Roskam's Airplane War Stories

An Account of the Professional Life and Work of Dr. Jan Roskam, Airplane Designer and Teacher

Dr. Jan Roskam

Ackers Distinguished Professor of Aerospace Engineering
The University of Kansas and President of DARcorporation

2002

120 East 9th Street, Suite 2 • Lawrence, Kansas 66044, U.S.A.

PUBLISHED BY
Design, Analysis and Research Corporation (*DARcorporation*)
120 East Ninth Street, Suite 2
Lawrence, Kansas 66044
U.S.A.
Phone: (785) 832-0434
Fax: (785) 832-0524
e-mail: info@darcorp.com
http://www.darcorp.com

ISBN 1-884885-57-8

In all countries, sold and distributed by
Design, Analysis and Research Corporation
120 East Ninth Street, Suite 2
Lawrence, Kansas 66044
U.S.A.

Printed in the United States of America
First Printing, 2002

Table of Contents

Contents

List of Acronyms

ACADS	Aircraft Computer Aided Design System
ATLIT	Advanced Technology Light Twin
AVRO	A.V. Roe Aircraft Company (Division of BAC)
AE	Aerospace Engineering
AEB	Aerospace Engineering Board
AFN	American Forces Network
AGARD	Advisory Group for Aeronautical Research and Development
AIAA	American Institute for Aeronautics and Astronautics
AMSA	Advanced Manned Strategic Aircraft
ASAP	As Soon as Possible
BAC	British Aerospace Corporation
BAM	Bataafse Aanneming Maatschappij
BSAE	Bachelor of Science in Aerospace Engineering
BTS	Boeing Technology Services
BTWT	Boeing Transonic Wind Tunnel
BuAer	Bureau of Aeronautics (Now NavAir of the USNavy)
CAD	Computer Aided Design
CD	Compact Disk
CEO	Chief Executive Officer
CRES	Center for Research in the Engineering Sciences, predecessor of CRINC
CRINC	Center for Research, Inc.
DARcorp.	Design, Analysis and Research Corporation
DC	Douglas Commercial
DEAE	Doctor of Engineering in Aerospace Engineering
Delft UT	Delft University of Technology
DFBW	Digital Fly-by-Wire
DH	DeHavilland
EADS	European Aeronautics, Defense and Space Company
FAA	Federal Aviation Authority

Acronyms

FAR	Federal Airworthiness Regulation
FRL	Flight Research Laboratory
GCA	Ground Controlled Approach
GD	General Dynamics
GLC	Gates Learjet Corporation
HBS	Hogere Burger School (Type 3 High School in Holland)
IFR	Instrument Flight Rules
JPATS	Joint Pilot Aviation Training System
JSF	Joint Strike Fighter
KLM	Koninklijke Luchtvaart Maatschappij (Royal Dutch Airlines)
KSR	Kohlman Systems Research
KU	Kansas University (The University of Kansas)
MBA	Master of Business Administration
MHB	Messerschmitt-Heinkel-Blohm
MD	McDonnell-Douglas (now Boeing)
MIT	Massachusetts Institute of Technology
MSAE	Master of Science in Aerospace Engineering
NAA	North American Aviation (later Rockwell now Boeing)
NACA	National Advisory Committee on Aeronautics
NASA	National Aeronautics and Space Administration
NASP	National Aerospace Plane
NATC	Naval Air Test Center
NATO	North Atlantic Treaty Organization
NAWC	Naval Air Warfare Center
NBAA	National Business Aircraft Association
NIV	Nederlands Instituut voor Vliegtuigontwikkeling (Netherlands Institute for Aircraft Development)
NSF	National Science Foundation
NYU	New York University
OSU	Ohio State University
PC	Personal Computer

Acronyms

PhDAE	Doctor of Philosophy in Aerospace Engineering
RAEC	Roskam Aviation and Engineering Corporation (1972-2001)
RAF	Royal Air Force (Great Britain)
RATO	Rocket Assisted Takeoff
RC	Radio Controlled
RFP	Request for Proposal
RNAF	Royal Netherlands Air Force
ROTC	Reserve Officers Training Corps
RTAC	Research and Technology Advisory Council
SAC	Strategic Air Command
SAE	Society of Automotive Engineers
SBIR	Small Business and Innovative Research
SFIM	Societé de Fabrication des Instruments de Mesure
SNECMA	Societé Nationale des Etudes et des Moteurs d'Aviation
SOCATA	Societe de Construction Aeronautique et de Transport Aerienne
SPIFR	Single Pilot Instrument Flight Rules
SRI	Stanford Research Institute
SSSA	Separate Surface Stability Augmentation System
SST	Supersonic Transport
STC	Supplemental Type Certificate
STOL	Short Takeoff and Landing
STOVL	Short Takeoff and Vertical Landing
TFX	Tactical Fighter Experimental
TU Delft	Technological University Delft, The Netherlands
TWA	Trans World Airlines
UofW	University of Wichita (Today Wichita State University)
USAAF	United States Army Air Forces (predecessor of USAF)
USAF	United States Air Force
USN	United States Navy
VATLIT	Very Advanced Technology Light Twin
VSTOL	Vertical and Short Takeoff and Landing

Acronyms

VTOL	Vertical Takeoff and Landing
VSV	Vliegtuigbouwkundige Studie Vereniging (Aeronautical Engineering Students Organization)
WPAFB	Wright-Patterson Air Force Base

List of Figures

Figures

Figures

Introduction

This book represents an overview of my life experiences as an airplane designer, a teacher and a sometimes pilot. I have been very fortunate to have been involved in more than 36 aircraft programs, 24 of which made it into flight, and 12 of which never got beyond the "drawing board." I also have had the opportunity to pilot 38 different types of airplanes.

I became "nutty" about airplanes when I was ten years old. I continued to be fascinated by airplanes all my life and, I can honestly say, I have had a ball helping in the design and development of many airplane types, and teaching others how to analyze, design and build them. I also have had a lot of fun flying many. Flying was always a pleasure for me although I never accumulated more than a total of about 500 flying hours.

My career spanned 13 years of full-time work in industry with Aviolanda, Cessna and Boeing, and 35 years with The University of Kansas (KU). At KU I taught airplane design and airplane flight dynamics. I also developed a research program in airplane design, engaged in many consulting activities in the USA and in Europe, and wrote and published 11 textbooks.

In addition, I have taught more than 144 one-week (short) courses on stability, control, automatic controls, airplane design and airplane performance. This all started in 1976 with a short course on flight dynamics taught in Wichita at the request of NASA and Cessna Aircraft Company. The demand for these classes kept increasing until I was doing five to eight per year which continues as this book is being written.

As a teacher, I have been privileged to teach airplane design, stability and control to more than 600 students at KU and more than 2,000 students in various short courses.

During my regular classes, as well as during my short courses, I illustrate my material with a large number of what I call "war stories." Most of these stories directly involve certain airplanes. The majority of these stories are based on actual events that happened in the design and development of aircraft programs, many of which (but not all) I was associated with.

Students enjoyed hearing these war stories and kept asking me to record them in a separate book. In responding to these requests, I decided to combine the war stories with what has become my professional autobiography. I thought it might be of interest to see how a professional's life can evolve, and how actual airplane experiences became "war stories." Pictures of these airplanes are included at the end of each chapter or section.

In the text, many airplane types are mentioned with which I had no, or very little, technical or flight involvement but which somehow "touched my life." I decided to include pictures of these airplanes as well. I hope that young engineers will recognize in these pictures the tremendous evolution of airplanes during one professional's lifetime.

I hope that the book will serve as interesting reading for those who, like me, are "nutty" about airplanes. I also hope that there is value in the book from a viewpoint of learning about many aspects of the complex airplane design and development process. I fervently hope that this book can serve as an inspiration to future airplane designers and teachers. To the latter end I have included an extensive list of references, many of which deal with the history of aircraft designs and aircraft manufacturers. Aspiring airplane designers should read all these books.

An account of my professional life would not be complete without listing publications, theses supervised, etc. Appendices A through F take care of this.

Appendix A contains a chronological list of my publications. Not included are minor papers and conference presentations of which there are several hundred.

Appendix B lists all master's and doctoral theses which I directly supervised. Not included are many more for which I served as a committee member.

Appendix C lists all airplane types I piloted and also those with which I had major or minor association during the design and development stage.

Appendix D contains my latest curriculum vitae, excluding publications which are listed in Appendix A.

Appendix E presents a summary of my short course involvement.

Appendix F contains a chronological listing of honors and awards which were bestowed on me. I particularly cherish those given to me by my students.

As I finish this book I have also announced my retirement from full time teaching at KU by December 31, 2003. It is time for a younger generation to carry on.

I do owe a lot of thanks to my wife, Jan Thomas Barron, who read the manuscript and made many suggestions for changes. As a result, countless errors were corrected and the book became more readable.

I also need to thank Walt Whittaker who took many of the photographs and who also arranged most of the photographs in digital format.

Finally, I have to acknowledge the many comments and suggestions made by William Anemaat. He was also very helpful in familiarizing me with various aspects of the softwares which I used to produce this book.

Chapter 1: Years Before High School

I was born February 22, 1930, in the city of The Hague,* The Netherlands. My sister Ada was born two years later. My father, Kommer Jan Roskam, was a bookkeeper and later became a registered accountant. My mother, Agatha Roskam Bosman (in Holland, the wife's name is put after the husband's name), was a full-time housewife and mother. I remember very little of my earliest childhood. I do remember that my parents were very much in love and they raised us in a loving but firm manner.

My first memories are of living on the fourth floor of an apartment building in the town of Scheveningen, a suburb of The Hague. Scheveningen had a fisherman's harbor on the North Sea. I remember the smell of fish and the sight of many trawlers and other fishing vessels in that little harbor. I also remember the fried sole and fried herring that my mother used to fix: absolutely delicious.

As a youngster of about four I remember watching trains go by from our upper story apartment. A large window allowed us to look out over a sand dune landscape. In the distance were railroad tracks for the line The Hague-Scheveningen. I was fascinated by the nicely streamlined, green-red painted, diesel-electric trains which were used on that line. On our side of the railroad tracks was an equestrian trail. I remember watching groups of people riding horseback, mostly on weekends.

My parents, particularly my mother, spent a lot of time reading to us and with us from various books, well-illustrated with color pictures, long before we went to school. My sister and I memorized a number of fairy tales and children's rhymes. As a result, we knew how to read before we went to elementary school. We also played quite a bit with construction type toys.

At one time, to my mother's dismay, I managed to completely disassemble an alarm clock. I must have had an early knack for things mechanical.

My parents insisted that all of us have at least breakfast and dinner together as a family. We had to come to the table on time with our hands scrubbed. My mother was a great cook and made the most wonderful desserts. We quickly learned that you always had to empty your plate before dessert was served. As a result, we never took more than we could eat. There was no way we were going to miss out on her delicious desserts.

I fondly remember that as we matured, we had frequent after-dinner conversations about politics, economics, religion and topics of contemporary importance. We learned a great deal from those discussions.

An early exposure to aviation came as a consequence of the KLM Douglas[(1)] DC-2 *Uiver* (Dutch for stork) winning the handicap air race (and placing second in the speed race) in the McRobertson Air Race from London, England, to Melbourne, Australia, in 1934. Figure 1 shows a picture of that airplane.

---

* Although the Dutch parliament and most government buildings are located in The Hague, it is not the official capital city. Amsterdam is the official capital of The Netherlands.

Winning second place in the speed race was probably the most significant aspect of this KLM victory. Here was a passenger airplane, carrying fare-paying passengers, beating all (except one) specially designed racing airplanes in flying from London to Melbourne. The exception was the beautiful, red-gloss painted DeHavilland(2) Comet, called *Grosvernor House*, flown by Campbell and Black. Figure 2 shows what that really neat airplane looked like. More about that airplane later in Chapter 6.

The Dutch obviously were elated over this remarkable feat. So were the designers of the DC-2 at Douglas Aircraft Company in Santa Monica, California! The acquisition of the sleek DC-2 was the start of a long, and mutually profitable, relationship between KLM and Douglas. KLM ended up buying and flying all Douglas models DC-3, DC-4, DC-5, DC-6, DC-7, DC-8, DC-9, DC-10 and MD-11. This relationship lasted until Boeing(3) edged out Douglas in the 1970's with the 747 and later with the 737 and 767.

One day my dad brought home a large cardboard sheet with wings, fuselage, tails, nacelles, propellers and landing gear of the DC-2 *Uiver* printed in color. My dad did most of the work putting the model together. It hung from the ceiling in my bedroom for many years.

My family moved to a rented row house in the Harderwijkstraat in 1935. This house was located in the middle of The Hague. There was a nice back yard with large hydrangia bushes.

I vividly remember one Sunday in 1936 when my parents took us to the beach at Scheveningen. The big passenger airship the *Hindenburg* (Figure 3) flew low across the beach on its way from Frankfurt, Germany, to Lakehurst, New Jersey. Passengers were waving from the airship promenade deck to the people below. This was an unforgettable sight for me.

I remember some of the experiences of our early schooling at the Comenius School, a Christian school. It was only a 20-minute walk.

Each Monday morning we brought small monetary gifts to school which were put in a little statue on the teacher's desk. The statue was a Javanese lady in a praying position. Her head nodded when coins were deposited. In those days what is now the Republic of Indonesia was called the Dutch East Indies. The island of Java was, and still is, the most influential of the hundreds of Indonesian islands.

I also remember the annual celebrations of the birthday of Princess Beatrix. She was the daughter of Princess Juliana, and the granddaughter of Queen Wilhelmina. Juliana became queen shortly after WWII. (Beatrix is the queen at the time of the writing of this book.) Every Dutch student was treated to a Dutch biscuit with colored sugar candy whenever a royal birthday occurred during the school year. Figure 4 shows my elementary school class during one such event in 1938. In Figure 5, I pose for an individual picture.

Because Holland was still suffering the consequences of the economic depression (started with the 1929 Wall Street crash and felt worldwide) my father held several poorly paying, part-time jobs. My parents had a hard time making ends meet but were never in debt; there always was good food on the table. My mother was a truly superb cook and knew how to get bargains. She also was an excellent seamstress and made most of our clothing. Obviously, my dad could not afford a car so we all moved around by bicycle or public transportation. We also could not afford a telephone. I remember the first telephone we got was after WWII.

One of my dad's extra jobs was giving private lessons in bookkeeping to various students. These lessons were given in our home. Our house at the Harderwijkstraat was really too small for such an activity. Therefore, my parents decided to move to a new, larger, but higher cost, row-house on the Veenendaalkade. I believe that happened in the spring of 1939.

There was a canal in front of that house. During the winter the canal froze and I remember learning to skate with the help of a wooden kitchen chair. I never became a fancy skater, but did credibly well in the "straight-and-high-speed" department.

We also had to learn to swim because my mother was afraid we might end up in the canal by accident. For our swimming lessons we went to a covered swimming pool facility in downtown The Hague. We were first taught to "dry swim" while lying face down on a bench beside the pool. Next, we were outfitted with an inflated tube to which a type of fishing pole was attached via a thin cable. The swim instructor controlled the length of the cable and shouted instructions to us. I liked swimming, but disliked diving and never took to entering the water that way.

Our house at the Veenendaalkade was at the edge of town. We took walks in the country and I began to notice (really notice) various types of plants and animals. Later, during my high school years, I joined a Youth Club for Nature Studies and learned a lot about our environment.

As it turned out WWII intervened. Germany invaded Poland in 1939, and England declared war on Germany. Rumors of a German invasion of Holland began to abound. As a result, my dad lost his students to the Dutch military draft and the house on the Veenendaalkade became too expensive.

Therefore, in late 1940, we moved to another new, lower cost row-house in the Rhenenstraat. Our living quarters were distributed on the second and third floors of the building. Our main entrance was on the ground floor with barely enough parking space for two bicycles. The other two were parked in a bicycle sales, repair and rental facility around the corner. This facility was run by a Mr. Veenstra who was always very helpful when there were mechanical problems with our bikes.

Moving to the Rhenenstraat actually turned out to be a stroke of luck for the entire family. Our neighbor downstairs, Mr. Van Donk, was a works-manager for the BAM (Bataafse Aanneming Maatschappij), a construction contracting company. It turned out they needed a full-time book-keeper. My dad applied and got the job.

One of our neighbor's sons, Henk van Donk, was studying to be a civil engineer at Delft University of Technology. From him I learned a lot about that university. Henk was also one of the best chess players in Holland and taught my sister and me how to play the game. We in turn taught our dad, and the three of us played a lot of chess until I emigrated to the United States. My dad and I continued to play chess by mail until the late eighties.

I was in the fifth grade, when the second world war broke out for Holland. My first war story deals with this event.

War Story 1

For Holland, World War II began on May 10, 1940. I remember waking up that morning to a lot of noise in the sky. My bedroom was on the third floor. However, this did not afford me a good look at the sky. I rushed into my clothes, raced down the stairs and outside to look upwards. There were several air duels going on: Dutch Fokker[(4)] G1 and DXXI fighters in combat with German Messerschmitt[(5)] Me 109, Me 110 and Junkers[(6)] Ju-52 airplanes. I already knew the most important types of airplanes of that era. Figures 6-10 show these airplanes.

The Junkers Ju-52 transports were evidently trying to land paratroopers at the Ockenburg Airfield, southwest of The Hague. The Germans had begun their massive attack on the low countries (Holland, Belgium and Luxembourg) and none were properly prepared to defend themselves. The war against Holland lasted only five days after which a long five-year period of Nazi occupation began. The eventual defeat of Germany had to wait until the United States entered the war and put a stop to Nazi despotism.

Lesson: Much later in life, I realized the following very important lesson from that experience: If you want peace, prepare yourself for war! Or, after Julius Ceasar: Ci vis pacem, para bellum! I also learned that there is no substitute for total air superiority in war.

War Story 2:

One peculiar airplane type which I remember seeing several times during this five-day war, was the B&V 141[(7)] asymmetric, single-engine battlefield observation airplane. This oddly shaped airplane is shown in Figure 11. This design evolved for reasons of pilot-to-ground visibility in turns to the right. Most airplanes of that era had serious side visibility problems, whether they were twin-engined or single-engined. This was caused by a combination of weight, balance and engine/propeller installation considerations. The asymmetric engine installation used on the B&V 141 gave good visibility to at least one side.

Lesson: There is nothing in the laws of physics which says that airplanes must be symmetrical.

This lesson has been dormant in my mind for a long time. Late in my career as a university professor, I was instrumental in a student design study of asymmetrical jet transports. This is discussed in Chapter 6.

War Story 3:

I also remember seeing a Fieseler[(7)] Storch (Storch is German for stork) land on a street in the middle of The Hague to disembark a German officer. The Storch was a STOL (Short Takeoff and Landing) airplane with rather remarkable, short takeoff and landing capabilities

(Figure 12). The airplane had a large wing, very efficient flaps, slats on the wing and on the tail and a powerful engine.

Lesson: To get off and back onto the ground in a short distance takes a large wing, a high maximum lift coefficient and a lot of power (or thrust).

One dreadful measure taken by the occupying Nazis was to confiscate all privately owned radios and substitute so-called "people's receivers" (made in Germany) on which one could only hear Nazi propaganda. We happened to have two radios and my parents decided to turn in one and keep the other. This was done by many Dutch families. We hid the remaining radio under the floor of a closet and many evenings tuned in for half an hour to Radio Orange*, broadcasting Allied news from London. I still remember the announcer's voice: "Here is Radio Orange in London," at the start of each broadcast.

During the first three years of the war the news was usually grim as the Nazis slaughtered their way through Europe and North Africa. Later in the war the news from London got better and better. A particularly positive event for us was when the USA entered the war as a result of the dastardly Japanese attack on Pearl Harbor.

A vivid memory of mine was the rather complete lack of moral fiber and leadership shown by the various churches in occupied Holland. When the Nazis started to round up Jewish citizens and transport them on cattle cars back east to their deaths, there was hardly any protest. I found this lack of leadership by the churches appalling, even as a young boy.

I also remember the belt buckles worn by German soldiers: they said "Gott sei mit Uns" (God be with us) in prominent letters. Who were they kidding?

One day I made a cardboard model of a Me 109 fighter and burned it. I guess I had to vent my anger at the Nazis.

My dad's employer had a contract from a German housing firm to build row-houses in Bramfeld, a suburb of Hamburg. That work already had started before WWII and, with agreement from the Dutch Contractors' Council in London, it was decided to continue but at the slowest possible pace.

My dad was appointed head bookkeeper for that job so we moved temporarily to Hamburg, but retained our house in The Hague. Therefore, in April of 1941 my sister and I found ourselves in a German school. It did not take us long to speak fluent German. Figure 13 shows a picture of my family taken in late 1941.

The regimentation in that German school was something my sister and I, being free-spirited Dutch, had to get used to. I distinctly remember numerous HJ's (Hitler Youths) and BDM's (Bund Deutscher Mädel or Club of German Girls) sporting their ugly uniforms and snapping out their Heil Hitlers. There was a rule which prohibited a non-Hitler Youth from having a fight with a uniformed member of the Hitler Youth. I managed to violate that rule.

---

* The Dutch Royal family is referred to as belonging to the House of Orange.

One day a particularly obnoxious Hitler Youth insulted Queen Wilhelmina during an exchange of arguments over political systems. This made me angry and I punched that ruffian in the nose. I was promptly arrested by two members of the SA (Sturm Abteilungen), the uniformed Nazi party hooligans. The next day, my mother and I had to appear in front of the local Nazi Gauleiter (District Leader) and we were given a warning that I was never to do that again. After that the offending Hitler Youth was called in, and the Gauleiter proceeded to tell that young man that he should never again insult a foreign head-of-state. Apparently, there still was a certain amount of fairness amongst some Nazis in those days.

My dad and several of his Dutch coworkers engaged in a slowdown conspiracy which came to the attention of the Gestapo (Geheime Staats Polizei or Secret State Police). One day the Gestapo arrested my dad and subjected him to a lengthy interrogation. We were all terrified. However, there was nothing they could prove so they released him with a stern warning. This happened one other time, luckily with the same result.

By 1942 we were having air raids carried out by the RAF (British Royal Air Force) almost every other night. These raids were primarily conducted by the famous AVRO[(8)] Lancaster bomber shown in Figure 14. As a result of these air raids, my sister and I spent many nights in a bomb shelter and did not have to attend school the next day. We missed a lot of schooling and, needless to say, fell way behind our friends in Holland.

Some nights, despite the air raid alarm, we ventured outside to see what was going on. I remember seeing search lights crisscrossing the sky and sometimes catching a Lancaster bomber. The fate of the bomber was often sealed after being caught by search lights.

The Germans developed a nasty trick which was particularly effective with partly overcast skies. They would aim search lights at neighboring clouds. This lit up a large area of the sky in such a way that Lancaster bombers would appear as sharply focused images above the clouds, thus falling easy prey to night fighters patrolling at higher altitude. One could tell what the Germans were up to because antiaircraft guns remained silent during such episodes.

I believe it was also in 1942 when the RAF began the first radar-guided carpet bombardments of the city. These bombardments were very effective in destroying large sections of Hamburg. One night was particularly terrifying in terms of noise and explosions. When we came out of the bomb shelter the next morning many houses in our general neighborhood were destroyed, or on fire. The roof of our house received relatively minor damage, but there were several conspicuous holes. Upon inspection, my dad and I found three phosphorous bombs, resembling hexagonal sticks, on the upper floor. Miraculously these bombs had not gone off! After that experience my parents decided to move back to Holland. This was in July of 1942.

As a result of the many schooling interruptions, I was at least one year behind in learning compared with most Dutch children of my age. For some strange reason the education experts in Holland did not put me back but placed me in a class according to my age. This turned out to be a disaster. I flunked most subjects and had a terrible year from a scholastic viewpoint. I wanted to become an aeronautical engineer and this did not appear possible in view of my unacceptable scholastic performance. This was a very demotivating experience for me. An explanation of the Dutch school system is in order.

In those days Holland had three types of high school.

Type One prepared students for vocational, blue-collar occupations.

Type Two prepared students for trade type, white-collar occupations.

Type Three prepared students for entry into a university.

These schools were separate entities with their own teaching staffs, facilities and prescribed curricula.

As a result of my terrible academic performance, I was judged unsuitable for a university education. Therefore, I was assigned to a Type Two high school. Since I wanted to get into aero engineering, something drastic had to be done. Luckily, my mother strongly disagreed with the judgement of the educators and got me placed in a special, preparatory school. This happened in the fall of 1943. The purpose of that school was to prepare students, who were academically poor performers, for entry into the Type Three high school.

My dad told me that this would be my only chance and that I better put it to good use. I did just that. Because of a great teacher, I managed to develop a real liking of science and mathematics.

I also remember family trips by train to visit relatives in the country. On several occasions the train in which we were riding was attacked by rocket firing, Hawker[9] Typhoon fighters of the RAF (Figure 15). On one occasion, an attacking Typhoon managed to stop the train we were on. There were quite a few German soldiers on board. They jumped out and started shooting at people who were running away from the train. Several were killed.

In the spring of 1944, much to my relief (and that of my parents), I passed the preparatory school exit examination. With that, I was officially admitted to the Type 3 high school from which I eventually hoped to get into the aeronautical engineering department at Delft TU.

Figure 1 Royal Dutch Airlines (KLM) DC-2, *Uiver* (Courtesy Dutch National Aviation Museum, The Netherlands)

Figure 2 De Havilland Comet I, *Grosvenor House*

Figure 3 Airship *Hindenburg* (With Permission from the Royal Aeronautical Society Library)

Figure 4 My Elementary School Class During a Celebration of Princess Beatrix's Birthday (Author is standing, second from the left)

Figure 5 The Author as an Eight-Year Old on a Typical Elementary School Bench

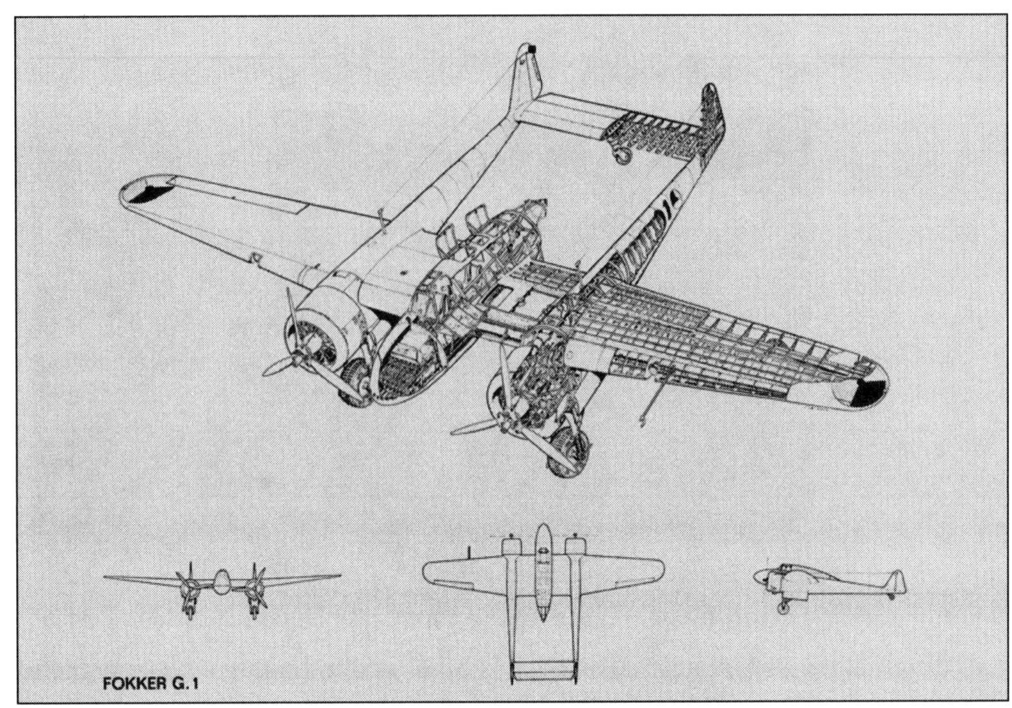

Figure 6 Fokker G-1 (Courtesy Fokker)

Figure 7 Fokker D XXI (Courtesy Fokker)

Figure 8 Messerschmitt Me-109 (With Permission from the Royal Aeronautical Society Library)

Figure 9 Messerschmitt Me-110 (With Permission from the Royal Aeronautical Society Library)

Figure 10 Model of the Junkers Ju-52

Figure 11 Model of the Blohm & Voss B&V 141

Figure 12 Fieseler Storch (With Permission from the Royal Aeronautical Society Library)

Figure 13 My Parents, my Sister and the Author in Late 1941

Figure 14 AVRO Lancaster (Courtesy British Aerospace)

Figure 15 Hawker Typhoon (With Permission from the Royal Aeronautical Society Library)

Chapter 2: High School Years

In the fall of 1944, my sister and I entered the much coveted, Type Three high school. Although my sister was two years younger than I, she managed to get placed directly from elementary school whereas I had lost two years as a result of my earlier, poor academic performance.

We were both lucky to get placed in the prestigious HBS Beeklaan, as that school was called. The acronym HBS stood for Hogere Burger School or, freely translated, Higher School for Citizens. Because the actual school facilities were located in a German "Sperr-Zone" (Forbidden Zone), the school occupied temporary quarters in an old school building not far from our home. In fact, we could walk to and from school.

I entered this five-year high school with great enthusiasm and a real desire to learn. The entire curriculum was prescribed. It consisted of four languages (Dutch, French, German and English), world geography, biology, chemistry, physics, mechanics, mathematics, government, world history, economics, Dutch history, drawing and physical education.

Classes were held 9:00 a.m.-12:00 noon and 1:00 pm-5:00 pm, Monday through Friday, and 9:00 a.m.-12:00 noon on Saturday. There was a total of two months vacation. Homework was required in all classes. Class attendance was mandatory.

Because there were too many students for one classroom, the students were split into two groups: one class with boys only and the other one mixed. My sister was placed in the mixed class (there were only six girls) and I was placed in the all boys class. This mix of classes continued during our entire five year stay at the HBS Beeklaan. Students were passed from one grade to the next only if their grade point average was 60% or better.

During my high school years I spent much of my time in serious study of the hard sciences. Mathematics, mechanics, physics, biology and chemistry were definitely my favorite subjects. In this type of high school we got into linear algebra, analytic geometry and physics, including some quantum physics. In the last year we even got into the fundamentals of differential and integral calculus.

I had some really superb teachers. I have never forgotten Messrs. Visser (mathematics), DeKok (physics), Taverne (chemistry), Koote (Dutch literature), Dommering (French literature), Chavonnes Vrught (English literature), Lehnen (German and Esperanto literature) and Saayes (world history). These were definitely my favorite teachers. Learning Esperanto was optional but I decided to take it anyway.

I also remember Mr. Mulder, our school director. He ran the school firmly but fairly and was always ready to help with student projects.

I owe a great deal of gratitude to these individuals for giving me a first class education in the broadest sense of the word. They were all very demanding, highly motivating, and fair.

I mentioned earlier that our neighbor's son, Henk van Donk, taught me how to play chess. For one of my birthdays I received several books on chess opening and middle game theories by ex-world chess champion Dr. Max Euwe. Dr. Euwe was a mathematics teacher in Amsterdam and had an unusually clear style of writing. As a result, I managed to memorize many opening lines and became quite a credible chess player.

Our high school had a rule that freshmen could not join the school chess club. The rationale was that chess could easily take up all your time and therefore leave little time for studying. However, there was one exception to this rule. If a freshman could beat the top chess team of the school in a simultaneous exhibition then he, or she, could join. I was the first freshman to accomplish this feat and beat the team 9-1 on a Saturday afternoon in October of 1944. As a result I was allowed to join the chess team and eventually worked my way up to become the school chess champion. My sister also was good at chess and together we played on the top chess team of our high school.

By the end of 1944 the Germans had stolen virtually all food from Holland and the civilian population was left to its own devices to stay alive. The stores were mostly empty of food stuffs. Many people traded their valuables for food which they could sometimes obtain from farmers if they had bicycles and the physical ability to ride long distances. These bikes were mostly equipped with wooden rims around the wheels because rubber tires were no longer available. The wooden rims were very, very, uncomfortable to ride on.

Worse, there was no city gas, no electricity and no coal (used for heating by most people at that time).

There were soup rations (one per person) served in official soup kitchens. These soups consisted of water with very little nourishing substances thrown in; we called them boiled water. One had to stand in line for hours just to get this.

We ate tulip bulbs and cooked on little stoves using as fuel asphalt chipped from the streets, and green wood sawed from live trees in the parks. My dad and I chipped a lot of asphalt and cut quite a few trees. I knew people who even used wood stripped from rooms in their homes.

I clearly remember scores of V-2 rockets (Figure 16) being fired from the outskirts of The Hague (from a town called Wassenaar) toward England. Those V-2's were not very reliable and many fell back on The Hague. As a result, a lot of Dutch citizens were killed. The Germans did not care about that.

Right after the war, two Dutch engineers published a book about the workings of the V-2. The book was called *Ballistics of the Future*[(10)]. This book was my first exposure to rocketry from an engineering/scientific viewpoint. I still have a copy in my personal library.

War Story 4

The Gestapo (German Secret Police) maintained a headquarters building in the center of The Hague. In that building were records of people who were suspected of working for the Dutch resistance forces, called the underground. The Dutch underground had communicated this fact to the RAF (Royal Air Force). In the RAF served a number of Dutch pilots who were very familiar with downtown The Hague.

One day, three DeHavilland Mosquito bombers (Figure 17), flown by Dutch pilots managed to destroy that building and all the records in it. To the Dutch, this was a joyous occasion which gave hope for the future.

Lesson: Precision air strikes get everyone's attention, particularly the enemy's.

The allied invasion of Western Europe started in 1943. My dad and I kept track of the progress of American and British forces with the help of a map and a lot of colored pins. Radio Orange kept us informed. We also kept track of the progress made by the USNavy and USArmy against Japan.

As indicated before, by years-end 1944 and early in 1945, there rarely was any electricity, gas or coal for heat. We had little bitty oil lamps by which we read and studied. Luckily, city water services were maintained so that sanitary facilities did work. There was no train service anymore and no one, except Germans, had cars. We walked or used wooden-rim bicycles.

We all lost weight and became undernourished. In January of 1945, my parents managed to place me temporarily with a farming family up north, the Roozenbroeks. This way, my parents and my sister could share four rations between the three of them.

The Roozenbroek family (two parents and six children) lived near the town of Anna Paulowna in a very nice villa. They owned and operated a huge tulip bulb farm. They were very good to me. Although I had to participate in chores, I could spend some time gathering food from other local farmers. I also was given plenty of time to do my schoolwork.

Once every two weeks my father or my mother would make the ten hour bicycle trip to carry some of the food back home to augment meager soup kitchen rations.

War Story 5

One time my mother had made the trip and, with a lot of food on her bicycle, was on the way home. I accompanied her several miles south. In the middle of nowhere we were stopped by a German patrol and our bicycles and food were confiscated.

My mother was outraged and I did not know what to do. She decided that we should visit the local German Kommandant and protest that treatment. She managed to impress this German officer with the terrible injustice that had been done to us. To our surprise, the officer actually agreed that what his soldiers had done was illegal. After some telephone calls and a long wait we got everything back and my mother was on her way home again.

Lesson: In the midst of all that inhumanity, certain German officers maintained the ability to do the right thing.

By early spring of 1945 the southern part of Holland (the part below the big rivers) had been liberated primarily by Canadian and British forces. However, we lived north of the rivers and the Germans were still in control.

War Story 6

In late April of 1945, the Nazi general in charge of German troops in Holland apparently made a deal with the American Eighth Air Force to allow American bombers to drop food over the starving population of Holland. It was impressive to see the scores of Boeing B-17 and Consolidated-Vultee [11] B-24 bombers (Figures 18 and 19) flying low with crews waving and dropping canisters filled with food out of the bomb bays. This was the famous Operation Manna, which literally saved many Dutch families from starvation.

Lesson: If it had not been for massive American and British air power, many Dutch people would not have survived the war.

Liberation came May 5, 1945, when the Princess Irene Brigade (Dutch troops serving under General Montgomery of the British Army), Canadian and American troops entered our part of Holland. Luckily, we were spared significant street fighting. It was amazing how quickly, thanks to enormous American support, the Dutch economy recovered and the shops filled again with good food.

Our high school moved back to permanent quarters. These quarters were much farther from our house than the temporary quarters. Therefore, my sister and I took an electric street car (tram) to school; good bicycle tires were not available for the first year after WWII. From early 1946 we used bicycles to go to school except in bad weather when we took the tram.

Figure 20 shows my high school class in 1947. One of my classmates, Olaf von Michalofski, also was very interested in airplanes. We often had discussions about the relative merits of various WWII airplanes like the North-American[12] P-51, Mustang, Republic[13] P-47, Thunderbolt, Lockheed[14] P-38, Lightning, Grumman[15] F6F Hellcat, and the Chance Vought[16] F4U Corsair. These airplanes are shown in Figures 21 through 25.

Olaf and I kept track of where this fighter technology might be going. We were very impressed with the jet engines and the various new jet fighters coming out of the USA and England. Airplanes we found particularly intriguing were the Gloster[17] Meteor and the Lockheed P-80, Shooting Star (Figures 26 and 27). We had many debates about the relative merits of swept wing fighters such as the North American F-86, Sabre and the revolutionary delta-winged Gloster Javelin (Figures 28 and 29).

Olaf and his family had repatriated from the Dutch East Indies after the surrender of Japan. From them I learned firsthand about the terrible conditions under which Dutch citizens lived in Japanese occupation camps.

During their occupation, the Japanese trained a large number of Javanese (people, native to the island of Java) to hate the Dutch and, as a result, various revolutionary actions were taken against the Dutch. The Dutch responded with two police actions. These were in fact fairly sizable military operations launched against the centers of revolution. Soekarno, a graduate of Delft University of Technology, was the leader of the Indonesian revolution.

What interested me about the police actions was the aviation aspect of these events. During both police actions, North-American B-25 bombers and Supermarine[18] Spitfires (Figures 30 and 31) were used by the RNAF (Royal Netherlands Air Force) in a ground support role. During the second police action, the United Nations enacted an embargo against Holland to prevent the Dutch from waging war on Java. Several countries did not honor this embargo. Therefore, it became possible for KLM (Royal Dutch Airlines) to establish an air bridge from Amsterdam to Batavia (now Djakarta) via South Africa and the island of Mauritius.

In view of the relatively primitive means of navigation, it was a real tribute to the Lockheed Constellation and the Douglas DC-4 (Figures 32 and 33), as well as to the KLM crews who operated these airplanes, that hundreds of flights were conducted without any problems.

As it turned out, this was all for naught. By 1949 the Dutch had agreed to give up the East Indies and the Republic of Indonesia was established. Soekarno became the first president.

During my high school years, I wrote letters to many aircraft manufacturers in the USA and England, requesting information and pictures and/or drawings of their airplanes. Most of these companies responded. As a result the walls of my room were full of airplane pictures. I remember that Douglas of Santa Monica, Boeing of Seattle, Martin[19] of Baltimore and DeHavilland Aircraft of Hatfield were particularly generous. I still have most of these materials in my airplane files.

War Story 7

Our neighbor downstairs, Mr. Van Donk, had a company car for his use: a US built Studebaker. This was the streamlined Studebaker model with the jet-inlet type ornament in front. One Sunday, the Van Donks and my family were riding in the countryside when the car developed a serious leak in the gas tank. In those days there were no service stations open on Sunday except for dispensing gasoline. Mr. Van Donk and my dad wondered what to do because we were a long way from home.

At that point I remembered having read about USArmy Air Corps crews using chewing gum to temporarily fix leaks in aircraft tanks. I suggested we do that and it was agreed that this was worth trying. We bought chewing gum at a restaurant which I proceeded to chew and then stick into the tank rupture. It worked like a charm! Mr. Van Donk drove the car in that condition for two weeks until it could be repaired.

Lesson: Look for simple solutions to difficult problems. Also, here is another application of lessons learned by other people. Therefore, keep on reading!

Right after the war, Dutch radio stations began broadcasting a lot of American big band music. I really enjoyed the music of Glenn Miller, Benny Goodman, Harry James, Count Basie, Louis Armstrong, Duke Ellington and Tommy Dorsey. There was an American radio station in West Germany, AFN (American Forces Network), which had special programs on big band music and I was a frequent listener. I still like big band music and now have much of that music on CD's.

My sister and I had a great-aunt and great-uncle (Aunt Trien and Uncle Jo) who lived in the city of Alkmaar in the north of Holland. They had two daughters who were approximately our ages (Willy and Jo) and we became good friends. My sister and I spent many wonderful vacations at their home. They were very hospitable people.

Uncle Jo carried a subscription to *The Saturday Evening Post* from America. I read every issue from cover to cover and became fascinated with life in the USA. I was particularly impressed with Norman Rockwell's drawings and the always funny *Hazel* cartoons. Reading *The Saturday Evening Post* probably gave me the idea that I would eventually like to live and work in the USA. I later became, and still am a subscriber to *The Saturday Evening Post.*

I also had become a student member of the library associated with the US Information Service in The Hague. That library was stacked with many aeronautical publications. It was nice to talk to the friendly American staff and exercise my English.

As a result of these exposures I became convinced that I wanted to emigrate to the USA and work for an American aircraft company. When I told my parents they, understandably, passed it off as a teenage phase.

Whatever spare time was available I spent playing chess and tennis, and acting in the school theater club. The latter came about in an interesting manner.

War Story 8

As part of a course in Dutch literature in the first year of high school, Mr. Koote required that students give class presentations on a subject selected by the students. I was extremely nervous when my time came and did poorly while speaking in front of an audience. Afterwards, Mr. Koote said this would be a significant hindrance to my future career. Therefore, he strongly suggested that I take up acting in the school theater club. I did and the experience completely cured my nervousness in front of audiences. In fact it made a rather credible public presenter (if not a ham!) out of me. Figure 34 shows me on stage. This turned out to be of significant help in my eventual career as a teacher.

Lesson: Public speaking is a skill that can be acquired with very little effort by taking acting lessons. It is important for engineers to acquire this skill as early as possible.

The experiences in acting even gave me the courage to perform as singer with our high school jazz band. Once a month there was a high school dance with big band music, mostly played by the high school jazz band. For about two years I sang with that band; Sentimental Journey, Chattannooga Choochoo were my favorites.

As part of our language curriculum in our high school, we were given low cost tickets to matinee stage performances by famous theater groups such as the Old Vic and the Young Vic from England. I fondly remember attending classics like *Hamlet*, *A Midsummer Night's Dream*, *The Amazing Quest of Mr. Ernest Bliss* as well as a variety of operas and operettas.

My dad played soccer competitively until his retirement. Almost every Sunday he played for a local soccer club. I also joined that club as a junior. I liked soccer (still do) but I was never very good at it.

I got interested in tennis mostly because my parents were. They decided to make this a family affair and the four of us received lessons from a real pro, a Dutch nobleman with the impressive name of Van den Bergh Van Heemstede. He was a very good teacher and all four of us became credible tennis players. Later, when I had my first job, I joined the Dordrecht Tennis Club and played competitively (albeit on weekends only) for two years before emigrating to the United States.

War Story 9

My sister and I received a weekly allowance from our parents. At one point in 1948 we had saved enough money to charter an airplane and, for the first time, experienced what it means to fly.

Together with several friends we chartered a Cessna[20] UC-78 Bobcat from Aero Holland, a Dutch air charter company. Aero Holland had acquired several Bobcats as surplus from the US Army Air Corps. Figure 35 shows our airplane, the PH-NCL, taxiing in. Figure 36 shows the entire group of friends with our pilot.

It was a wonderful experience to fly above our home town of The Hague, the beach at Scheveningen, and the North Sea. That flight reinforced my resolve to get into aeronautical engineering and eventually learn to fly. It also got me interested in the Cessna Aircraft Company, which later employed me as an aircraft design engineer.

Lesson: Flying is fun and very motivating.

Figure 37 shows a model of the Bobcat which was referred to as the "Bamboo Bomber" by US airmen who flew it in WWII. The model shown in Figure 37 is actually a T-50, Crane. This was the Canadian trainer version of the Bobcat. Externally, the airplanes were alike.

During my high school years I devoured every issue of *Vliegwereld* (World of Flight), a Dutch monthly aeronautical magazine. Frequently, *Vliegwereld* contained cut-away drawings of airplanes. I copied these cut-aways on white paper with the help of carbon paper and one of my mother's knitting needles. Making and studying the cut-away copies really helped me understand how airplanes were put together, down to the systems and manufacturing level.

During the summer of 1948 I also designed and built a large balsa wood model of a twin jet fighter resembling the English Electric[21] Canberra bomber (Figure 38). I told my dad that real passenger jets were only a decade away. As things turned out, I was right about that! I also predicted that he and my mother would visit me in the United States by transatlantic jet.

Dad thought that was absurd. Jet airplanes were considered dangerous in those days. Besides, why would I want to go to America?

My parents actually made several trips to visit me by jet. The first one was in 1965 on the occasion of my graduation from The University of Washington with a Ph.D. in Aeronautics and Astronautics. How proud they were!

War Story 10

In 1948 my high school class elected me class representative. The function of a class representative was to discuss student grievances and other problems with school officials and to assist in their resolution. I enjoyed this role. However, I made myself very unpopular with one particular teacher, Mr. Van Putten.

Mr. Van Putten had a habit of coming late to class. This problem was known by the administration but ignored. Our classroom had a large hatch in the back. The hatch led to a huge attic with plenty of space to hide an entire class. One morning Mr. Van Putten was extremely late. I suggested that the class hide in the attic. We all did. Pretty soon the teacher came into the classroom, did not see anyone, and decided to go to the teachers' lounge. As soon as he left we returned to our seats and I went to the school director, Mr. Mulder, to ask if Mr. Van Putten was sick that day. I used to get A grades from this teacher. After this my grades were reduced to B or even C. However, he was never late again!

Lesson: It is unprofessional for students and/or teachers to be late to class.

During my high school years I also had several pen pals: young ladies in the USA, England and Finland. We exchanged letters about once a month. These contacts taught me quite a bit about different countries and personalities. It is regrettable that I never met any of my pen pals in person.

I graduated from high school in May of 1949 as number one in my class and had no difficulty being admitted to Delft University of Technology. I was finally on my way to becoming an aeronautical engineer. My university years (Chapter 3) were about to begin.

By the summer of 1949 I had saved enough money for yet another flight. This time I decided to fly from Schiphol (near Amsterdam) to Leeuwarden (a city in the north of Holland) and back as a passenger on a KLM Douglas DC-3. At that time KLM operated a three times daily service between Amsterdam and Leeuwarden.

I used my bicycle to travel from The Hague to the Schiphol Airport.

These flights were another wonderful and motivating experience for me. A good view of a DC-3 is seen in Figure 39. Figure 40 shows me in front of a KLM DC-3. Little did I know that I was going to be piloting a DC-3 many years later.

Figure 16 V-2 Ballistic Missile (With Permission from the Royal Aeronautical Society Library)

Figure 17 DeHavilland Mosquito (With Permission from the Royal Aeronautical Society Library)

Figure 18 Boeing B-17, Flying Fortress (Courtesy USAF Museum)

Figure 19 Consolidated B-24, Liberator (Courtesy Convair)

Figure 20 My High School Class in 1947 (Author is on the last row, far right)

Figure 21 North American P-51B, Mustang (With Permission from the Royal Aeronautical Society Library)

Figure 22 Republic P-47, Thunderbolt (With Permission from the Royal Aeronautical Society Library)

Figure 23 Lockheed P-38, Lightning (With Permission from the Royal Aeronautical Society Library)

Figure 24 Grumman F6F, Hellcat (With Permission from the Royal Aeronautical Society Library)

Figure 25 Model of the Chance Vought F6-U, Corsair

Figure 26 Model of the Gloster Meteor, Mark I

Figure 27 Lockheed P-80, Shooting Star (With Permission from the Royal Aeronautical Society Library)

Figure 28 North American F-86, Sabre (From Van Steenderen; Vliegende Vleugels, Deel II, 1947)

Figure 29 Gloster Javelin (With Permission from the Royal Aeronautical Society Library)

Figure 30 Model of the North American B-25, Mitchell

Figure 31 Vickers Supermarine Spitfire (With Permission from the Royal Aeronautical Society Library)

Figure 32 Lockheed 049, Constellation (With Permission from the Royal Aeronautical Society Library)

Figure 33 Douglas DC-4 (With Permission from the Royal Aeronautical Society Library)

Figure 34 The Author During a Stage Performance

Figure 35 Cessna UC-78, Bobcat, PH-NCL

Figure 36 Our Group of Friends After Our First Flight in 1948 (Author is Second from the right)

Figure 37 Model of the Cessna T-50, Crane (Canadian Version of the UC-78 Bobcat)

Figure 38 English Electric Canberra (With Permission from the Royal Aeronautical Society Library)

Figure 39 Douglas DC-3 (Courtesy Douglas)

Figure 40 The Author in 1949 in Front of a KLM Douglas DC-3

High School Years

Chapter 3: University Years

In the fall of 1949 I entered the Delft University of Technology as a freshman in AE (Aeronautical, later Aerospace Engineering). At that time, the Delft AE curriculum was a five-year-program leading directly to the equivalent of the American MSAE (Master of Science in Aeronautical Engineering) degree. There was no intermediate BSAE (Bachelor of Science in Aeronautical Engineering) degree, and still isn't.

The city of Delft is located about ten miles southeast of The Hague. I usually made the daily trip from my parent's house to the university by bicycle, a 50 minute ride each way. Most of this was through open country. These bicycle rides were good exercise and, except in bad weather, very enjoyable. Only when the weather was really bad did I take the train. The door-to-door time was in fact longer by train.

The first two semesters I spent studying advanced calculus, mechanics, dynamics, kinematics, thermodynamics, physics, steam engines, piston engines, turbines, material science and theory and design of mechanisms. As part of the physics and thermodynamics courses many experiments had to be conducted and documented with emphasis on the calibration of any measuring equipment. We also were required to take courses in aircraft manufacturing and shop practice. As part of these courses we were taught various riveting, welding, machining and assembly techniques. I remember being in awe of my instructor in these shop courses. His name was P.A. van den Broek.

Mr. Van den Broek was the KLM flight engineer on the first flight (1924) from Amsterdam, Holland to Batavia (now Djakarta) in the then Dutch East Indies (now Indonesia). He was fond of recounting the hair-raising events encountered during that record breaking flight in a single-engine passenger airplane, the Fokker FVII. Figure 41 shows the FVII, an early transport which could carry six passengers and a crew of three.

The chairman of the AE department was Professor H.J. Van der Maas. He was a former test pilot/engineer for the NLR (National Aeronautical Research Laboratory). His expertise was flight mechanics, stability and control. One of his claims to fame was test flying the Douglas DC-5. This little known airplane (shown in Figure 42) was ordered by KLM for use in the Dutch West and East Indies. However, WWII intervened after the first five were delivered. Most of the DC-5 airplanes destined for KLM were interned for service in the USNavy, where they became known as the RD-5.

The DC5 was designed under the leadership of famous Douglas designer Ed Heineman[(22)]. There are some interesting comments about Professor Van der Maas in Reference 22.

Professor Van der Maas was an extremely busy man. In addition to his teaching he was instrumental in getting the Fokker Aircraft Company off the ground after WWII via some very clever political maneuvering. He got the Dutch government to let him organize the NIV (Netherlands Institute for Aircraft Development). This NIV was to take tax payer money and use it to underwrite several airplane programs. The idea was to pay this money back with interest over the life of the production airplanes. This resulted in the development of Fokker models F-25, S-11, S-12, S-13, S-14, F-27 and F-28. The taxpayers got their money back via royalty payments on F27 and F28 sales. Figures 43 through 49 show renditions of these airplanes.

Professor Van der Maas also was instrumental in helping with the formation of AGARD (Advisory Group for Aeronautical Research and Development, a division of NATO).

Because of his many outside activities, Professor Van der Maas was away from his office a lot. I still remember seeing him dash into his car (a really fast, French built Citroen) and charge around the corner with screeching tires, almost on two wheels.

Another, internationally known faculty member was Professor Van der Neut. He was an expert in structural analysis and design. He and Assistant Professor Van Buuren, a former Fokker and Koolhoven* designer, really motivated me toward airplane structural design.

One very attractive feature of the Delft Aero Department was that it maintained an extensive aircraft collection. It had actual airplanes such as a B-25 bomber (Figure 30), a P-38 fighter (Figure 23), a P-51 fighter (Figure 21) and a P-47 fighter (Figure 22). These airplanes were obtained (for $1.00 each!) from the USArmy Air Corps which had declared them obsolete.

The department also had several older Fokker airplanes: the Fokker T-8 and the Fokker C-5 as well as an old Dornier(7) Do-24K amphibious airplane (Figures 50 - 52).

It was very instructive wandering through the collection and learning how airplanes are put together. Two of the airplanes were mounted solidly on jacks so that the flaps and the landing gear could be exercised by the students. What a wonderful way to learn! I remember exercising the B-25 gear and flaps quite a bit.

One reason the B-25 held special interest for the Dutch was the fact that there was a Dutch Mitchell Squadron flying for the RAF during WWII, and there were four Mitchell Squadrons flying for the RNAF in the East Indies during, and after, WWII.

As part of an early flight test course in my freshman year we made a number of flights in a Koolhoven FK-43 airplane (Figure 53). During one flight, heavy smoke began pouring from the nacelle. An emergency landing was made in a farmer's field. A hydraulic line to the variable pitch propeller had broken, sending a stream of hydraulic fluid over the engine cylinders.

Another degree requirement of the Delft Aeronautical Engineering Program was that all AE students were expected to undergo a minimum of six weeks practical training (industry internship), every summer for four years.

In all cases students were paid a fair wage. The European Association of Aircraft Manufacturers had struck an agreement with various universities to provide aeronautical engineering students with meaningful internship experiences. I believe this was a great program and I certainly learned a lot from it.

---

* Before WWII, Frits Koolhoven operated an airplane manufacturing company (Koolhoven Vliegtuigen) at the Waalhaven Airport of Rotterdam. The company was about the size of Fokker. The Germans destroyed the Koolhoven plant in May 1940.

I spent one summer working as an apprentice-machinist with a machine-tool manufacturer in The Hague, two summers at Fokker in Amsterdam, and one summer at Percival[(23)] Aircraft Ltd. in Luton, England.

War Story 11

My first summer as an intern in 1950 was spent working for the Escher Machine Construction Company in The Hague. On my first day, the shop foreman took me to a corner in a storage area and pointed to a heap of parts. He said, "That heap of parts used to be an automatic welding machine. It stopped working. Someone took it apart to try and fix it. However, he left the company before finishing the job. Your job is to fix it. By the way, there is also a manual. Come see me if you need any help."

It took me about two weeks to unscramble the mess, figure out what was wrong, repair it, and put the whole thing back in operation. Figure 54 shows the result.

This experience gave me a lot of insight into a fairly complex system, including the interaction of many components. It also taught me how automatic welding can fit into a manufacturing process. It was personally very satisfying to get that machine back in operation.

Lesson: Sometimes the "sink or swim" technique is an effective way to acquire a new skill.

The rest of my work at Escher consisted of helping with welding and assembling various types of construction machinery. Although all of this machinery was not destined to fly, I learned a great deal.

I spent the summer of 1951 at Fokker, located at the Schiphol Airport near Amsterdam. For details about the Fokker Aircraft Company see Reference 4.

At Fokker, I was assigned the task of helping with the disassembly of Douglas C-47, Dakota* transports and checking systems on the Gloster Meteor, Mark IV (twin jet fighter) assembly line. Figure 55 depicts this jet fighter, the first jet in the RNAF.

These experiences taught me a lot about detailed design, manufacturing, and assembly. I also gained first hand experience with the famous "ilities": accessibility, maintainability, inspectability, repairability and manufacturability. Later this greatly helped me in my early career as an airplane structural and systems designer.

The following three war stories are from my early Fokker experience.

---

* The C-47 was a military version of the Douglas DC-3. Thousands of these airplanes were built during WWII.

War Story 12

During my first summer internship at Fokker, I was assigned the job of helping to take the outer wing panels off 12 Douglas Dakota (military version of the DC-3) airplanes. Fokker had a contract from the RAF (Royal Air Force) to zero-time these airplanes.

The outer wing panels were attached to a flanged rib just outboard of the nacelles. The attachment consisted of many, many bolts. After removing the outer wing panels I remember looking at the inside of these wings and spotting a lot of corroded skin stiffeners. In fact, the corrosion was so bad that one could break off all the skin stiffeners by hand. This must really be appreciated in view of the fact that these airplanes had flown all the way from India to Amsterdam. Here was a classic case of overdesign of a wing structure.

I observed that the corrosion was impossible to spot before wing removal because no access panels were included in the basic design of those wings.

Lesson: In modern airplanes, wings are stressed much more accurately. Corrosion is prevented, or delayed, by various chemical treatments. Finally, in modern airplanes the structure must be easily inspectable in the field.

War Story 13

One of the Dakotas was parked in a hangar with a low ceiling. Mechanics had taken the tail surfaces off the airplane for inspection and repair. One day two inspectors entered the airplane from the rear fuselage door and walked (uphill!) to the cockpit. As they entered the cockpit, the c.g. of the airplane shifted forward of the main gear, and the airplane ponderously tipped onto its nose, crashing the rear fuselage into the roof girders of the hangar.

Lesson: When taking major components off an airplane during repair keep in mind that the center of gravity can move in ways that can result in damaging consequences. These should be prevented by proper procedures and retaining devices.

War Story 14

While being assigned to the Gloster Meteor (Figure 55) final assembly line, I participated in the checking of various systems with the airplane on jacks. Two jacks were mounted under the wings and one under the front fuselage. This allowed the flaps, gear and other systems to be freely exercised and checked.

There was a procedure in place for lowering the airplane from its jacks symmetrically by slowly bleeding off hydraulic pressure in each individual jack. This procedure required three people (one at each jack) and one supervisor. The task of the jack people was to slowly bleed off pressure in each jack at the command of the supervisor. The task of the supervisor was to watch that the airplane stayed level.

One day the supervisor decided to expedite matters while two jack people were at lunch. I was the only jack person around and was told to slowly lower the left wing jack. I suggested to the supervisor that it would be safer to wait until the other jack people returned and that it was against established procedure for me to lower one wing jack by myself.

The supervisor became rather obnoxious and shouted at me to do my job as instructed. I told him that if I did so the airplane might slide off one jack which could damage the airplane. He told me to do it or be fired.

Against my better judgment I proceeded with the task and slowly let the left wing jack down. Suddenly the airplane slid off the jack but was stopped by the main gear which, of course, was in the down position. However, the top of the jack put a big dent in the lower wing skin.

Luckily for me there were several witnesses and the supervisor was severely reprimanded. The damage to the wing skin was repaired.

Lesson: It is usually smart for everyone to follow established procedures in the shop.

Not all the courses I had to take in Delft were easy for me. I disliked the courses in aircraft stability and control, although I did well in them. Little did I know that, eventually, I would become an expert in that subject. I particularly dreaded the courses in fluid dynamics. The next war story deals with that.

War Story 15

We had to take several courses in fluid dynamics. These classes were given mostly by Professor Burgers, who was well known in the field. Although his lectures were good, there was something about the topic that turned me off, and I did not prepare thoroughly for his intermediate exams. As a result I got a conditional pass. That meant that I had to come in for an oral examination in his office. I had memorized the material but I must say that, at that time, I still could not claim to understand it. Professor Burgers quizzed me quite exhaustively and I answered every one of his questions. When he was done he looked me in the eye and said, "Mr. Roskam, you have done a marvelous job of memorizing the material. For that, I will allow you to pass this course. But you did not fool me: I do not believe you really understand fluid dynamics."

Lesson: Some professors are smarter than students think they are.

According to the Delft aeronautical engineering curriculum students were required to take at least one course in a non-aeronautical engineering subject. I elected to take a class called "Construction of Railroad Vehicles" because I always had an interest in railroading*.

The course was taught by Professor Van Eldik Thieme, an excellent teacher and an experienced railroad car designer. I still have my lecture notebook of that class; there were no textbooks available on that topic.

---

* As I am approaching retirement, I have built a credible HO model railroad in my home.

After his second lecture Professor Thieme invited me to his office and asked me to join his research group as a research assistant. In March of 1951 I did.

The first task assigned to me was to develop analytical procedures for the design of the suspension systems for new, high speed railroad cars. I learned a lot from this experience, particularly about how to apply the theory of dynamics to real world problems. This was also my first exposure to the practical application of Lagrange's Equations.

After two years of working on railroad cars, I was invited by Professor Van der Maas to become his research assistant in the area of aircraft manufacturing, planning and organization. That experience gave me a lot of insight into how and why airplanes are broken down into certain sub-assemblies and how these sub-assemblies in turn are produced.

As part of this work I built a large model of a fighter assembly line. The model was used by other students in the study of manufacturing and assembly problems. All this turned out to be a great help to me, not only in my senior airplane design project, but also later in my career as an airplane designer.

War Story 16

Professor Van der Maas decided that his students needed more insight and exposure to the general subject of manufacturing, planning and organization. Because he was too busy to prepare lectures on these topics, he asked me to prepare four lectures for him. I did.

Professor Van der Maas had the unique gift of being able to scan material and immediately present it in a very credible manner. He had total retention and a photographic memory. This was a good thing because he certainly did not have the time to study my material in any detail.

Part of what I prepared for him included some general discussions about industrial organization and the relationship to government. Professor Van der Maas was on the conservative side of the political spectrum, I was on the liberal side. The part of my material dealing with industrial organization and the relationship to government took him a bit by surprise.

His reaction was wonderful to watch. After presenting the material, he suddenly interrupted himself. "Obviously this is the opinion of my assistant, Mr. Roskam, but that does not mean that I agree." He then proceeded to set things straight, the way he saw them.

Lesson: Speechwriters have to be watched carefully.

During the spring of 1951 another interesting opportunity arose for me. The travel agency De Vrije Wereld (The Free World), in Amsterdam, was looking for aspirant tour guides to give tours in the mountains of Switzerland. I applied and was accepted.

During my first tour I was an apprentice and learned the trade from Mr. Cor Kramer. For two subsequent years, 1952 and 1953, I served as a full-fledged guide. Each tour usually had 20 to 30 participants. We went by motor coach from Amsterdam, Holland, to a Youth Hostel in Stechelberg, Switzerland. From there I led the group over a wide variety of trails into the mountains. We all carried backpacks with food and water.

I will never forget the visual evidence of the Battle of the Bulge. Our bus trips on the way to Switzerland took us through the Ardennes in Belgium and Luxembourg. Nearly all tree tops in about 60 miles of forest had been cut off by the immense bombing and artillery fire during WWII. This was six to seven years after the war and much of the Ardennes were still devastated.

These tours were a very pleasant way to learn how to get along with people from various backgrounds, and to get free trips to that most beautiful country: Switzerland. Since I was responsible for the safety of these people, I also learned how difficult it was to discourage some people from doing downright dumb things. I was lucky; there was never an accident even during glacier traverses.

Late in 1952 my attention was caught by an announcement that AE students could apply for flight training leading to a private and/or a commercial pilot license. The training was to be conducted at the Dutch National Flying School at the old Ypenburg Airport between The Hague and Delft. Every year about ten AE students were being selected for this flight program.

I applied and was accepted into the private pilot program (my eyesight was not adequate for the commercial pilot program). However, because I was not of legal age to make such a decision myself, I had to obtain my dad's signature.

One evening during our usual after dinner family discussions I asked my dad to sign the application. He refused on the grounds that flying was dangerous and he did not want to lose me in a silly flying accident. I was angry and very disappointed.

Three evenings later my dad informed me that he had changed his mind and would sign the papers. This was a happy turn of events and I was on my way to realizing another dream: becoming a pilot. I learned to fly on Piper[(24)] J-3 Cubs belonging to the National Flying School. Figure 56 shows a picture of this classic of the air.

Years later, my dad told me what happened. The day after he refused to sign my papers, he told one of his friends at work about it. His friend counseled him that he handled the situation all wrong. What my dad should have done was sign the papers and let me take my first flying lesson. After all, that would scare the living daylight out of me and I would never bring it up again! The advice obviously backfired. My first flying lesson convinced me that flying was to be part of my life.

I must say that my parents were very good sports about all this. As soon as I received my private pilot's license my mother was my first passenger, and my father my second! By the way, when I received my pilot license (in April of 1954) I did not yet have a driver's license. I did not get that until later that same year. I used my bicycle to go back and forth to the airport. When I finally took driving lessons my instructor was very impressed that he was teaching a licensed pilot who could not even drive a car!

War Story 17

One day I was landing a J-3 in a significant crosswind. I did a miserable job getting the airplane on the ground (meaning I really did not control it very well) and ended up in a ground-loop. Luckily this did not cause any physical damage.

Lesson: There are two types of pilots of tail-wheel airplanes: those who will and those who have ground-looped an airplane. With luck the latter will only damage one's ego!

War Story 18

Because the J-3 had a very low stall speed (around 32 kts) it was possible to perform the following "stunt" which was impressive from a ground observer's point of view.

In strong, steady winds, one could perform a takeoff, stay on the runway heading, climb a bit and then slow the airplane down to just above the stall speed. The wind would then blow you backwards, relative to the ground. With proper timing you could then land again and repeat the process. I remember having quite a bit of fun doing this.

Lesson: As long as you have steady winds, this type of maneuver can really teach you how to control an airplane close to the stall.

War Story 19

Early in 1953 there was a major northwest storm which coincided with an unfavorable moon-earth conjuncture. The resulting massive storm broke the Dutch sea dikes in several spots and flooded large parts of the country. I and my fellow students volunteered to "man the dikes" and shovel sand into bags and carry them to close off gaps in the dikes. We spent several miserable nights and days doing this labor. We took brief naps in tents, and were fed sandwiches and coffee by local residents who were glad to have our help.

When the main danger had passed, the Dutch Parliament insisted on hearings to determine how this could have happened. It was learned that the dikes had been designed to the so-called 1-per-200-year storm criterion. The Dutch actually have storm records dating back to the time of the birth of Christ!

Anyway, at the instigation of Parliament, a trade study was made to determine the cost of reconstructing the dikes against the 1-per-200, 1-per-500 and 1-per-1,000 year storm criterion. As a result, Parliament voted overwhelmingly to reconstruct the dikes to the 1-per-500 storm criterion. The country could simply not afford to do any better!

However, there is no guarantee that the 1-per-500 year storm won't happen tomorrow!

Lesson: Mankind cannot design anything with zero probability of failure. Trading the cost of increased safety versus the fatal accident rate is a fact of life for many design engineers.

Another way of interpreting this lesson is that a price must be put on human life when major design decisions are made. This is a very basic lesson which certainly applies to the design of airplane structures, engines, and flight crucial systems.

The new system of dikes was finally finished in 1986. Two years later all reconstructed areas were accessible by highways. Anyone visiting Holland should go and see the incredible engineering job that was done to protect the country from the sea.

War Story 20

My first solo cross-country flight took place in the middle of the winter of 1953. I had to fly to a small airport with a grass runway located in the east of Holland. There was snow all over the countryside. It really was cold and the J-3 had no heating system and leaked cold air all over the place. My toes felt frozen most of the way.

Before landing, I first had to make two low passes over the runway to chase the sheep away. I set the airplane down and parked in front of a little building where the airport keeper treated me to a cup of hot chocolate. Before I could leave he took his jeep and chased the sheep away again.

Lesson: Sheep don't mind the snow as long as they know there is grass underneath.

War Story 21

My final cross-country was to the island of Texel, located in the north of Holland. To fly there from Ypenburg required one to fly over the North Sea along the coast, but far enough out to avoid a military training area. I must have been a bit chicken flying over water so I decided to keep the coastline in clear view. I should have known better. This took me through the military area and pretty soon I had a Spitfire of the RNAF on my tail. Spitfires (Figure 31) were used in those days as squadron hacks and to chase undesirable airplanes out of certain areas. I don't remember which made me more nervous: flying over water or having that Spitfire circle around me until I finally could begin my descent into the Texel Airport.

Lesson: Always stay clear of forbidden zones.

During the summer of 1952, again at Fokker, I was lucky to work for the already famous Jan Schliekelman in his manufacturing research group. New metal bonding procedures were being developed, tested, and then applied to the twin-turboprop F-27 and the twin-jet F-28 transports (Figures 48 and 49).

My job was to keep track of test specimens and test them to destruction while recording pertinent stress and strain information. I also had to inspect for any signs of mis-bonding. It was interesting to work in the "clean room" facilities used in the metal bonding process. It was also useful to be exposed to working with various tensile and shear test machines and learn to record and interpret stress and strain data.

In September of 1952 I attended the Farnborough Air Show in England. I spent two days talking to various airplane company representatives and collecting data on airplanes. I also witnessed a spectacular accident which came close to ending my life.

War Story 22

During one of the flying displays, the De Havilland Company was demonstrating its brand new carrier-based fighter, the DH 110 Sea-Vixen. This was one of the first supersonic, twin-jet, fighters. The airplane was configured as a twin-boom airplane (Figure 57). Reference 2 contains interesting details about many DeHavilland airplanes.

There were two prototypes at the show: one had a known aileron-tab-flutter problem resulting in a maximum speed limitation, and the other which had been modified to eliminate the problem. The "problem" airplane was at the show for static display only; the other was for demonstration flights.

One morning it was discovered that the flight demo prototype had developed a serious oil leak that would take at least a day to fix. Therefore, it was decided to fly the other airplane. The test pilot, John Derry, and his flight engineer, Tony Richards, were briefed on the problem and the need to observe the speed limitation.

Part of the scheduled flight demo included a high speed, very low altitude pass perpendicular to the line of spectators followed by a steep pull-up maneuver. I was standing amongst hundreds of spectators as the airplane approached straight at us at high speed. As soon as the pull-up maneuver started, I saw parts separate from the airplane. A split second later the entire airplane broke into many pieces. The two engines separated from the airframe and fell into the crowd, killing many spectators. The pilot and flight engineer had no time to eject. The front fuselage with both crew members crashed into the ground about 50 yards from where I was standing. The entire sequence of events is still like a horror movie in my memory. I was not able to move for quite a while after the crash. I was completely stunned.

The first thing I did after regaining my composure was to find a telephone, call my parents in Holland and let them know that I was all right. They had already heard of the tragedy and were very worried.

Lesson: It is vital that flight test crews observe all speed limits to which they are briefed. It is also not smart to release an airplane and crew if a serious problem is known to exist.

War Story 23

One course all engineering students at Delft had to take and pass was called Government Organization Types. The course was taught by a prominent Dutch journalist and nobleman with the impressive name of Professor Josephus Jitta. He was also editor-in-chief and owner of the newspaper, *De Haagsche Courant*. His office was on the top floor of a building in the center of The Hague. That office was huge. A lengthy red carpet led from his office door to his desk.

Professor Jitta was feared by most students because he had a habit of flunking the great majority on their first attempt to pass his oral examination. These exams were always held in his office. Early in 1953 it was my turn. In those days students were expected to appear for an oral examination dressed in a formal suit with black tie.

When I entered his office he motioned me to approach his desk and astounded me by saying, "Mr. Roskam, you will be pleased to hear that you have passed this examination." Naturally I was dumbfounded because I had not yet uttered a word. He then motioned to some comfortable chairs around a conference table, and invited me to sit down. When we were seated he said, "What I would like to do is to discuss the Korean War with you."

He summoned his secretary for afternoon coffee and cake and we proceeded to have a lively discussion about the Korean War. It lasted well over two hours. He then thanked me and I left. The next day I found out that he had given me an A for my "performance."

Lesson: You never know what to expect from certain professors.

My fourth summer internship in 1953 was spent at Percival Aircraft Ltd. in Luton, England. At that time, Percival was manufacturing the Percival Prince (twin-engined, propeller-driven, utility transport) and the Percival Provost (single-engine, propeller-driven, primary trainer for the RAF). Percival was also working on the prototype of the Percival Pembroke, a navalized, larger version of the Prince, as well as the Percival Jet Provost, which was to be a high-commonality, jet-powered version of the Provost. Figures 58, 59, 60 and 61 show pictures of the Prince, Pembroke, Provost and Jet-Provost respectively. Reference 23 contains more detailed information on the Percival Aircraft Company.

Because I was not a wealthy student I could not afford to fly from Amsterdam to London. Therefore, I bought a ticket on a ferry from Hoek van Holland to Norwich. The crossing of the North Sea was my first experience traveling by ship. The sea was pretty rough and I was sick and miserable most of the way.

After I arrived at the boarding house in Luton where I was to stay, the first thing I did was book a return flight on a British European Airways flight from London to Amsterdam. I was not about to travel by ship again if I could help it.

This resolve changed much later in my life when I was given the opportunity to spend some time on the USNavy aircraft carrier *Lexington.*

My time in Luton and at Percival Aircraft was very enjoyable. I was invited to join the Luton Tennis Club and played a lot of tennis during evening hours. I also attended several professional soccer games.

One of my fellow engineers at Percival also was staying at my boarding house. He had a small, red, two-seat MG sports car and invited me to ride with him to work. That solved my transportation problem very nicely.

War Story 24

My first assignment at Percival was to verify the structural design, load-paths and stress calculations which had been done on the wing tip extension of the new Pembroke. To do this I was given copies of all appropriate drawings, which had already been released to prototype manufacturing. The Pembroke was a slightly larger version of the Prince, a twin-engine, propeller-driven, high wing, utility transport airplane.

I discovered a major flaw in the design which would have caused the wing tip to come off on the very first flight. As it turned out, this flawed design had already been installed on the first prototype. I proposed a redesign which was approved and installed.

Lesson: All flight crucial structural design aspects of an airplane should be cross-checked by an engineer other than the original design engineer.

The chief stressman was very grateful and asked what favor he could do for me. I suggested he get me approved for some test hops in Percival airplanes. He introduced me to the chief test pilot and arrangements were made. That week I had the good fortune to get rides on the Prince and the Provost. I also was invited to ride as a pseudo flight test engineer on the first flight of the Pembroke. Needless to say these were wonderful experiences.

War Story 25

Percival also was working on a jet powered version of the Provost, called the Jet Provost. The basic idea was to create a low cost, jet-powered version of the very successful Provost, the standard propeller-driven trainer of the RAF which was in production at that time. To achieve this objective it was decided to utilize a high degree of commonality between the two airplanes.

Figure 62 shows a side-by-side comparison of the two airplanes. It is evident from Figure 62 that commonality in this case is largely an illusion.

Lesson: Retaining commonality between two designs with widely differing powerplants and widely differing flight envelopes (altitude and Mach number) often proves impossible. History shows that in most cases a better and lower cost solution is to start with a fresh sheet of paper (or today, with a new CAD file).

My final assignment at Percival consisted of documenting and verifying its administrative system of shop orders and the associated man-hour and cost accounting. That assignment was particularly interesting because it gave me insight into how shop orders come about and how difficult it is to account for hours and cost of any given project.

War Story 26

After completing my internship at Percival, I flew back to Amsterdam on an Airspeed[(25)] Ambassador of British European Airways. Figure 63 shows that airplane, a rather attractive design. It looked like a high wing, twin engine Constellation. During cruise flight (conducted at fairly low altitude because of the short distance between London and Amsterdam), I felt and heard a sharp thump somewhere in the back of the airplane. Pretty soon the copilot showed up to look out of the right side windows to visually inspect the tail. With a shrug he strolled back to the cockpit.

Upon arrival at Amsterdam I got out with the pilots and walked around the airplane (we did not have jet-ways in those days) to look at the tail. There was substantial damage to the leading edge of the right vertical tail. The pilots thought that we had been hit by a large gull. There were blood smears and feathers at the leading edge.

Lesson: Airplanes are going to get hit by birds. At low altitudes some of these birds are bound to be larger than the regulatory four pound birds we are designing for now. Perhaps these regulations should be revised.

Also in 1953, I ran for vice president of the Organization of Aeronautical Engineering Students (VSV) and was elected. The board of the VSV was invited to various European functions and that was good for networking and finding out what was going on.

I remember one memorable trip to France for a visit to the Breguet* Aircraft Factory. Breguet at that time had the four-engine Deux Ponts (Two Bridges) transport airplane in production. This was a very impressive airplane although not many of them were built. Figure 64 shows a three-view of the Deux Ponts.

Breguet also was engaged in the production of a jet powered missile with wings made out of prestressed concrete!!! It had developed a special technique of casting fine-grained concrete in thin molds with a few steel ribs and piano wire to pre-stress the concrete. The wings were very thin (six percent) and the French designers claimed that they were not only cheap to make, but weighed little more than aluminum wings. They also claimed that they could make six wings per hour.

During my last year at the Delft TU, I remember attending several lectures by disciples of Professor Deeming of MIT (Massachusetts Institute of Technology). Their emphasis on quality management and customer satisfaction made a lasting impression on me. One of their famous conjectures was that 90% of all mistakes made in industry are the fault of management, not the workers. That really caught my attention. More about that later in the book, see Page 69.

---

* Named after Louis Breguet, aircraft designer and the first to derive range and endurance equations for airplanes. These formulas are known to aero engineers as the Breguet equations.

My final design project at Delft consisted of the preliminary design of a large, four-engine piston-propeller transport with detachable fuselage.

My design looked like a larger, four-engine version of the Fairchild(26) C-119 Packet which served as my inspiration. Armand Thieblot, the chief designer at Fairchild, had been very kind to send me data on the C-119 (Figure 65).

I did a lot of work on that design, including the very challenging landing gear. I even built a large model of the airplane which I named the Pallas Athene after a Greek goddess of trade. A detailed structural design and corresponding loads analysis of the tail surfaces was an accompanying requirement of that design study. All this taught me a lot about the steps leading from conceptual design, to structural layout design, load analysis, stress analysis, resizing of the structure and final structural layout for manufacturing.

As a student I clearly liked preliminary design and structural layout design the best. I also enjoyed analyzing a design from a manufacturability viewpoint. I remember distinctly disliking the subject of stability and control. However, since this was an extremely important aspect of preliminary design, I believe I did a credible job in it. Circumstances would eventually transform me into an international expert on that subject.

I finished all required course and project work for the Delft MSAE degree during the late spring of 1954. Therefore, I was officially scheduled to graduate that fall. My plan was to serve my required two years in the Royal Netherlands Air Force and then emigrate to the USA.

However, in May of 1954 I received an unsolicited job offer to become assistant chief designer at Aviolanda(27) Aircraft Company. That company was located in Papendrecht, Holland. That job offer represented such a challenging and attractive opportunity that I could not turn it down. Later I heard that Professor Van der Neut had recommended me for the job.

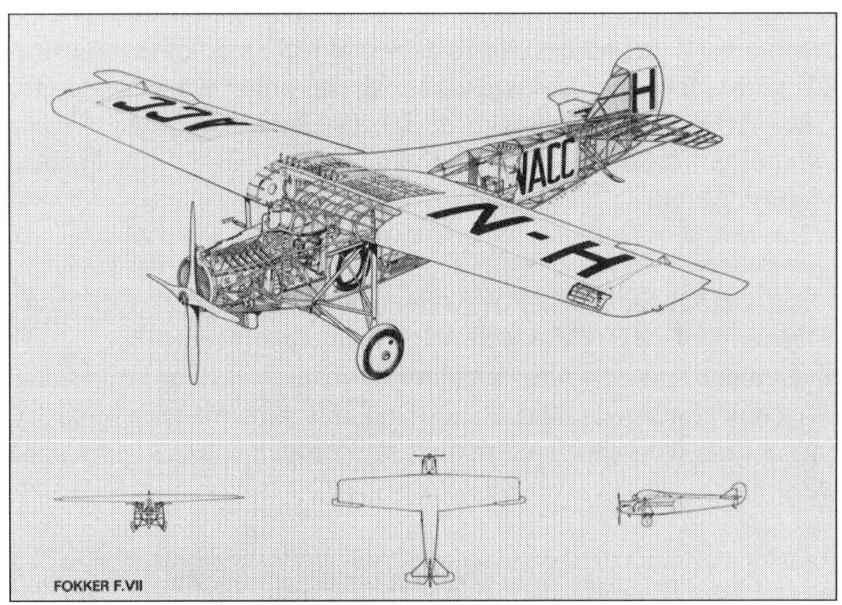

Figure 41 Fokker FVII (Courtesy Fokker)

Figure 42 Douglas DC-5 (Courtesy Douglas)

Figure 43 Fokker F-25 (Courtesy Fokker)

Figure 44 Fokker S-11 (Courtesy Fokker)

Figure 45 Fokker S-12 (Courtesy Fokker)

Figure 46 Fokker S-13 (With Permission from the Royal Aeronautical Society Library)

Figure 47 Fokker S-14 (Courtesy Fokker)

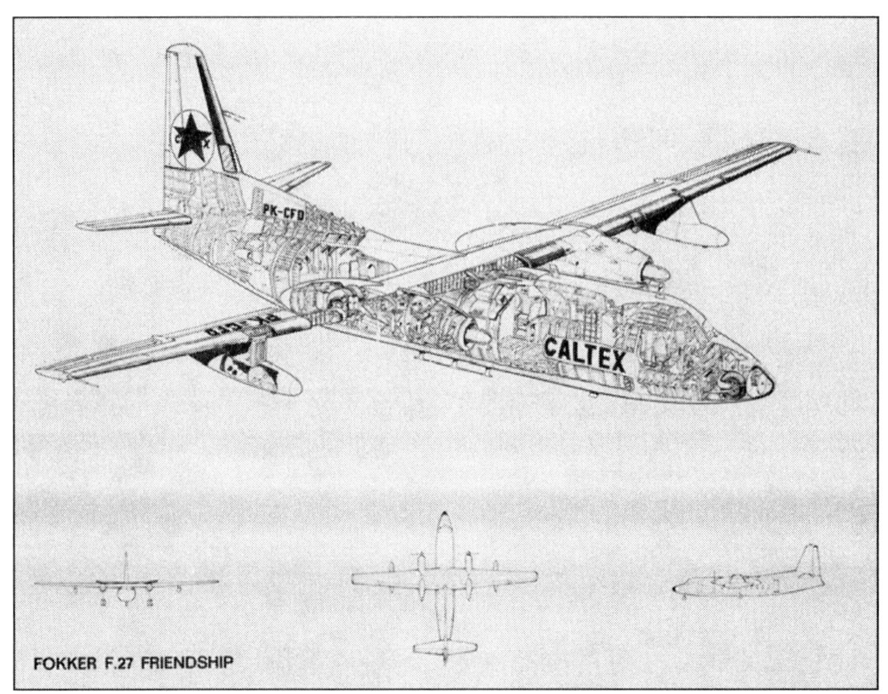

Figure 48 Fokker F-27 (Courtesy Fokker)

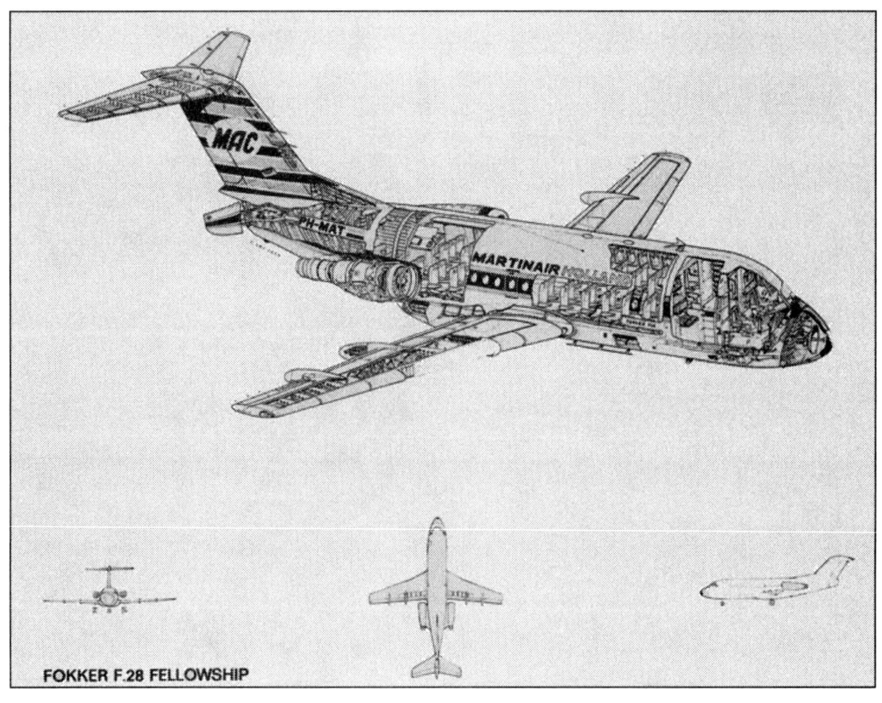

Figure 49 Fokker F-28 (Courtesy Fokker)

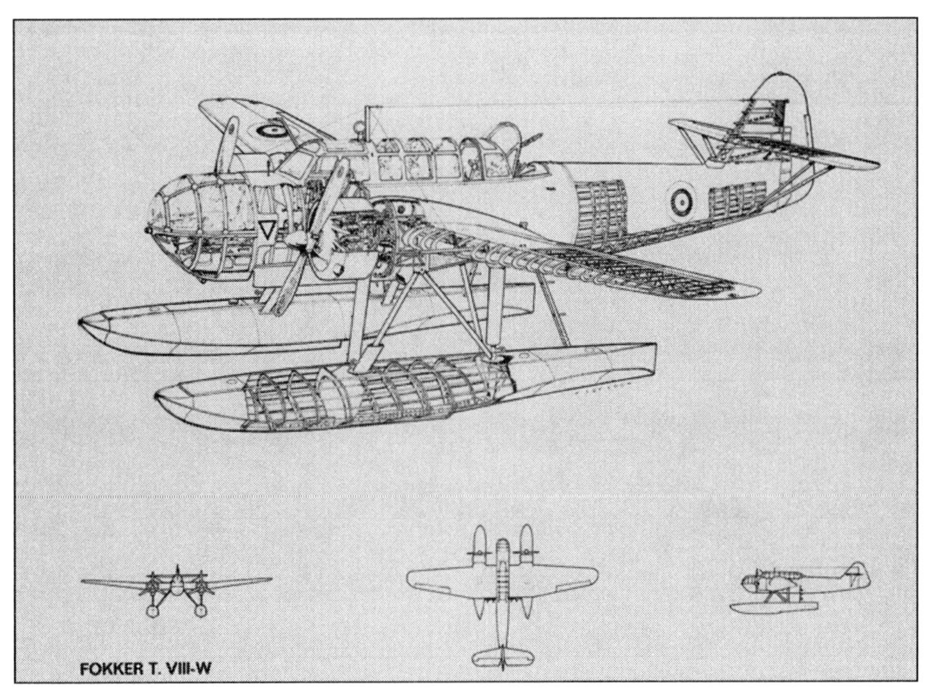

Figure 50 Fokker T-8 (Courtesy Fokker)

Figure 51 Fokker C-5 (Courtesy Fokker)

Figure 52 Dornier Do24K (With Permission from the Royal Aeronautical Society Library)

Figure 53 Frits Koolhoven FK-43 (With Permission from the Royal Aeronautical Society Library)

Figure 54 Escher Welding Machine Repaired by the Author (Courtesy Escher)

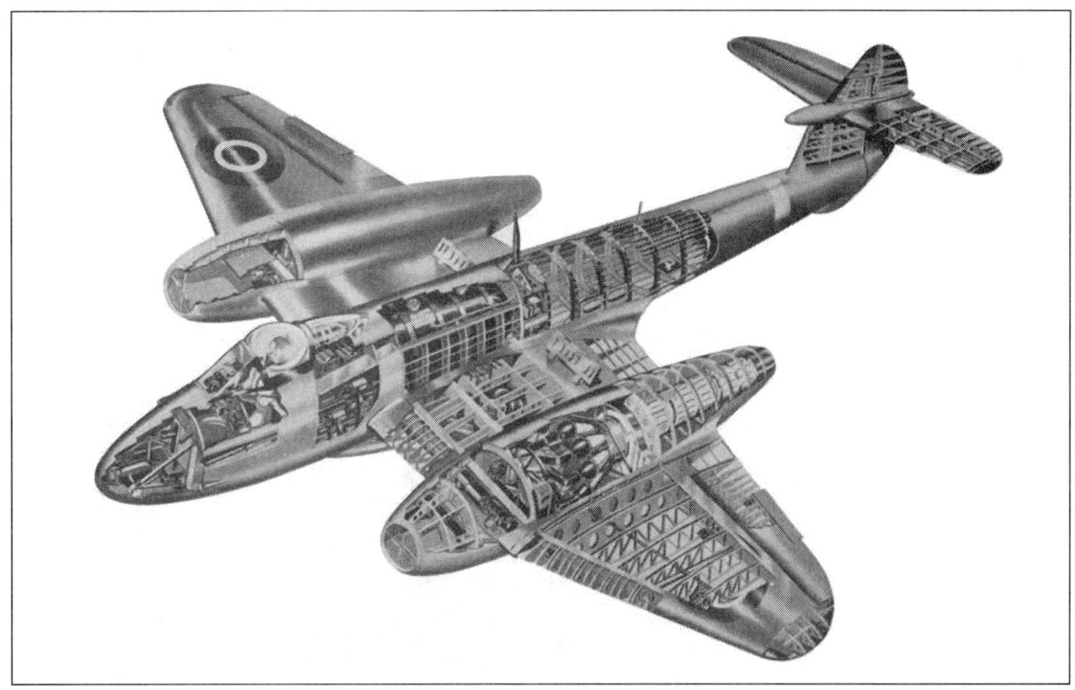

Figure 55 Cutaway of the Gloster Meteor, Mark IV (Courtesy Gloster)

Figure 56 Model of the Piper J-3, Cub in which the Author Learned to Fly

Figure 57 De Havilland 110, Seavixen (With Permission from the Royal Aeronautical Society Library)

Figure 58 Percival Prince (From Ref. 23 with Permission from Mrs. B. Silvester)

Figure 59 Percival Pembroke (From Ref. 23 with Permission from Mrs. B. Silvester)

Figure 60 Percival Provost (From Ref. 23 with Permission from Mrs. B. Silvester)

Figure 61 Percival Jet-Provost (From Ref. 23 with Permission from Mrs. B. Silvester)

Figure 62 Commonality Lost: Provost and Jet-Provost (From Ref. 23 with Permission from Mrs. B. Silvester)

Figure 63 Airspeed Ambassador (Courtesy Airspeed)

Figure 64 Three-view of the Breguet Deux Ponts (From De Jong, A.P. and P.A.; Vliegtuigen van de Amerikaanse Luchtmacht; Uitgeverij Born, Amsterdam, The Netherlands, 1954)

Figure 65 Fairchild C-119, Packet (From De Jong, A.P. and P.A.; Vliegtuigen van de Amerikaanse Luchtmacht; Uitgeverij Born, Amsterdam, The Netherlands, 1954)

Chapter 4: Years at Aviolanda and in the Royal Netherlands Air Force

When I joined the Aviolanda[27] Aircraft Company in the summer of 1954, it had a distinguished record of producing flying boats for the Royal Netherlands Navy, and major aircraft subassemblies for various types of military and civilian aircraft. The company also carried out aircraft repairs and heavy maintenance work. The company headquarters and main manufacturing facilities were located in Papendrecht. Papendrecht is a small community, just across the Merwede River from the city of Dordrecht. Reference 27 describes some of the history of the company which later became integrated into the Fokker Aircraft Company.

The bread and butter line of Aviolanda in 1954 was the series production of fuselages for the Hawker Hunter jet fighter (Figure 66) which was being assembled by Fokker in Amsterdam for several European air forces, including the RNAF (Royal Netherlands Air Force). The Hunter was to take over from the Gloster Meteor which was becoming obsolete.

When I started working for Aviolanda, the company had just initiated design studies of a pulse-jet powered, remotely controlled, target drone system called the AT-21. The vehicle was a high wing, remotely controlled airplane with a horizontal tail and twin vertical tails. The customer was primarily the Royal Netherlands Navy.

The structural design was an interesting hybrid. The fuselage and control surfaces were made from aluminum alloys. The wing, horizontal tail, and vertical tails were made from foam-in-place filled fiberglass. This was fairly revolutionary for that time.

The engine was a valveless (acoustical) pulse-jet, the AS-11, designed and manufactured by SNECMA of France. The engine had an installed thrust of 150 lbs. Figure 67 shows a cut-away rendition of the Aviolanda AT-21. Note the cowling around the engine. This cowling also functioned as a thrust augmenter. Also note the air bottles forward of the fuel tank. These air bottles served, via a reduction valve, to keep the fuel tank pressurized and force fuel into the atomizers inside the combustion chamber of the pulse-jet. It was a very simple system and it worked.

The AT-21 was to be launched with two solid rockets of the same type as used to RATO (Rocket Assisted Takeoff) Dutch naval Hawker Seafury fighters (Figure 68) during carrier* takeoffs. Figure 69 shows the AT-21 on its launcher.

The design engineering department of Aviolanda consisted of a chief engineer (Jan de Vries); an aerodynamicist (Evert Eveleyn); a manufacturing and stress engineer (Peter Linssen, a friend and former fellow student); another stress engineer (Dolf Pegel, also a former fellow student); a systems engineer (Olaf von Michalofski, a former high school classmate); two detail design engineers, and me. My job title was assistant-chief-designer. When required,

---

* In those days the Dutch Navy operated the aircraft carrier *Karel Doorman* which was later sold to Argentina.

we could call on the company draftmen's office for the translation of design concepts into actual manufacturing drawings.

In many ways we functioned very much like the Lockheed Skunk Works, although at that time we did not know it.

Shortly after entering employment at Aviolanda, my colleague, Dolf Pegel, and I were drafted for a two year service period by the Royal Netherlands Air Force. In those days, every Dutchman was legally obligated to serve two years in the armed forces.

When I told my boss about my orders to show up at boot camp he told me not to worry. Sure enough, a week or so later Dolf and I received new orders from the RNAF to show up at officers' candidate school for a lightning training course which would make us second lieutenants for special technical services in Her Majesty's RNAF.

The course lasted about three weeks. I got a good background in how to handle small weapons, including various types of machine guns. Most importantly, we were even taught how to dig a fox hole. Figure 70 shows Dolf and me in such a foxhole. Figure 71 depicts the entire officer candidates' class in battle fatigues, with rifles ready.

Weekend travel from home to our training base was cumbersome. With the help of a loan from my father, I purchased my first car, a really small Renault 4CV. Figure 72 shows me as the proud owner of that vehicle. This made traveling much more agreeable.

After being commissioned, my orders were to return to my civilian job but now in uniform! Administratively, I was detached to the Royal Netherlands Army which had a garrison in the city of Dordrecht, across the Merwede River from Papendrecht. This was a fortunate way to fulfill my military service.

My main responsibilities at Aviolanda were the structural design of the fuselage, the fuel system, the nacelle and the powerplant testing, and systems-to-airframe integration for the AT-21 target drone system. I also supervised the design of the ground control cab and the launch bridge. The design and testing of the launch system was also my responsibility. A three-view of the AT-21 vehicle is shown in Figure 73.

War Story 27

A one time interesting side duty, which I remember vividly, was dropping flowers on members of the Dutch Royal House. I believe the year was 1955. There was to be a big air show at Ypenburg Airport* and many members of the House of Orange were invited as guests of honor. A RNAF colonel was in charge of organizing the air show.

The colonel asked me to drop flowers over the grandstand from a height of 1500 feet from a Piper J-3 Cub owned by the National Flying School. To get ready for the show, my orders

---

* This airport was located just south of The Hague. It no longer exists.

were to takeoff from Ypenburg in the early morning and to land at Valkenburg, a Dutch Naval Air Station, located north of The Hague. Valkenburg was used to dispatch all airplanes for the show.

After landing at Valkenburg, a group of four Hawker Seahawks, carrier-based fighters from the British Royal Navy arrived. Figure 74 shows this very attractive airplane which was also participating in the air show. I remember being surprised when the flight leader stepped out of his cockpit: he had a long, black beard! How he managed that with his oxygen mask still puzzles me today.

At the proper time, my Piper Cub was loaded with hundreds of flower heads. My passenger was to drop them over the side at my signal. We latched the side window in the down position and took off for Ypenburg where we managed to unload the flowers right over the target: the Dutch Queen Juliana, her husband, Prince Bernhard, and their children. After dropping our flowers, we landed to the applause of the crowd.

As I remember, this was the only occasion that I piloted an airplane while in RNAF uniform.

Lesson: In those days, nobody worried much about security. Today, this would be a real nightmare for security people, and probably would not be allowed.

Back to the AT-21. For ease of sea-recovery the wings and tails of the AT-21 were attached to the fuselage with explosive bolts. The design, development and testing of these bolts was also part of my job. Since none of us at Aviolanda had any experience with explosives, and since there were no explosive bolts on the market at that time, we decided to develop them on our own. To do this we enlisted the help of a Dutch fireworks' manufacturer. After quite a bit of trial and error testing we were able to come up with a design that worked, was cheap, and promised to have a good shelf life.

The propulsion component of my job took me to Paris on many occasions to consult with French SNECMA engineers regarding the engine, for which Aviolanda also had negotiated the manufacturing rights.

While in Paris I also was assigned the job of coordinating with SFIM, a company that furnished much of the sensors and instrumentation for the AT-21.

Looking back on my Aviolanda experience it is amazing how much we got accomplished with very few engineers and technicians, and very little calendar time. We had a major advantage: total freedom to do whatever we thought was right. We all developed into generalists simply because we did not have the specialists.

Later in my career I learned that this operating environment was very similar to that used by Lockheed[(14)] in its Skunk Works, by Burt Rutan[(28)] in his Scaled Composites Company, and by Dassault of France.

War Story 28

It was decided that we needed to verify the AS-11 thrust and fuel flow predictions made by SNECMA. For that reason we put together an instrumented test-stand. This test-stand was built adjacent to a very large, and very wide, concrete ramp. This ramp had been built before WWII for the launch of flying boats into the Merwede River. Aviolanda was manufacturing these flying boats for the Royal Netherlands Navy. The concrete ramp conveniently separated the thrust-stand from the factory and various offices.

The "business end" of the stand was pointed at the Merwede River which was so wide that a ferry service had to be used to go from Papendrecht to Dordrecht. I vividly remember the tremendous noise made by our pulse-jet during bench testing; it put out an amazing 160 decibels at full throttle. As the crow flies, the test-stand was located about four miles from the market square in Dordrecht. Soon after starting engine testing we received angry complaints from the Dordrecht police that the people and merchants in the market square could not converse in a normal tone of voice! Needless to say we had to agree to certain curfew times to carry out further testing.

Lesson: Noise, and the fact that this can pose a nuisance to other people, is something aircraft designers must consider. Nowadays there exists a regulation which defines how much noise airplanes may perpetrate on communities. The regulation is FAR 36.

War Story 29

The second pulse-jet we tested had been manufactured at Aviolanda (under a licensing agreement with SNECMA). One day, while running an endurance test during which the combustion chamber ran red hot, a horrible noise emanated from the test-stand and the engine quit. After turning off the fuel supply we looked at the engine and found that it had imploded. Figure 75 shows a photograph of the imploded pulse-jet.

The problem was traced to a "lower than specification" sheet gauge used in the manufacturing of the combustion chamber of the pulse-jet.

Lesson: Pulse-jets undergo a rapidly oscillating pressure cycle. During that part of the cycle where the inside pressures are below atmospheric pressure, implosion can occur. This is made easier because the walls are red hot which reduces the ability of the sheet metal to withstand external pressures.

War Story 30

In 1956 there was a lot of political tension in Hungary. In those days, Hungary was still under Soviet control. Various freedom movements were stirring and getting ready to overthrow the communist government. These movements were being actively encouraged by the USA and by NATO. At one point things got so hot that all NATO forces were put on high alert.

Once a week I had garrison night duty. What that meant was that I had a room in the local Dutch Army barracks where I could sleep. In addition to a bed, the room was equipped with two red telephones, a regular telephone, and a locked cabinet which contained envelopes with contingency plans. One red phone was there to alert the duty officer that something was going on. The other red phone was a secure line to the commanding officer of the garrison.

One night I had just fallen asleep when a red telephone rang. The message was to "proceed with plan A." I opened the locked cabinet which held all the classified plans, and opened the envelope marked A. According to plan A, I had to call the officer in command and inform him what had transpired and then put everyone in the barracks on alert. I did all this and took temporary charge of the barracks.

As it turned out, the Hungarian Revolution had broken out and the Soviets were in the process of moving tanks and troops to crush the uprising. The next evening we were told that the alert had been lifted because President Eisenhower had decided not to intervene on behalf of the Hungarian revolutionaries. NATO was powerless without American help.

Lesson: When starting a revolution toward democracy don't necessarily count on your friends.

At Aviolanda, as a side task, Peter Linssen and I also were given the job to follow-up on manufacturing errors which occurred in the production of Hawker Hunter fuselages.

War Story 31

Aviolanda at that time was manufacturing a major part of the fuselage for the Hawker Hunter jet fighter (Figure 66). A side responsibility assigned to me was the structural analysis of misdrilled bolt and rivet holes in skins, stringers and frames of the Hunter.

This misdrilling of holes came about as follows. Every Monday morning workers had to check out the drill bits needed for their work. These fairly expensive drill bits were checked in every Friday evening before the weekend. At that point I did not know that the lighting conditions in the storeroom were rather below par and workers often grabbed the wrong size drill bits. As a result, overdrilling of holes was a fairly frequent occurrence!

My job was to determine whether or not the skin or frame was still usable, repairable, or had to be discarded. The latter outcome was obviously very expensive for the company. I became rather proficient at using the well-known book by Bruhn[(29)], which contains many procedures for analyzing aircraft structures.

After several weeks I became curious about the reason behind these mistakes. By visiting workers and foremen I soon found out that the main reason for the mistakes was the extremely poor lighting in the store room. I suggested to management that a minor investment in better lighting might eliminate most of the mis-drilling of holes and therefore end up saving the company money in the long term. My suggestion was accepted and worked.

Lesson: This was my first real life exposure to the thesis espoused by Professor Deeming of MIT that 90% of the mistakes made in industry are the fault of management and not of the workers! There is a lot of truth in this.

The following war story deals with another interesting experience I had with what is called, “reverse” engineering.

War Story 32

Aviolanda received a contract to zero-time a number of Royal Air Force Consolidated-Vultee (later Convair) PBY-3 Catalina[30] flying boats. The Catalina was a very popular military flying boat during WWII. It served mostly as a search and rescue airplane although torpedo-bomber versions of the airplane also were in use. Figure 76 shows one of many types of Catalina flying boats which were built.

The airplanes that showed up at Aviolanda (they were landed on the Merwede River, adjacent to the plant) had major corrosion problems in the fuselage and in the outer wing panels. The management of Aviolanda decided, basically, to rebuild the outer wings. To do this, access to the appropriate wing drawings was needed. Upon contacting Convair in San Diego it was found that the originals of the Catalina drawings had been destroyed and that copies were no longer available.

At that point I was called into a meeting with our management and asked what might be done. I suggested that we could simply reverse-engineer the drawings by carefully measuring the existing spars, stringers, ribs and skins.

Needless to say I was assigned the task to see to it that this work would be done. With the help of our drafting office we reverse-engineered the entire outer wing panels and validated the dimensions via Bruhn-type stress analyses (Reference 29). The latter was necessary because we had to use metric aluminum gauges whereas the airplane had been built with American gauges. This meant that the empty weight of the airplane went up a bit. But it worked, and the RAF was happy with the zero-timed Catalinas.

Lesson: Reverse-engineering an existing design sometimes is the most cost-effective way to replace components for which drawings are not available. However, don’t forget that the empty weight will probably increase!

War Story 33

In the summer of 1955 I had to attend a conference on the south coast of England, more or less near Brighton. I had been requested by my boss, Mr. De Vries, also to take care of some AT-21 business with the Dowty Company.

Dowty was working on the design and development of several pressure reduction valves for the AT-21. It was agreed that the company would pick me up by airplane at a small airfield close to where my conference was being held. A company pilot was to fly me to Dowty headquarters and return me the same day.

At the appointed time a Percival Proctor showed up and landed. Figure 77 shows a picture of the Percival Proctor. The pilot judged the runway too short for a normal takeoff with me and my heavy briefcase on board.

At the suggestion of the pilot we pulled the Proctor about 150 feet onto the access road. We then boarded the airplane, ran through all the checks, and started the takeoff run. Rounding the corner of the access road onto the runway turned out to be easy and we were soon airborne. This surely was the strangest takeoff I ever experienced. Figure 78 shows the runway and access road arrangement of the airfield.

Lesson: Sometimes you have to throw away the book.

War Story 34

My job on the AT-21 program specifically did not include the design, development and testing of the avionics and the remote control system. That was in the hands of other people mainly outside our design department. Our boss, Mr. De Vries, kept us out of that loop. As a consequence all I could do was ask questions during our weekly project meetings. It became apparent to me that this part of the project was rapidly becoming its Achilles heel.

Some of my questions about avionics system design, system integrity, system testing and system schedules began to irritate my boss. At one point, to pacify the Dutch Navy, Mr. De Vries decided to schedule a test launch of the AT-21 without a functional control system but with a functional parachute recovery system. I thought this was a total waste of time and money and again made myself very unpopular by pointing it out. We did launch the test dummy, and it worked but what did it prove?

Lessons:

1) When a company embarks on a project which has a brand new technology side to it, which is also critical to the success of the project, it is essential that management establish clear design, test and systems integration objectives and schedules.

2) It is critical that all project team members be properly informed and given the opportunity to ask questions during design reviews.

3) Company management and the customer need to be given completely honest reports on progress, or the lack thereof.

It was evident to me that the project suffered from poor management decision making. In addition, the customer, the Royal Dutch Navy, was not kept properly informed.

It also seemed to me that very poor control was exercised over the critical avionics component of the AT-21 project. As it turned out, after I had left the company the entire project was cancelled because of these problems.

Since I still had the desire to emigrate to the USA after my military service, I decided to quit my job. After a surprisingly amicable discussion with Mr. De Vries, and with the fiat from my military bosses, I left Aviolanda and spent the last three months of my military service working at the Department of Defense in The Hague on procurement issues surrounding the Hawker Hunter fighter. My boss, Lt.Col. Ooyens, later became a general in the RNAF.

This turn of events actually became very useful for me. It gave me a lot of insight into the political workings behind the scenes of military/civilian contractor negotiations.

Late in 1956 I wrote a letter to Cessna Aircraft Company in Wichita, Kansas. I had decided that I wanted to work for Cessna after doing considerable research on various US aircraft manufacturers. I liked Cessna, its product line, and in particular, the Cessna T-37 and potential attack version derivatives. In my letter to Cessna I offered my services in the area of structures design. To my amazement Cessna offered me a job as a structures layout designer on the Cessna T-37. Cessna also took care of all the immigration formalities and visa requirements.

For the interested reader, References 31 - 33 contain useful overviews of the development of Cessna commercial airplanes. These excellent books were written and published by Bill Thompson who served as head of aerodynamics and chief test pilot for the Commercial Aircraft Division of Cessna.

Figure 66 Hawker Hunter (With Permission from the Royal Aeronautical Society Library)

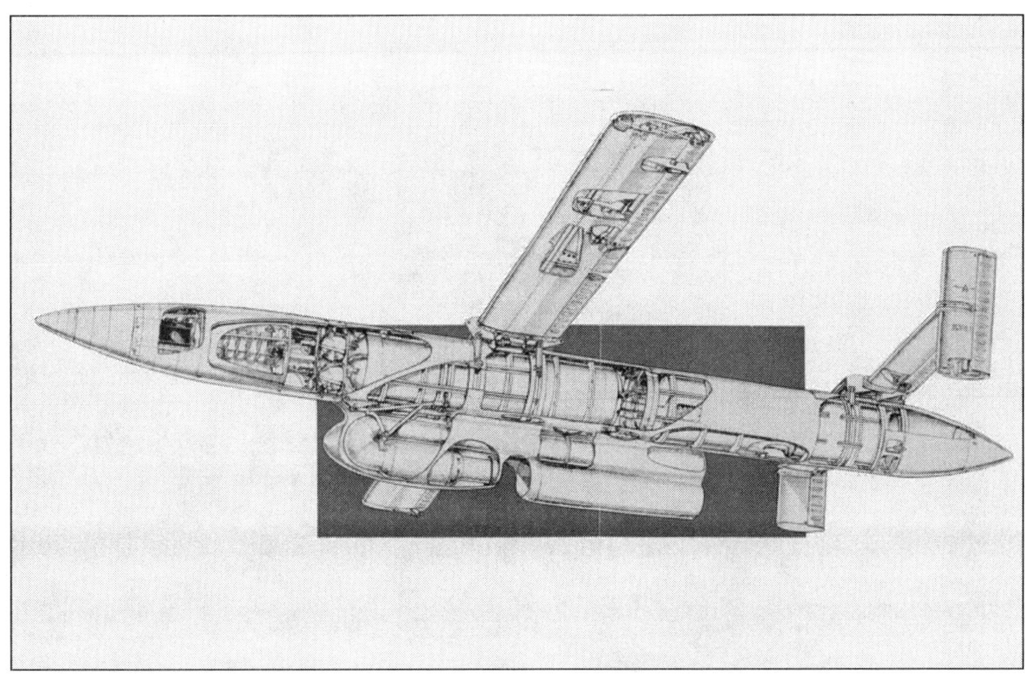

Figure 67 Cutaway of the Aviolanda AT-21 (Courtesy Aviolanda)

Figure 68 Model of the Hawker Seafury

Figure 69 Aviolanda AT-21 on its Launcher (Courtesy Aviolanda)

Figure 70 Dolf Pegel and the Author in a Foxhole

Figure 71 My Officer Candidates' Class (Author is left on the first row)

Figurc 72 Thc Author with his First Car in 1955

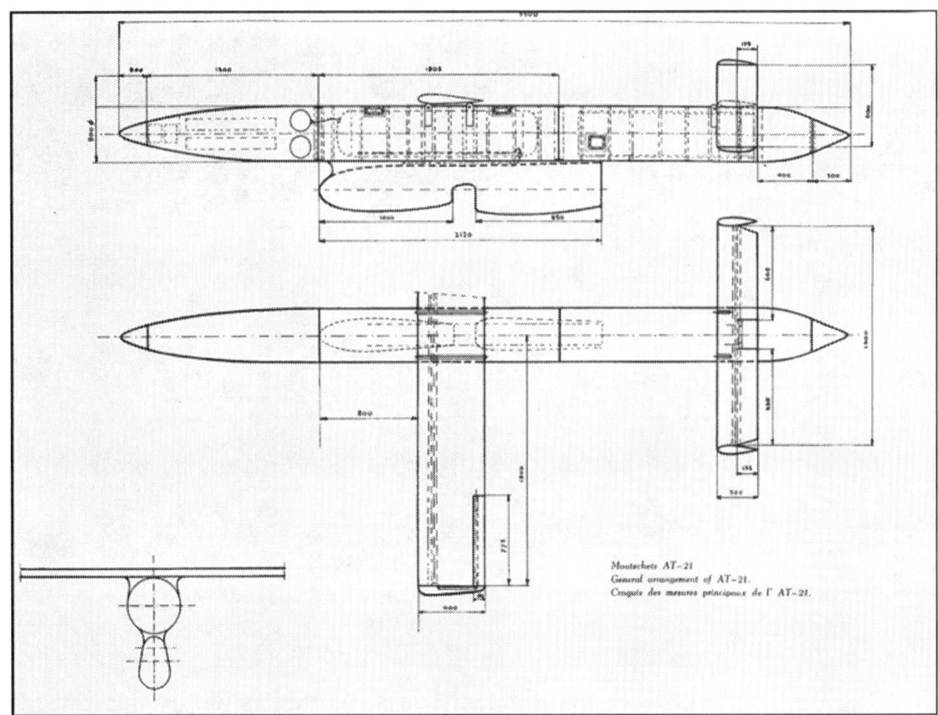

Figure 73 Three-view of the Aviolanda AT-21 (Courtesy Aviolanda)

Figure 74 Hawker Sea Hawk (With Permission from the Royal Aeronautical Society Library)

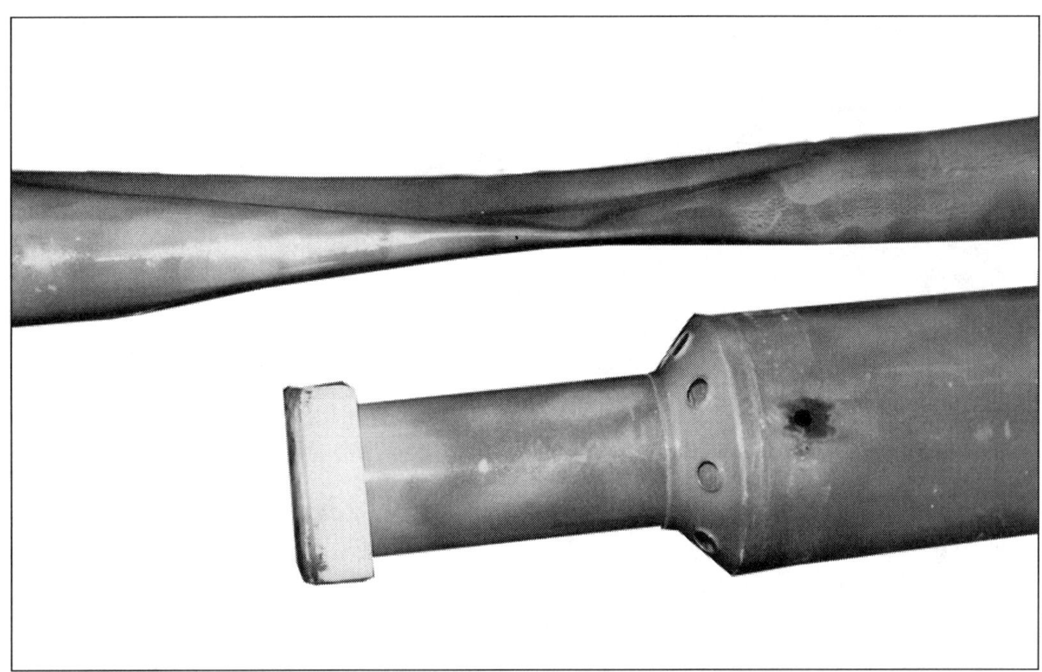

Figure 75 The Imploded Pulsejet of the Aviolanda AT-21 (Courtesy Aviolanda)

Figure 76 Consolidated-Vultee PBY-3, Catalina (With Permission from the Royal Aeronautical Society Library)

Figure 77 Percival Proctor (Courtesy Hunting/Percival)

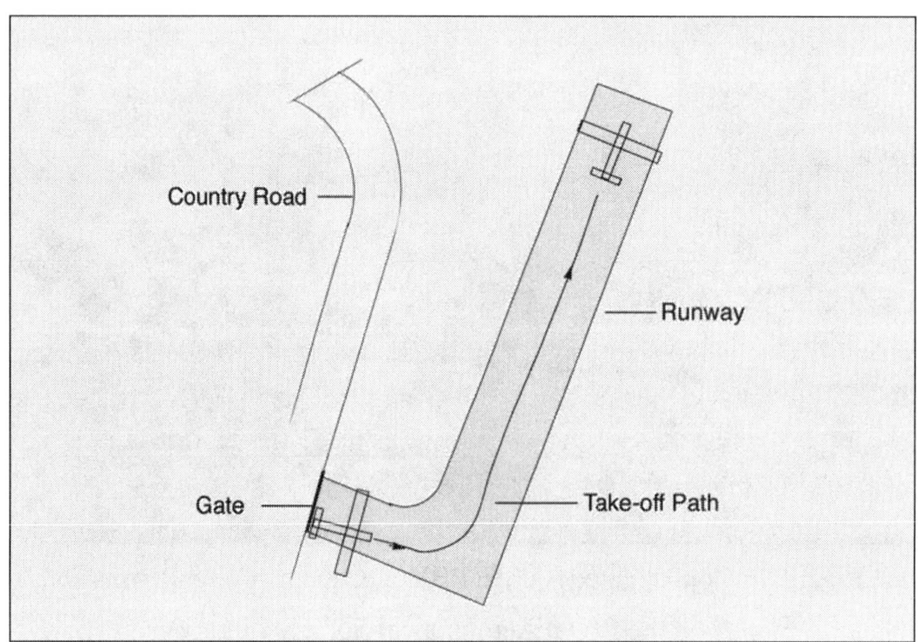

Figure 78 Access Road and Runway Arrangement Used for Takeoff in the Proctor

Chapter 5: Years at Cessna and Boeing

On March 12, 1957 I boarded a KLM Lockheed 1049, Super-Constellation, in Amsterdam for my immigration flight to New York. Figure 79 shows a 1049 operated by the Kansas City "Save a Connie" organization.

War Story 36

I was very surprised when, midway over the Atlantic, a cabin attendant asked if I were Mr. Roskam. I said I was. She invited me to the first class cabin where I was introduced to the Dutch Minister of Defense. He wanted to know why I had decided to emigrate to the USA. I told him, and he merely expressed his regrets that Holland was losing a promising aeronautical engineer. That was all.

Lesson: Never underestimate intelligence operations.

After landing in New York and clearing immigration, I changed flights and boarded a TWA[34] Lockheed 049, Constellation (Figure 80), for the flight to Wichita, with an intermediate stop at Indianapolis. One of the TWA flight attendants asked me why in the world I was going to live in Wichita, Kansas. After all, that was just about the bottom of the barrel in the USA. During subsequent conversations, I found that I knew a lot more about Wichita and Kansas than she did. I certainly have enjoyed living there.

The following war story has a bearing on future developments of the way airplanes will be controlled.

War Story 37

Contemplate how many cockpit crew members were required to fly the piston engine passenger transports across the ocean. There were five: a radio-telegraph operator, a navigator, a flight engineer and two pilots.

In the early 60's we could safely eliminate the radio-telegraph operator. Automation was the enabling technology, and cost reduction was the economic driver.

In the early 70's we could safely eliminate the navigator. Automation was the enabling technology, and cost reduction was the economic driver.

In the early 80's we could safely eliminate the flight engineer. Automation was the enabling technology, and cost reduction was the economic driver.

I will give you one guess who will be next.

Lesson: Flight crews don't like hearing me say this. Like it or not, with the exorbitant pilot salaries and the fact that a large number of accidents are caused by crew mistakes, further automation is inevitable.

On March 15, 1957, I began working for Cessna Aircraft Company in the Military Aircraft Division in Wichita, Kansas. My general job assignment was in the area of structural design and systems design layout on the T-37, twin jet trainer.

Figure 81 shows a three-view of that wonderful airplane of which many hundreds were built. USAF pilots affectionately refer to the airplane as the "Tweetie Bird." At the time of publication of this book, the T-37 is still serving with Air Training Command in the USAF, although it is gradually being replaced by the Raytheon JPATS T-6* shown in Figure 82.

My immediate bosses at Cessna were Harry Ballard and Ken Yeoman. Harry was a former bombardier on B-17 bombers during WWII. Ken was a very experienced design engineer.

The chief engineer for the Military Aircraft Division was Hank Waring, a former test pilot. Ozzie Mall was in charge of preliminary design. I had quite a few opportunities to discuss technical matters with Harry, Ken, Hank and Ozzie. They certainly knew what questions to ask and when to ask them. They knew their business. I enjoyed working with them.

A vice president of Cessna at that time was Del Roskam. Because Roskam is a relatively rare name in Holland as well as in the USA, he wondered if we were related. His wife finally figured out that somewhere, three generations ago, we had a common ancestor in a province of Holland called Friesland. As I always put it: Del and I were not related closely enough to be useful to me. We frequently did get our company mail mixed up, until his secretary straightened that out.

A mild cultural shock for me was the fact that everyone was immediately on a first name basis, including the company presidents and vice presidents. In Holland, one only called friends and daily acquaintances by their first name. Otherwise it was always Mr.

My first specific assignments at Cessna involved flap-system layout and design, tip-tank layout and design and hard-point design for various weapons stores. These design features later became standard on the A-37 called the Dragonfly which, much later, served with distinction in the Vietnam War. Figure 83 shows the first attack version of the T-37.

Figure 84 shows me and Ken Yeoman trying to "fit" a tip-tank to the wing tip. In those days, CAD had not yet been invented. Therefore, everything had to be "mocked-up" to check for fits and interferences.

War Story 38

When I started working at Cessna, I did not have a US secret security clearance. However, much of the work I did was stamped secret every evening. To get my work back the next day required a special procedure. This went on for months until my clearance came through. The process of getting that clearance was interesting. I heard from relatives in Holland, that certain people had been asking questions about me.

---

* The Raytheon JPATS T-6 is in fact an extensively modified Pilatus PC-9 turboprop trainer developed by Pilatus Aircraft Company of Switzerland.

At one point an FBI operative came to see me at Cessna asking if I had listed all organizations to which I had belonged in Holland. I said that to the best of my knowledge I had. Well, what about the Youth Organization of the Dutch Labor Party? I said that I had indeed been a member and that I forgot to list it, which I had. That satisfied him. It also satisfied the "system" because I got my clearance. The fact that as an officer in the RNAF I had a secret NATO clearance, probably also helped.

Lesson: As I said before, never underestimate intelligence operations.

Much of my design work required inputs from the loads group to allow me to properly size various aspects of the structure and structural attachments. However, the loads group was very busy and simply did not have the manpower to respond in due time. As a result, I soon began estimating my own air- and inertial-loads. I also documented the results in reports or memos. After several months this was noticed by the head of aerodynamics, Harry Clements. He suggested I be transferred into the advanced design component of his aerodynamics group. That is how, with the gracious consent of Ken Yeoman and Hank Waring, Harry became my boss.

A very nice aspect of my job at Cessna was that at any time I could walk into the factory and watch T-37 airplanes being built. I learned a lot by just watching and talking to assembly line personnel.

War Story 39

The first prototype of the T-37 ran into a serious problem when Bob Hagan, the company test pilot, had to bail out because the airplane would not recover from a spin. For a training airplane that was a very serious problem which absolutely had to be solved.

During a meeting with Harry Clements and Ken Yeoman, Harry suggested that a flat strip of aluminum wrapped around the nose of the airplane might break up the flow around the nose at high angle of attack. This could reenergize the air flowing toward the rudder, and just might provide enough rudder control power to allow spin recovery.

No better ideas came forward, so I was assigned the task of drawing up the strip and seeing it installed on the second prototype that same day. This was done.

Bob Hagan flew the airplane the next day in and out of spins without any trouble.

I remember being asked by our chief engineer, Hank Waring, what it would take to find out why and how this strip worked. I suggested a wind tunnel test but Hank did not want to spend money finding out why a solution which was known to work, really did work.

So, to this day, we can only conjecture why the T-37 nose strip helps in spin recovery.

In Hank's defense, Cessna was operating on a tight budget with the T-37 program and I probably would have made the same decision in his place. Figure 85 clearly shows this stall strip on the nose of the second airplane in the lineup.

Lesson: If a solution to a problem works, don't spend any more money finding out why, particularly when you are in a tight budget spot.

The following war story shows how I got involved in the sweeping aft of the vertical tail of the Cessna 172.

War Story 40

We were working a lot of overtime on the T-37 program. One evening in 1957, a gentleman approached me and introduced himself as the director of Cessna 172 marketing in the Cessna Commercial Aircraft Division (also known as the Pawnee Division, because it was located on Pawnee Avenue). That is where all the non-military airplanes were being built. The Cessna 172 at that time had an unswept vertical tail as shown in Figure 86.

He proceeded to show me an artist's rendition of a Cessna 172 with a swept vertical tail and asked me what I thought of it. I told him that it looked like a much jazzier airplane than the basic 172 with its unswept vertical tail.

He said that I was the first engineer who did not poo-poo the idea and that he thought that the swept tail would result in much greater sales. He also told me that he could not get anyone in the commercial division to take his suggestion seriously. All its engineers opined that more weight, more drag, less effectiveness and less performance would be the result.

He asked if I would spend some time and analyze this swept tail. I agreed to do so. About a week later I reported to him that the swept vertical tail was a washout in terms of weight, drag, effectiveness and performance, but that the enhanced looks probably would sell more airplanes. He took my data back to the Commercial Division and managed to convince the decision-making hanchos that they should adopt the swept tail.

That fall, Cessna proudly announced the "new swept look" for the 172 model. It improved sales by 30% and the swept tail became a standard feature on other Cessna models. The airplane with the new vertical tail is shown in Figure 87.

Lesson: Good looks can really improve airplane sales, particularly if nothing else gets harmed.

A serious cultural shock was the realization how strongly imbedded racial discrimination still was in 1957.

War Story 41

While working overtime several evenings I noticed a young black janitor who seemed to be very interested in the work I was doing. One evening I struck up a conversation with him. I was surprised to find out how much he knew about airplanes and engineering so I asked him how he had acquired his knowledge. It turned out that he had a BS degree in aeronautical engineering! When I asked why he was doing janitorial work instead of engineering work he told me that, as a black, he could not get an engineering job at Cessna, Beech or Boeing. He said that all his relatives lived in Wichita and he did not want to move to another part of the country. I found this so hard to believe that the next day I asked my bosses about it. They confirmed that most companies (including Cessna) had a policy of not hiring blacks into "white- collar" positions.

This was my first encounter with outright discrimination. It really bothered me to think that the country in which I had chosen to live, work and become a citizen, could be so inconsistent in the application of the idea of "equal rights for all."

Lesson: It is amazing how long it took a nation of good people to recognize that racial discrimination is only one thing: wrong. Equal rights for all means precisely that: equal rights for all.

In July of 1957 I was approached by Norman Bauer, who was head of the the propulsion group on the T-37 program. Norman explained that he was supposed to teach a night course in aircraft propulsion at the University of Wichita (UofW, now WSU, Wichita State University) that coming fall semester. However, because of a family problem, he could not honor that commitment. He asked if he could recommend to the AE department chairman that I take over his assignment. I did not hesitate and said he could.

After meeting with the chairman, Professor Mel Snyder, I was duly appointed as a lecturer in aeronautical engineering at the UofW. Cessna also gave its blessings to my evening job.

At that time, the only thing I knew about airplane propulsion was what I had learned in two propulsion courses at Delft University in Holland. Therefore I boned up and prepared, with the help of several textbooks, a series of handwritten lectures which eventually covered the entire semester. I found it a great challenge to stay ahead of my students, most of whom were practicing engineers at either Cessna, Beech or Boeing.

I must have done a credible job of teaching because toward the end of the semester, Mel asked me to teach a course in fluid mechanics in the 1958 spring semester. And so it went. I found myself teaching part-time throughout the year (including the summer semester) and particularly enjoying the fact that it was making a well-rounded generalist out of me.

Flying also had become a very important part of my life. Shortly after starting my work at Cessna, I became a member of the Cessna Employees' Flying Club. With the help of a Cessna pilot, Ray Starr, I got my US private pilot license. My Dutch license really helped shorten the time to do this. It did not take very long to get used to flying nose-gear airplanes. One never has to worry about ground loops anymore.

The Cessna Flying Club basically allowed employees to check out airplanes and only pay for fuel and oil. It was a really good deal. I was eventually checked out to fly the 172, the 150, the 180, and the 182. See Figures 87, 88, 89, and 90.

It was very enjoyable to be able to check out an airplane after work, fly over the city of Wichita at night, and practice night takeoffs and landings.

To get some experience with Instrument Flying Rules (IFR) approach flying, we were allowed to use the Ground Controlled Approach (GCA) system the USAF had at McConnell Air Force Base on the east side of Wichita. This also enabled the USAF GCA controllers to get a lot of practice. I remember performing many landings with absolutely zero visibility simulated by wearing a hood. Those GCA controllers were very good indeed.

One day, during a trip to the Lake of the Ozarks in Missouri, I got checked out to fly a Cessna 195 on floats. It was quite an experience to find out just how rough water really is when you land on it. Figure 91 shows the Cessna 195 on floats albeit in the USAF LC-126 version. The USAF used these airplanes in Alaska for search and rescue missions.

The next war story describes an event which is being repeated too frequently.

War Story 42

One Saturday I was flying a Cessna 172 with the intent of landing at the Cessna airstrip on the east side of Wichita. That strip was more or less located underneath the north-south runway approach to McConnell Air Force Base.

I had not been paying much attention to a Boeing B-47, Stratojet bomber (Figure 92 shows the XB-47) which was flying around the pattern at McConnell. As a result of my carelessness, I flew through one of the B-47 wing tip vortices and suddenly found myself upside down. Luckily, Ray Starr had taught me to roll on through and by doing so, I recovered.

Lesson: Always keep an eye out for bigger airplanes and stay clear of vortex turbulence.

War Story 43

Another Saturday I was practicing touch-and-go's at the Wichita Municipal Airport on the west side of town. During one downwind leg I received a frantic call from the control tower operator with instructions to make an immediate climbing turn to the right. He had a TWA Constellation with one engine inoperative* right behind me for landing. I followed his instruction literally.

---

* Some pilots remember the Constellation as the world's best three-engined airplane.

Some seconds later I realized that, because of the much larger turn radius of the Lockheed Constellation (Figure 80), I might be turning right into him. Because the 172 is a high wing airplane it was not possible to see the Connie without banking out of the right-hand turn. So, I banked left, and there was a scary sight: the Connie flying right over me. I think I came within 50 feet of that airplane.

Lesson: Always think about the consequences of a sudden instruction to change flight direction. The controller should have told me to turn to the left. I should have questioned his instructions.

We ran into several other interesting problems with the T-37. War stories 44 and 45 deal with these.

War Story 44

During one test flight Bob Hagan reported that the airplane was becoming extremely left wing heavy. Bob finally landed the airplane with full right aileron. The cause was obviously asymmetric fuel transfer. It turned out that the left and right wing-tip fuel vent lines had been mis-installed. The angular difference between the vents caused differential tank pressures sufficient to precipitate uncommanded fuel transfer from the right wing into the left wing.

Lesson: In fuel system design much attention has to be paid to details. If it is possible to install a component the wrong way, Murphy's Law predicts that someone will do it. It is therefore up to the design engineer to figure out a way to make misinstallation impossible, or, at least inconsequential.

War Story 45

The USAF had insisted that it be possible to lower an engine vertically out of each nacelle onto a maintenance cart. To accomplish this the lower spar cap in the front spar of each wing had a swing-link designed into it. Figure 93 shows the arrangement. A demonstration had to be given to USAF personnel to show that engine replacement could be done within a short period of time. Nobody had given any thought to a dress rehearsal.

The day of the demonstration came and turned out to be very embarrassing. A crowd of important USAF watchers were right there.

The bolt allowing the swing-link to be moved downward was duly removed. The link swung down. The engine fittings were disconnected. The engine was lowered onto its cart and then moved away. Another cart with another engine was moved into position. The engine was raised into the nacelle. All fittings were reattached. Someone swung the swing link upward and... oops, the bolt holes were no longer aligned.

Now look at the airplane, sitting on its landing gear in Figure 93. It should have been obvious that when the lower spar link is taken away there will be just enough deformation (because of bending) to prevent realignment.

Lesson: It is usually not a good idea to have to remove primary structural components to exchange engines. It is also not a good idea to arrange for customer demonstrations without a dress rehearsal.

The next war story sheds light on how I learned about airplane Dutch roll.

War Story 46

One day, Harry Clements asked me to analyze the Dutch roll characteristics of the T-37 at high altitude. There had been some pilot comments about low damping. I must have given him a really blank stare because he continued, "you know what Dutch roll is don't you?"

I told him that I had never heard the term. He explained what the airplane motions are in the Dutch roll. At that point I knew what he was talking about and said, "I learned about that at Delft University but we called it the lateral-directional oscillation." After we had agreed that we were talking about the same subject I asked Harry why it was called Dutch roll instead of, for example, American roll. He said he did not know but that was what he had been taught in college.

I carried out my assigned task and showed Harry why the Dutch roll was so poorly damped with suggestions of what might be done. As it turned out, we never did anything about it because it really was not critical on that airplane, just a bit of a nuisance.

This Dutch roll business made me curious so I decided to look into the matter by going to the Cessna Engineering Library. I found a very interesting book by Richard Kolk, *Modern Flight Dynamics*[(35)]. In the chapter dealing with lateral-directional dynamic stability I found the term "Dutch roll" mentioned with a footnote. It explained that the reason this motion is called the Dutch roll is because it reminds one of a fat Dutchman skating down a canal.

That explanation was not only funny, but seemed to make sense. Much later in my life I found that the origin of the term Dutch roll is still mysterious. Jerome C. Hunsaker already used the term in *Dynamic Stability of Airplanes*[(36)], in 1916. However, he does not explain where the term comes from!

Lesson: It is not always easy to find out where aeronautical terminology originates.

War Story 47

In the Commercial Division, Cessna was working on a new airplane, the Cessna 620. This was a very impressive, stand-up cabin, four-engine, propeller driven transport aimed at the executive market. Figure 94 shows a three-view of the airplane. Ralph Harmon was the chief engineer on that project. Two prototypes were built with "soft" tooling to minimize the required development investment. The airplane flew very well and had good handling qualities.

However, in 1958 Cessna was confronted with the decision to invest in "hard" tooling to launch the airplane into production. Before doing this Cessna management decided it wanted a definitive marketing study done. This job was given to a well-known marketing firm in Chicago. It came up with a very negative report about the marketability of that type of executive transport. Cessna cancelled the project and all engineers working on the 620 were given "pink slips."

Management also made the strange decision to have both prototypes destroyed.

Some years later this market really blossomed. Beech[37] Aircraft eventually walked away with that market with an airplane called the King-Air of which thousands were built.

Lesson: Marketing is not an exact science. Also, management should preserve prototypes. The least they could do is donate them to a museum.

War Story 48

Several people at Cessna thought that a logical development from the T-37 program might well be a civilian version. Such an airplane would have to be at least a four-place airplane. Ozzie Mall, one of the proponents, several engineers and I were assigned the task of carrying out preliminary design studies.

This led to the Cessna 407, a four-place, twin jet, based on the T-37. A mock-up was built with a functional cabin and functional cockpit controls. Figure 95 shows a photograph of the attractive Cessna 407 mock-up.

One day Del Roskam, our vice president, came to inspect the 407 mock-up. He climbed into the pilot seat, put his feet on the rudder pedals, pushed really hard, and promptly broke the pedal-assembly-to-floor attachment. Very embarrassing to all concerned.

Lesson: In a functional mock-up it is important to account for the maximum forces which pilots can exert on the cockpit controls.

It turned out that the specific fuel consumption of the Turboméca Marboré engines was unacceptably high for a commercial airplane. As a result the range was rather inadequate. This led to cancellation of the 407 project.

Another project I was asked to participate in was the preliminary design of the hydraulic actuation system which rotates the outer wing tips on the supersonic North American XB-70A Valkyrie jet bomber. A three-view of this airplane is shown in Figure 96. Cessna was bidding on that contract because it also operated a Hydraulics Systems Division in Hutchinson, Kansas, where hydraulic systems for various farm machineries were manufactured. The company hoped to get into the airplane hydraulic system business by this means.

My task was to size the actuators. It was an interesting job for me: sizing actuators meant determining their loads. This, in the case of the XB-70, involved estimating air loads over a very wide Mach range. I had never done that before, therefore, I learned a lot. As it turned out we placed second in the competition for that contract. However, that still meant we lost.

By this time I had become quite a pack rat when it comes to collecting books and documents on airplanes. The NACA (National Advisory Committee on Aeronautics) in those days published an annual report with all Technical Reports that had been produced in a given calendar year. These were the so-called “bound volumes.” They dated clear back to 1917 and I decided I wanted a copy of each. The problem was that most were no longer in print. Therefore, I contacted a famous book-finder in San Diego by the name of John Roby.

Two weeks later John called me with the message that he had located the missing volumes through a library sale. We made a deal and he shipped them to me. When I opened the boxes I found to my delight that many of the volumes were signed by Jerome C. Hunsaker, the famous MIT professor and one of the first members of NACA. They had come from his personal library. I am still the lucky owner of these books.

One evening in the fall of 1959 at the University of Wichita, I had an after class discussion with John Aydelotte who ran the aerodynamics groups at Boeing-Wichita. John also was teaching an evening course at the UofW. He mentioned that Boeing-Wichita had been tasked with the development of an advanced design group to work on a new commercial airplane and on several carrier based proposals coming out of BuAer, the USNavy Bureau of Aeronautics. He invited me to join Boeing as a lead engineer for the aerodynamic analysis and design efforts associated with these projects.

This sounded very attractive to me, particularly when he said, “By the way, we will pay you 50% more than what you are making at Cessna.” I could not afford to turn this offer down. That is why I left Cessna after only two years.

My bosses at Cessna were very understanding. I was offered a 20% raise to stay because that was all they could do in terms of the pay scales used at Cessna. Although I thoroughly enjoyed working at Cessna this was too much to turn down both in terms of job challenge and salary.

I knew I would miss working at Cessna. The learning environment was great. So many different projects, kicking tires on the production line, talking to shop people, the flying club, etc., etc.

Nevertheless late in 1959 I began working for Boeing-Wichita while continuing my evening teaching assignments at the University of Wichita.

My immediate boss at Boeing was Richard Wallace who reported to John Aydelotte. John in turn reported to Harry Higgins who was unit chief for aerodynamics and propulsion. Harry was a former P-38 pilot. He enjoyed talking about his P-38 experiences. Figure 23 shows a picture of that famous twin-engined fighter.

Harry was a dynamic individual who always was full of penetrating questions. He often said to his engineers: if you can't explain things to me in common language, I have to assume that you don't understand them yourself. I found Harry an inspiring mentor from whom I learned a great deal.

My first project at Boeing was the Boeing Model 909, a twin turbopropeller driven executive transport. Figure 97 shows a three-view of this neat looking airplane.

Project engineer on the 909 was Vernon Hudson. The always smiling gentleman in charge of preliminary configuration design work was Bob Burnham, a most gifted airplane designer.

Bob had a wonderful sense of humor. I fondly remember the many "liars poker" sessions we had during our working lunches at Boeing-Wichita. Bob and I would collaborate on many other Boeing projects.

War Story 49

Boeing, at that time, had an Industrial Products Division in Seattle. That Division had a gas generator in production for various types of armored vehicles. By adding a gear-box and a propeller to such a machine one had a turboprop engine. The next logical thought was to marry that turboprop to an airplane: the 909. The task to design and develop that airplane was assigned to the Wichita Division and I was the lead engineer for stability and control.

We did quite a bit of wind tunnel testing and ended up with what looked like a viable airplane. However, Seattle management had a change of heart. A marketing study (done by the same firm which torpedoed the Cessna 620) showed that there would not be a profitable market for such an airplane. The project was cancelled. Remember the Cessna 620 and the Beech King Air of War Story 47?

Lesson: One more time: marketing is not an exact science.

During the summer of 1960, I had an intern by the name of David Kohlman working in my group. He was a very smart engineer. That fall, Dave went back to MIT (Massachusetts Institute of Technology), to get a PhD in aeronautics.

Dave Kohlman was later instrumental in the biggest career decision in my life: leaving Boeing and becoming a professor at The University of Kansas.

At that time, the Boeing Wichita Division was tooling up for a major design change in the Boeing B-52 jet bomber. The earlier B-52 A-F models all had a rather large vertical tail and bladder type fuel tanks in the wings. They also ran on straight jet engines. Figure 98 shows the B-52D.

For the model G (and later the model H) several new features were added:

a) low bypass ratio engines replaced the straight turbojet engines (lower fuel consumption)

b) a wet wing was used (more fuel volume, the torque box in fact is the fuel tank)

c) the size of the vertical tail was reduced (lower empty weight and drag)

d) yaw dampers were added to compensate for the poor Dutch roll caused by the vertical tail size reduction.

The wet wing (often referred to as a wing with integral fuel tanks) allowed quite a bit more fuel to be carried in the wing. The net result of all the changes was a very significant boost in the payload-range capability of the airplane.

Figure 99 shows the B52G. Because, as it turned out later, an insufficient number of baffle ribs were added to the wing, a major operational problem arose. That is the subject of the next war story.

War Story 50

One day a B52G returning from a training mission was on final approach to a SAC (Strategic Air Command) base. There was about 30% fuel left in the wing tanks. Therefore, the airplane was at a rather low weight. Because of a fouled runway the airplane commander decided to initiate a go-around maneuver. Standard procedure is to advance all eight throttles forward and to pitch up the nose a bit. As a result of the large forward acceleration the fuel was forced toward the outboard wing which moved the center of gravity behind the aerodynamic center. This made the airplane statically unstable, so it pitched up sharply and the pilot lost control. The airplane crashed and burned, killing all crew members.

About a week later the same scenario caused the loss of another B52G airplane and crew. This time the fleet was grounded and an intensive investigation was carried out involving many Boeing engineers. The cause was established and a design fix had to be made.

Retroactively installing more baffles in the wing tanks would have been an obvious, albeit expensive, solution. However, a simpler and much lower cost solution was developed and adopted. A detent was installed in the throttle quadrant, as shown in Figure 100. The detent was placed so that it served as a warning to the pilot that suddenly demanding more thrust might result in a problem. The pilot could, if needed, move the throttles further forward beyond the detent, but would hopefully do so slowly. This solution has worked well: there have not been any more problems with the B52G and H models due to fuel motion.

Lesson: Simplicity is often preferred. Sometimes a $25 solution can be made to work to solve a $25 million problem.

One day, the Wichita newspapers reprinted an article which had appeared in the *Washington Post*. The article lambasted Boeing for charging more than $10 million dollars for each B-52 delivered to the USAF. How times have changed. We, as US taxpayers should be so lucky to be able to buy new B-52's for such a low price. By the way, as I write this book, the Boeing B-52's are doing yeoman's duty in Afghanistan. Some of these airplanes are now 35 years old and still going strong. What a bargain!

War Story 51

After the Model 909 was cancelled, I was assigned the stability, control and performance lead job on the Boeing Model 835, Missileer program. This was a twin jet, carrier based, airplane which was designed with the ability to fire 12 Phoenix missiles over long ranges. The missiles were to be mounted on rotary launchers in the internal weapons bay. An artist's conception of the Model 835, Missileer is shown in Figure 101.

Co-project engineers were Vernon Hudson and Bob Taylor, a former Boeing test pilot.

Bob Burnham and I were primarily responsible for the external configuration of that airplane. We did a lot of wind tunnel testing and also did quite a bit of detail design work on this proposal to the USNavy. Alas, we came in second to Douglas. However, the Douglas victory did not last long. The project lost high rank support in the Navy and was cancelled.

Lesson: By now the reader will have gotten the idea that many airplane design studies end up with a lot of paperwork but no airplane. There still is a lot of value in working on paper airplane designs. It hones the skills of a design team. It also keeps the competition honest.

As part of my job, I had to communicate and work with Boeing and Navy test pilots. With just propeller driven light airplane flying experience, I felt I had little credibility with these pilots. Therefore, I asked Harry Higgins to get permission for me to go through the altitude indoctrination program at Boeing-Wichita and be coached by Boeing test pilots in flying jets.

This request was granted. I soon found myself participating in a number of B52 missions. I even got to fly the B52 as well as the McDonnell[(1)] F-101 fighter, which Boeing used as a chase plane. Figure 102 shows the F-101. The B52G was already shown in Figure 99.

I believe that this jet experience really helped me to understand my job better. Besides, flying in these high performance jets was a real thrill.

Just when we received the news of the lost Model 835 competition, the USAF and the USNavy initiated studies toward a new, carrier- and land-based attack fighter, the TFX (Tactical Fighter Experimental). The TFX would combine Navy and Air Force requirements and result in a very high degree of commonality between the two airplanes. Supposedly, this would save the US taxpayers a lot of money.

One of the enabling technologies which had been extensively researched at NASA* Langley was the idea of a variable sweep wing. This NASA effort was led by Edward Polhamus.

---

* By this time NACA had become NASA, the National Aeronautics and Space Administration.

I became the stability and control lead engineer for Boeing-Wichita on the TFX program and made many trips to NASA Langley to find out all that Ed knew, which was quite a lot. I quickly learned to highly respect Ed for his grasp of airplane aerodynamic and design problems. Talking to him was an education in itself. Ed later would be very helpful to me in being appointed as a distinguished professor at The University of Kansas.

As usual by then, Bob Burnham and I were heavily involved in defining the external configuration of the Boeing TFX design.

Boeing management was very intent on winning that competition. For that reason it in fact employed a two-design-team approach. The other team was in Seattle where Bob Radoll was my counterpart.

The competition for the TFX program was strong, with all major fighter houses in the USA (Grumman, Douglas, McDonnell, Chance Vought, General Dynamics and also Boeing) in the running. After about one and one half years of multi-company competition, there was a "down select." As a result Boeing and General Dynamics went on to the final round of competition.

At that juncture, Boeing management decided to move the Wichita TFX project to Seattle and integrate the two teams. Thus, in 1962, I began working in downtown Seattle. Boeing rented an office building which was easily kept secure. The project by that time had become secret.

The TFX project was heavily staffed and the stability and control group was split in two: Bob Radoll leading the longitudinal aspects and I the lateral-directional aspects.

In our spare time, Bob and I were both model railroad fans and we had many discussions over the relative merits of various types of model railroads.

Both Bob and I reported to Harry Higgins who also had been moved to Seattle. Harry was in charge of overall aerodynamics of the airplane. Bob and I supervised about 24 engineers just in the stability and control area. Harry used to remind us that when he was involved in the Boeing B-47 project, only four stability and control engineers were required.

Also in 1962, I became a US citizen. Most of my friends were US citizens by birth. I am very proud of the fact that I am a US citizen by choice. The examining judge who gave me my citizenship suggested that I change my first name from Jan to John. I declined and kept the name given to me by my parents.

War Story 52

Because of the aft engine configuration of the TFX, the rear fuselage, from a structural viewpoint, had a T-cross section. Figure 103 illustrates this. It does not take a structures expert to realize that this can lead to severe torsional stiffness problems.

Because of the obvious lack of torsional stiffness, we worried about a new type of flutter mode: asymmetric horizontal tail bending driving fuselage torsion and, in turn, asymmetric wing bending, or vice versa. We built a very expensive flutter model and indeed found this flutter mode in the tunnel. The corresponding flight condition was Mach 1.2 at sea level, a USAF requirement. The Request for Proposal (RFP) of the TFX was very specific about there not being a need for this in the USNavy version.

To eliminate this flutter mode we decided to use a primarily titanium structure in the aft fuselage for the USAF airplane. The Navy version was to have a conventional aluminum structure. This cost a certain amount of commonality, but allowed a reasonably low weight in the USNavy version.

After a lengthy evaluation by the USAF and the USNavy, Boeing was declared the winner of the TFX competition. To everyone's surprise, Secretary of Defense McNamara, apparently for political reasons, decided to overrule his team of evaluators and awarded the contract to General Dynamics. He cited the lack of commonality in the Boeing airplanes as the main reason for his decision.

General Dynamics (GD) was teamed with Grumman: the idea was that GD would build the Air Force version and Grumman would build the Navy version. Thus were borne the F-111A (USAF) and F111B (USNavy). Figure 104 shows the F-111A.

Several major problems were encountered by General Dynamics well into the flight test program. One of these was the flutter mode which we had found at Boeing by simply doing the right homework in the wind tunnel. To fix that flutter problem required a massive weight increase of the aft fuselage: more aluminum! This made the airplane too heavy for carrier operations and the USNavy cancelled its part of the contract for the F-111B. The Navy then developed its own fighter which became the Grumman F-14A: see Figure 105.

The USAF was stuck with the F-111A and, to stay within reasonable development costs, decided to degrade the mission requirements: the supersonic, low altitude requirement was dropped. The US taxpayers ended up with a much less capable airplane.

Lesson: When a contract goes to the least informed company and technology transfer between companies is not required, the taxpayer ends up with a much less capable airplane.

War Story 53

One nice, sunny Sunday, I was to give one of the engineering aides in my group his first airplane ride. For the occasion I checked out a Beechcraft Musketeer (Figure 106) from the Bellevue Aero Service at the Bellevue Airport (no longer in existence). Because of the gorgeous weather I omitted checking the weather and missed the fact that there was a pretty strong easterly wind blowing. Such easterly winds were known to set up horizontal rotors on the lee side of a north-south mountain range.

I was flying north, parallel to the Cascade Mountain range, at a height of about 1500 feet above the terrain and my passenger and I were enjoying the scenery. The next thing I knew we were upside down. As before in Wichita (War Story 42) I rolled the airplane through and we returned to Bellevue unharmed. I don't think my passenger will ever forget that ride and neither will I.

Lesson: Never omit checking the local weather forecast. Mountain rotors are a well-known and predictable phenomenon. I should have taken the precaution to check the weather and fly at a safer height above terrain.

Boeing management had made no contingency plans for losing the TFX competition. As a result, management did not know what to do with its very large engineering staff. It was admirable that we were not laid off.

Instead, we were moved to the Boeing Developmental Center and given various military study and design tasks, mostly associated with VTOL (Vertical Takeoff and Landing) and STOVL (Short Takeoff and Vertical Landing) concepts. I remember working on a large number of different fighter designs with or without VTOL or STOVL capability. Bob Burnham cranked out one design after another, for me to analyze. We also evolved, together with NASA (National Aeronautics and Space Administration), a set of flying quality requirements for hovering and transitioning airplanes. The latter job involved many visits to NASA Ames at Moffett Field which was the center dedicated to VTOL and STOVL flight. Close to Moffett Field was a north-south ridge of hills which was ideal for soaring. My boss, Harry Higgins, and I rented sailplanes on several trips to Ames and spent hours soaring up and down that ridge. Figure 107 shows a picture of the Schweizer[38] Model 2-32 we flew.

Boeing management had made agreements with Dassault in France and Messerschmitt-Heinkel-Blohm (MHB) in Germany to cooperate in the area of V/STOL fighters. Therefore we learned quite a bit about the French and German approaches to various STOVL problems.

Dassault flew its Balzac airplane (Figure 108) but ran into uncontrollable rolling problems when transitioning in crosswinds. One of its test pilots got killed. MHB flew the VJ-101 (Figure 109). That airplane suffered an engine-out problem during a transition to a vertical landing but the Boeing test pilot was lucky to be able to punch out.

At Boeing we did a lot of engineering design and development work on the VTOL Boeing Model 837. Figure 110 shows a three-view of one of the many 837 variants we studied.

In the end it was the British approach, exemplified by the Hawker Harrier (Figure 111), which won out and became the only production STOVL airplane in the west.

Later, in the 1996-2001 era, another competition for the development of a STOVL fighter was held. This competition resulted in two Joint Strike Fighters (JSF), shown in Figures 112 and 113. As I am finishing this book it looks like a derivative of the Lockheed JSF may become the second such airplane. It may also become the last "manned" fighter.

While the F-111 development was going on, the USAF had become very interested in what the British were doing with the BAC* TSR-2 airplane, shown in Figure 114. This airplane promised to be much cheaper and Boeing was given a contract to look at a possible US variant. Bob Burnham and I did a lot of that work.

---

* BAC stands for British Aerospace Corporation

The TSR-2 airplane had a rather interesting mass distribution: it looked like a needle. As a result, the rolling moment of inertia was very much lower than the pitching and yawing moments of inertia. This in turn made us suspect that inertial roll coupling might become a problem. It was, but we found that by selective use of stability augmentation we could suppress that problem. My very first publication dealt with the analysis procedure we used (Ref.1 in Appendix A).

By this time I had also acquired a nickname as a result of always pointing out problems with directional stability and control on various designs I was involved with. That nickname was: Jan "the tail is too small" Roskam.

After all the fighter design work, I was assigned to work on the new Boeing Supersonic Transport (SST). That was quite a change in pace.

There had been a competition going on between Douglas, Lockheed and Boeing for an FAA supported program leading to a supersonic transport. After the usual "down select," Boeing and Lockheed were given contracts to proceed with more detailed design studies. I was assigned the task of leading the lateral-directional stability and control efforts on that study.

On the SST design project, I reported to Bill Kehrer, a very competent and agreeable boss. One of the engineers with whom I worked side by side was a young engineer by the name of Phil Condit. He was very sharp. Phil, at the time of this writing, is Chairman of the Board of Boeing.

I always had the desire, but never the opportunity, to get a PhD degree. I wanted to prove to myself that I could do it. Boeing had a program under which qualified candidates were financed by the company to pursue a PhD degree. Candidates had to make a proposal to Boeing and, if accepted, agree to get the PhD and then work at least two years at Boeing afterwards. Ten employees were accepted into this program each year.

I applied for this program and was accepted. That is how I started my PhD work at The University of Washington in the fall of 1962. Members of my dissertation committee were: Professor Victor Ganzer, Professor Bob Joppa and Professor William Bollard from the Department of Aeronautics and Astronautics, Professor Robert Clark from the Department of Electrical Engineering and a Professor from the Department of Mathematics (whose name I regrettably forget).

My research topic dealt with nonlinear aspects of airplane dynamics, particularly fighter aircraft. To solve the ensuing nonlinear equations of motion I developed a new numerical integration technique based on a series expansion of the Laplace Transform method. The method allowed real time integration on then existing main frame computers. Of concern also was the ability to predict under what conditions of perturbations the linear equations of motion would become invalid. I solved that problem by using a special version of the Lyapunov Stability Theory for nonlinear systems.

The professor from the mathematics department checked the validity of my proposed numerical integration scheme. Professor Clark kept me honest about the use of the Lyapunov method.

In those days all PhD candidates had to pass a twin foreign language requirement. I did not want to select Dutch, my native language, although I could have gotten away with it. Instead, I selected German and French. When the exams were given I found them full of errors. I nicely answered all questions and pointed out the mistakes. I passed.

The qualifying examination consisted of an extensive series of oral examinations and a written take-home exam. The take-home exam was of particular interest to me. I was asked to derive the dynamic equations of motion for a dirigible and determine (with an example airship) the dynamic modes and describe their characteristics. Airships differ from airplanes in that they, when accelerating through the air, carry with them a rather large mass of air which "sticks" to the vehicle because of viscous effects. This is referred to as the virtual-mass effect. As it turns out, it has a significant effect on the phugoid mode. Submarines have a similar problem. Anyway, I must have satisfied the examinators with my airship paper because they informed me that I had passed. References 39 - 41 present good insight into airship design and operational problems.

Next was the dissertation. Again, Boeing was extremely helpful. To develop and validate the new numerical integration techniques required a lot of computer programming. I was allowed to use a Boeing programmer to help with that job. The entire PhD program took a little more than two and one half years.

My parents made their first transatlantic trip (by jet) to attend the official graduation ceremonies. I remember how proud they were. My dad even reminded me that, years ago, I had predicted they would visit me by jet.

After earning my PhD degree in 1965, I was promoted to Senior Group Engineer, at that time the first step toward higher management positions. My boss, Harry Higgins, asked what I wanted to do next. I told him that I just wanted to work on any airplane design project that could use my expertise.

Harry put me to work on the AMSA (Advanced Manned Strategic Aircraft) project. This was a design study for the USAF which eventually led to the supersonic Rockwell B1A bomber. Figure 115 shows the B1A which turned out to be very similar to the Boeing AMSA design. Our design also used a variable sweep wing with all the aeroelastic problems this entails.

After the AMSA design study I was put to work on aeroelastic problems associated with the SST.

War Story 54

The Boeing SST design, conceived by Bill Cook[42], used a variable sweep wing, the trailing edge of which met up with the leading edge of a horizontal stabilizer. Four engines were mounted underneath the horizontal stabilizer.

To avoid negative g's from deflecting the wing in front of the engine inlets, the wing trailing edge had mechanical "grabbers" installed which "grabbed" similar devices installed on the leading edge of the tail. This way a delta wing was formed even though it had a “leak” path through it. Figures 116 and 117 show this very interesting configuration.

Wind tunnel studies showed this to be a promising configuration and Boeing decided to use it in the competition with Lockheed. And we won! The FAA (Federal Aviation Administration) gave Boeing the go-ahead to design and develop three prototypes.

During the ensuing detail design phase it was discovered that our structural weight estimates had been much too optimistic. We seemed to have an airplane that could meet all its mission requirements without a payload. In other words, we really did not have an airplane.

Boeing management did the right thing and confessed to the FAA and to NASA that we had fouled up. It was suggested to reopen the competition to be fair to Lockheed. This the government did not want to do and Boeing was given a contract to redesign the configuration. Thus was borne the Boeing 2707, a delta wing airplane with a horizontal tail and the engines mounted below the wing. Figure 118 shows a three-view of that design.

Lockheed never appreciated the fact that what we ended up with what was actually a design very much like the one it had proposed in the first place.

Lesson: In evaluating airplane designs submitted in a competitive environment, serious questions better be asked about the validity of weight estimates. This is particularly true when the proposed design contains brand-new unproven technology, or a brand-new unproven configuration. Even experienced companies can become victims of optimistic engineering predictions.

Some years later, the US Congress cancelled the entire project for environmental reasons.

War Story 55

Because the originally proposed variable sweep wing design had quite a bit of steady state, aeroelastic deformations, I was asked to help with its analyses. There were several questions:

a) Could we predict the bending and torsion of the outer wing panel with reasonable accuracy?

b) What was the effect of aeroelasticity on the stability and control properties of the airplane and how could this be predicted?

c) Was it possible to define the external shape to which the airplane had to be built in the factory (the jig-shape) so that in cruise the airplane would deform into the correct camber shape for the best possible lift-to-drag ratio?

At that time we had an aerodynamicist working at Boeing by the name of Frank Woodward. Frank had come up with a computational method to determine the aerodynamic influence coefficients of an arbitrarily panelled wing surface. In fact, his method applied to subsonic as well as to supersonic flow.

When I became aware of this development, I realized that by combining Frank’s panel method with a similar structural panel method and structural, flexibility influence coefficients, it would be possible to solve all these problems with a large set of matrix equations.

Chapter 7 in Reference 43 contains a step-by-step discussion of the methodology. When I first proposed this way of addressing problems a), b), and c) to my bosses, they wanted to know how I could prove that it really would work. I suggested that one way to prove it would be to design, build and test an aeroelastically scaled wind tunnel model. Since the variable-sweep SST wing had been heavily engineered in detail, I suggested we get some utility out of that work and validate the method by using the old, variable-sweep wing SST design.

That idea was approved and we proceeded to design and build an elastically scaled wing for testing in the Boeing Supersonic Wind Tunnel. The model was built to the model jig-shape. In the mathematical model of the wing we used 200 panels and therefore had 200x200 matrices.

One can imagine my concern when the critical day came and we mounted the model in the tunnel. The idea was that at a Mach number of 2.7 and at the cruise angle of attack, the wing had to deform into the desired cruise shape. We turned on the tunnel and much to my (and my bosses) relief, the model wing did what was expected. Figure 119 shows this wind tunnel model at zero dynamic pressure.

Lesson: To validate any new technology requires a sizable investment in calendar time, personnel and money. If a technology is perceived to be worthwhile, making such an investment on a timely basis can yield large benefits. Management has to be prepared to make such investments.

War Story 56

Another one of my assignments on the SST program was to determine what vertical tail size and shape would result in the lowest possible structural weight.

Because of fuselage side bending and because the tail itself was rather flexible at high dynamic pressures, this was a challenging problem. On that problem I interacted with Maynard Pennell, the overall engineering manager of the SST program. One day he stopped by my office to get briefed on the status of the vertical tail study. Afterwards I invited him to come and take a look at the latest vertical tail layout drawing (no CAD yet in those days!).

Maynard took a long look at the tail drawing and said, "Jan, this was a really good study and I want to compliment you on the engineering work. However, that tail looks terrible."

Maynard proceeded to sketch what he thought the tail should look like. As it turned out, all our studies had indicated that the so-called "optimum" was a very "flat" optimum. Therefore, it really did not matter much to the overall tail weight what it looked like. The tail that went on our proposal for the SST was the Maynard Pennell tail.

Lesson: Frequently, studies of optima in airplane design turn out to be relatively flat. If that is the case, the most important choice of a design is the one that is also aesthetically pleasing. Good looks do matter in an airplane.

War Story 57

A very interesting detail problem which had to be solved in the development of the elastically scaled wind tunnel model was the following. Figure 120 shows a schematic of the elastic wing. Note that it looks very much like a fish skeleton. This is also obvious from Figure 119. The entire torsional and bending stiffness of the model was represented by the spar. The "ribs" were there to maintain the shape. In between the ribs we needed a reasonably flexible filler material with the following generic properties:

a) Sufficient strength to support a good coat of white paint;

b) As little contribution to bending and torsion stiffness as possible;

c) Ability to withstand the high temperatures inherent in supersonic tunnel testing.

The wind tunnel model design group at Boeing tried all kinds of flexible materials, but none seemed suitable. One day Carmen Pecarero, a lead engineer in the wind tunnel, came up with the idea to try the flexible material used by the Mattel Company in its "Creepy Crawler" toy kits for children. As it turned out that material worked extremely well. We ended up buying lots of kits to have a good supply for future applications because Mattel advised us that the material was being discontinued.

Lesson: Sometimes the solution to a sticky problem is right at hand in your neighborhood toy store, and, at very low cost!

That spring, 1967, I also returned to part-time teaching. I taught a course in theoretical dynamics at Seattle University (with the fiat of my Boeing bosses). This experience reinforced my liking of teaching and probably was a signal of things to come.

War Story 58

Boeing had just lost the large USAF cargo-lifter competition to Lockheed. That became the C5A, affectionately known as the aluminum overcast. See Figure 121. Although losing that competition was a big disappointment, it quickly turned into a major blessing. There was a market for a large commercial jet transport for intercontinental services. Because of the work Boeing had poured into the C5 competition, a large pool of engineering talent was available to bring to bear on the big jet transport which was dubbed the Boeing 747. The prototype is shown in Figure 122.

Lesson: Losing a competition sometimes motivates the loser to pursue other avenues which ultimately lead to high profitability. That certainly was the case with the 747.

Even though the SST program was cancelled, the elastic wing part of its technology was immediately applied in the design of the Boeing 747 where it paid off handsomely. In the original 747 we ended up using 400 panels, for 400x400 matrices. It certainly was personally satisfying to see the aeroelastic methodology developed on the Variable Sweep Wing SST model applied in the jig-shape design of the 747 wings. To my knowledge, this was the first time the idea of a jig-shape, derived computationally from a desired cruise shape, had been applied to a production airplane.

Right about that time one of my former professors at Delft University, Professor Van der Neut, retired. Some of his assistants decided to honor him by publishing a book, *Contributions to the Theory of Aircraft Structures*(44), about the applications of various structural theories, advances and methods achieved by some of his former students. I was invited to write a chapter on the development of the aeroelastic methods at Boeing. I still have a copy of that book with a nice complimentary letter from Professor Van der Neut whom I always held in very high regard.

As a requirement associated with being a senior group engineer I had to take a number of management classes. Although these classes were certainly interesting and useful, I felt that further advancement into management was not something I looked forward to.

I did not like having to deal with people and budget problems at the expense of technical work and technical decision making. It was explained to me that this decision on my part would limit my financial future at Boeing.

In those days the company had not yet started the Boeing Fellow program whereby top engineers can reach fairly substantial salary levels.

Anyway, I felt that my personality was not suited for a high level management role.

One evening, at home, I got a call from Dr. David Kohlman (see Page 89) who had just been appointed chairman of the AE department at The University of Kansas. Dave explained that Dean of the School of Engineering, Dr. W.P. Smith, and he had decided that KU should become a top-level school in airplane design and airplane stability and control, including associated research. Would I be interested in joining the KU aero faculty?

Without hesitation I said "yes." So that is how I switched to KU from Boeing in the fall of 1967. It was one of the best decisions I ever made.

I enjoyed my job at Boeing and left on very good terms with all my bosses, particularly Harry Higgins. Later, Harry was instrumental in getting me my first research contract at KU.

Figure 79 Lockheed 1049, Super Constellation (Courtesy "Save a Connie," Kansas City, MO)

Figure 80 TWA Lockheed 049, Constellation (Courtesy Larry Meyers)

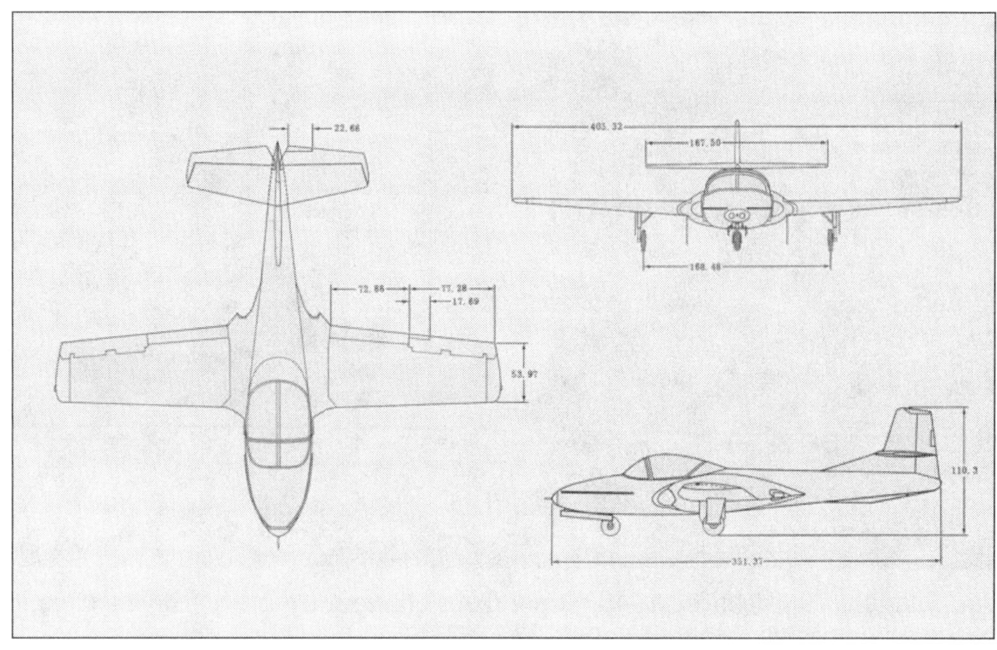

Figure 81 Three-view of the Cessna T-37A (Courtesy Cessna)

Figure 82 Raytheon JPATS T-6: Replacement for the Cessna T-37
(Courtesy Raytheon)

Figure 83 Cessna YA-37A, Dragonfly (Courtesy USAF Museum)

Figure 84 The Author Fitting a Tip-tank to the Wing Tip of the T-37A (Courtesy Cessna)

Figure 85 Nose Stall Strip on the Cessna T-37A, Second Airplane in the Row (Courtesy Cessna)

Figure 86 Cessna 172 with Unswept Vertical Tail (Courtesy Cessna)

Figure 87 Cessna 172 with Swept Vertical Tail (Courtesy Cessna)

Figure 88 Cessna 150 (Courtesy Cessna)

Figure 89 Cessna 180 (Courtesy Cessna)

Figure 90 Cessna 182 (Courtesy Cessna)

Figure 91 Cessna 195 on Floats, USAF LC-126 (Courtesy USAF Museum)

Figure 92 Boeing XB-47, Stratojet (From: Pedigree of Champions, Boeing D6-8988)

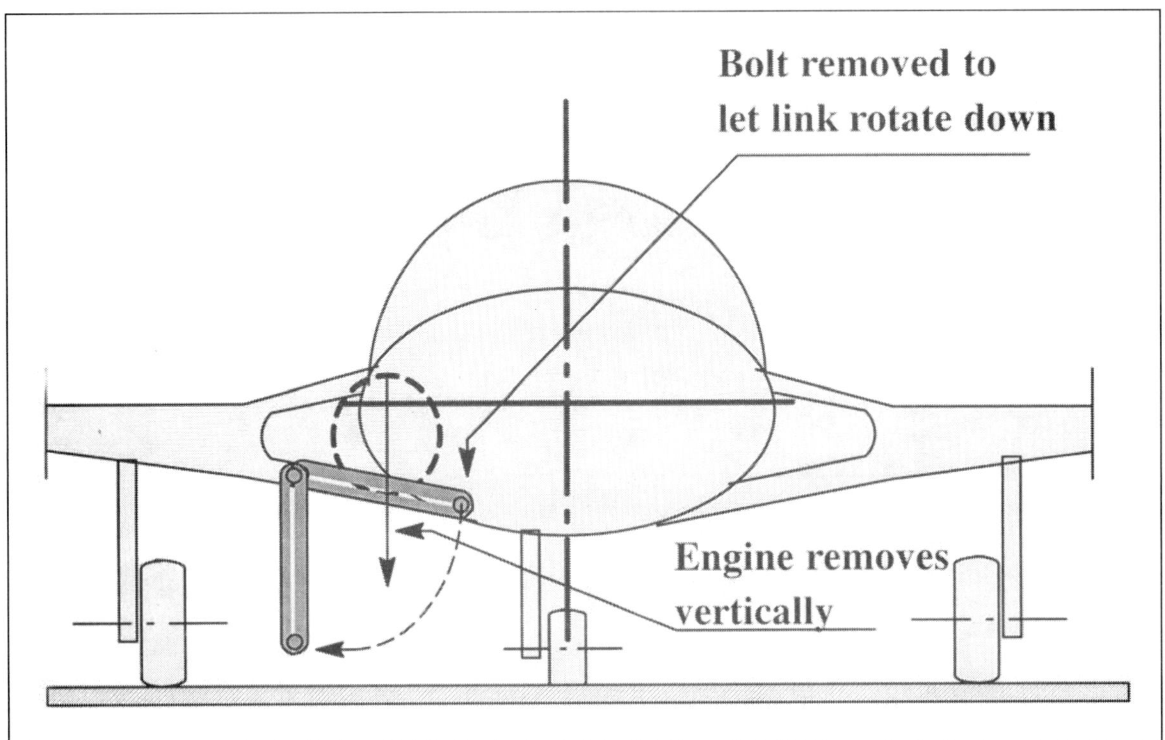

Figure 93 Swing Link Installation for the Lower Sparcap on the Cessna T-37

Figure 94 Cessna 620 (Courtesy Cessna)

Figure 95 Cessna 407 (Courtesy Cessna)

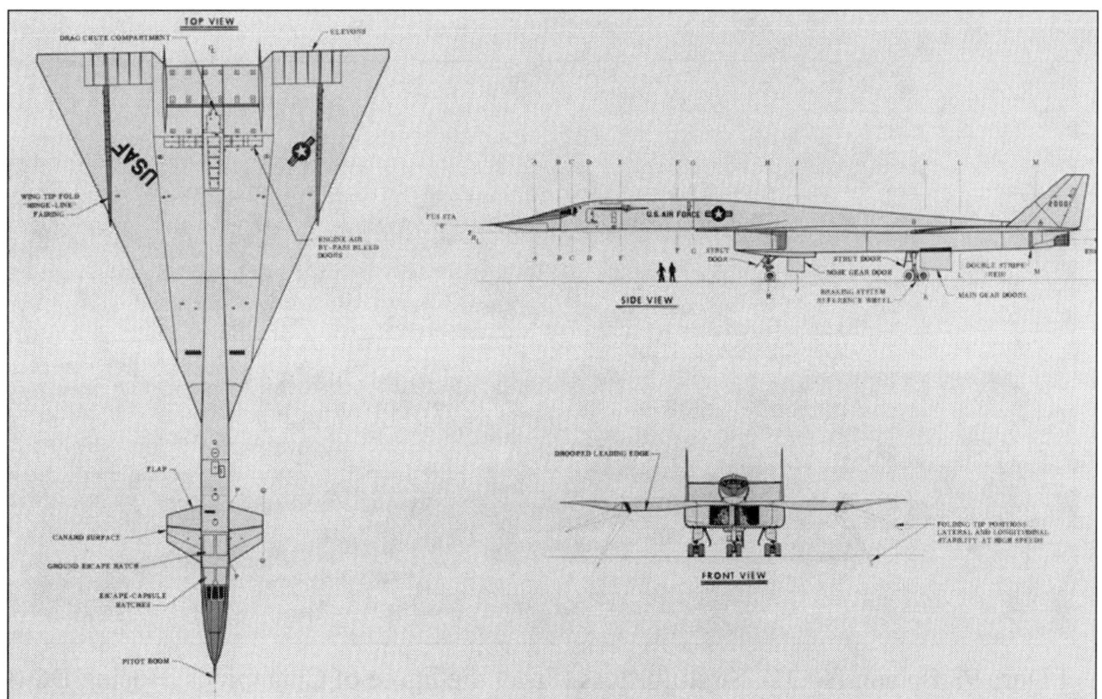

Figure 96 Three-view of the North American XB-70A, Valkyrie (Courtesy North American)

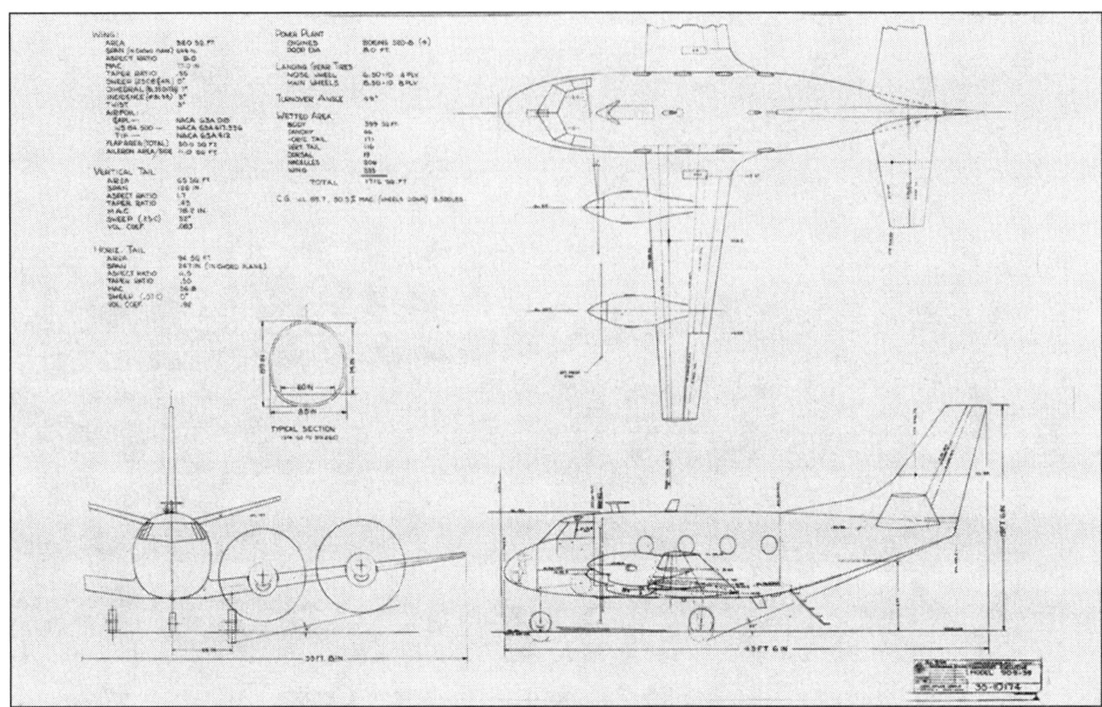

Figure 97 Three-view of the Boeing Model 909 (Courtesy Boeing)

Figure 98 Boeing B-52D, Stratofortress (From: Pedigree of Champions, Boeing D6-8988)

Figure 99 Boeing B-52G, Stratofortress (From: Pedigree of Champions, Boeing D6-8988)

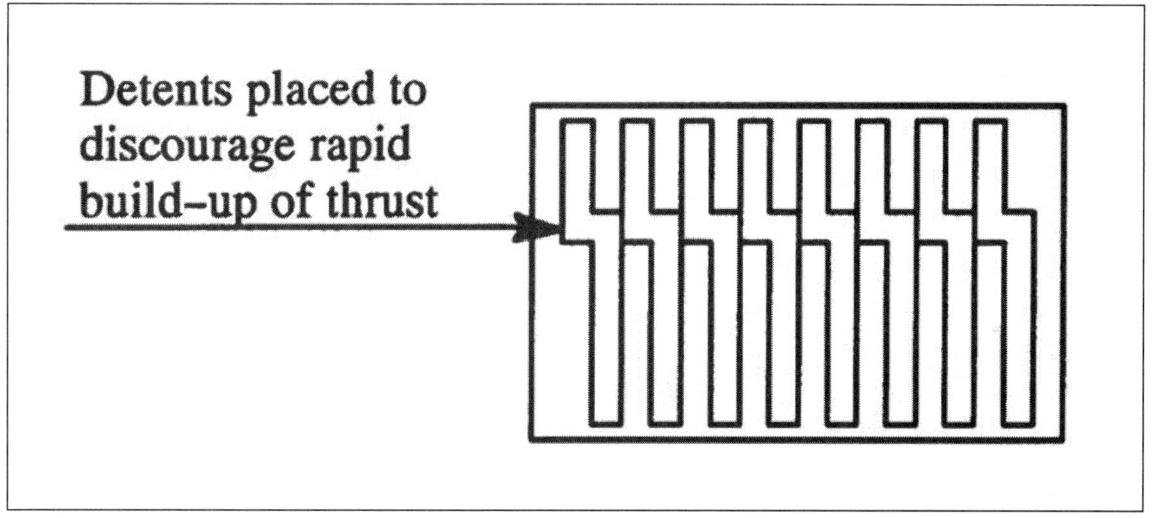

Figure 100 Detent in Throttle Quadrant of the Boeing B-52G, Stratofortress

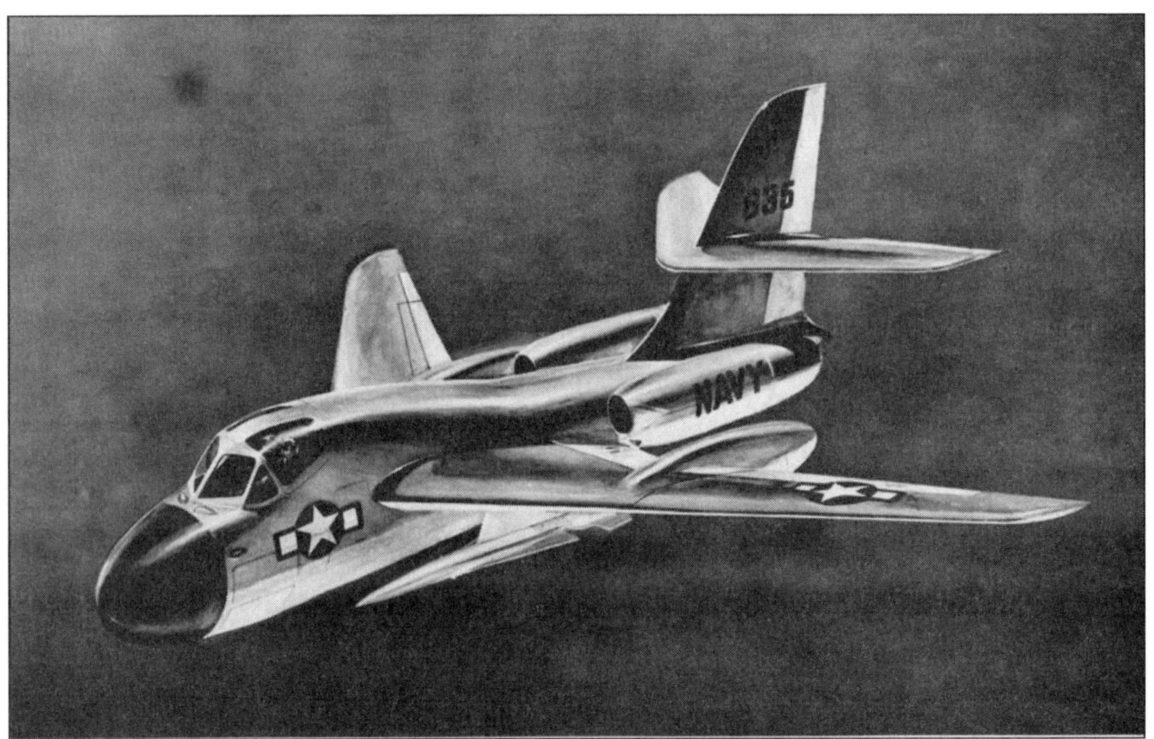

Figure 101 Artist Impression of the Boeing Model 835, Missileer (Courtesy Boeing)

Figure 102 McDonnell F-101, Voodoo (From: Hooftman, H.; Jachtvliegtuigen; Peters' Uitgevers Maatschappij, Deventer, The Netherlands, 1975)

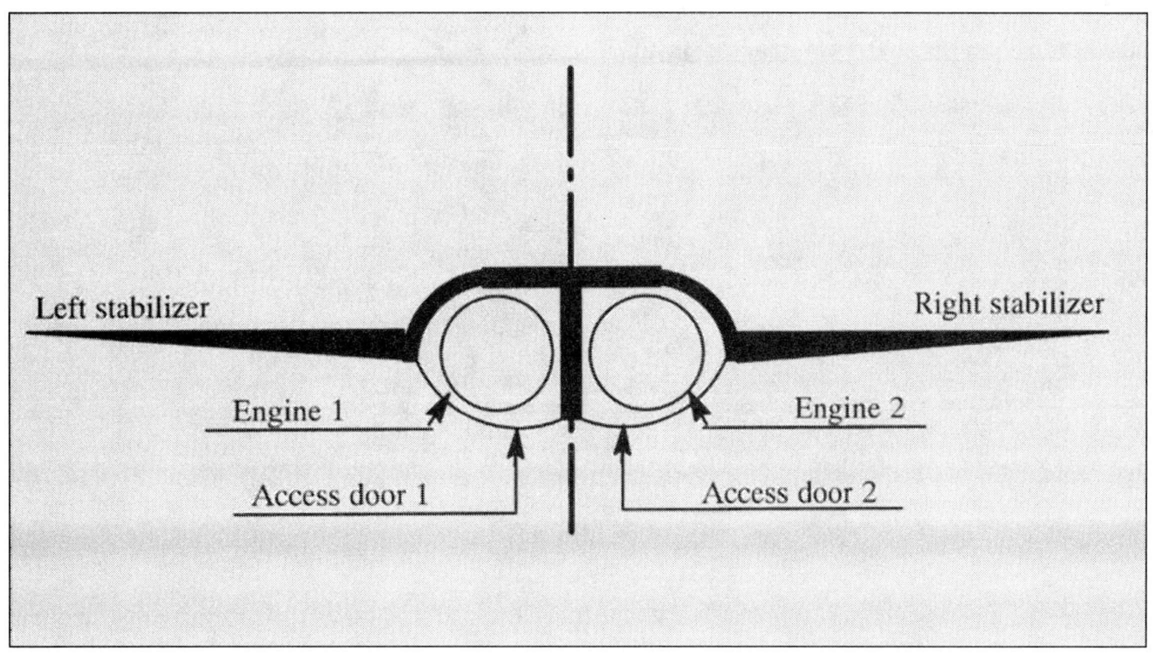

Figure 103 Schematic of the Aft Fuselage Cross Section of the TFX

Figure 104 Model of the General Dynamics F-111A

Figure 105 Grumman F-14A, Tomcat (With Permission from the Royal Aeronautical Society Library)

Figure 106 Beech Musketeer (Courtesy Beech Aircraft)

Figure 107 Schweizer Model 2-32 (Courtesy Paul Schweizer)

Figure 108 Dassault Balzac Experimental VTOL Fighter (Courtesy Dassault)

Figure 109 Messerschmitt-Heinkel-Blohm VJ-101 VTOL Fighter (With Permission from the Royal Aeronautical Society Library)

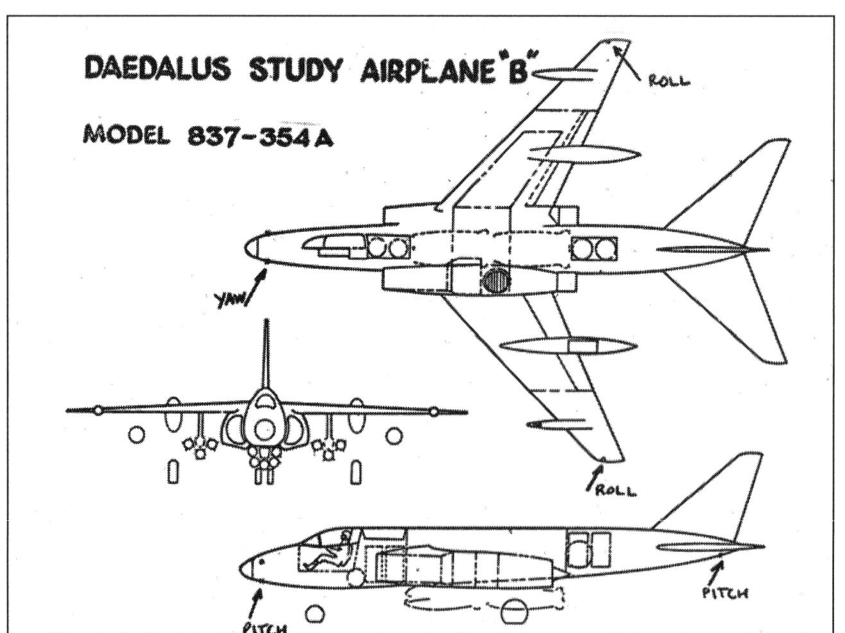

Figure 110 Boeing Model 837 VTOL Attack Fighter (Courtesy Boeing)

Figure 111 Hawker Harrier (Courtesy British Aerospace)

Figure 112 Model of the Boeing Joint Strike Fighter (X-32)

Figure 113 Model of the Lockheed Joint Strike Fighter (X-35)

Figure 114 British Aerospace Corporation (BAC) TSR-2 (With Permission from the Royal Aeronautical Society Library)

Figure 115 Rockwell (Now Boeing) B1-A, Lancer (Courtesy Rockwell)

Figure 116 Boeing Variable Sweep SST Design in the Cruise Configuration (Courtesy Boeing)

Figure 117 Boeing Variable Sweep SST Design in the Landing Configuration (Courtesy Boeing)

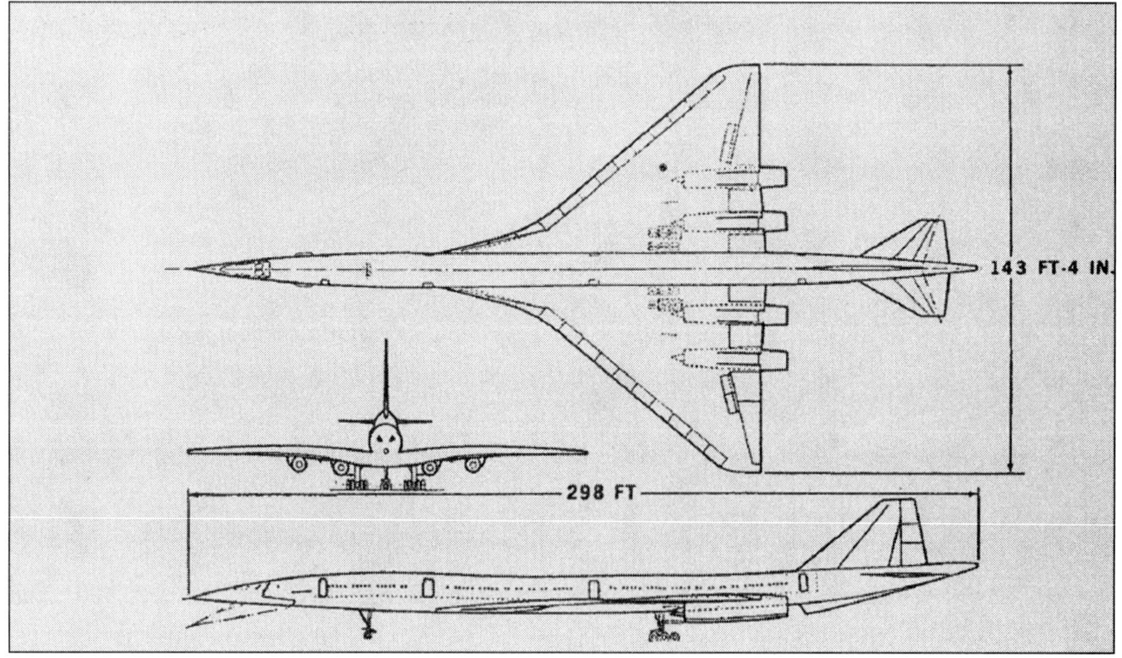

Figure 118 Three-view of the Boeing Model 2707 Delta Wing SST (Courtesy Boeing)

Figure 119 Elastically Scaled Wind-Tunnel Model of the Boeing Variable Sweep SST (Courtesy Boeing)

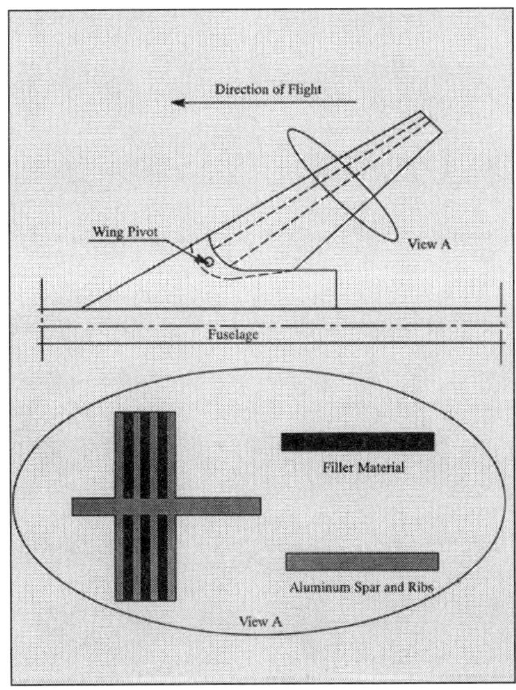

Figure 120 Schematic of the Elastically Scaled Wing of the Boeing SST

Figure 121 Lockheed C5-A, Galaxy (Courtesy Lockheed-Martin)

Figure 122 Boeing 747-100 (Courtesy Boeing)

Chapter 6: Years at The University of Kansas

During the fall of 1967 I began my career as a faculty member of the Aerospace Engineering Department at The University of Kansas (KU). This was not as big a career change as it might have seemed. Because of my various part-time teaching activities in Wichita and Seattle I knew what I was getting into. I had developed a strong liking for teaching. However, I did not want to quit my involvement with airplane design and development activities.

Happily, the way things turned out, there was an easy way to combine these activities. The reason is that The University of Kansas was a teaching, as well as a research university. Therefore, an engineering faculty member was expected to perform in three areas:

a) Teaching

b) Research

c) Service to the school, state, country and community.

The areas of research and service left me ample room for continued involvement in aircraft design and development projects.

A major advantage of an academic career is the tremendous freedom it provides. Typically, a university will give a professor a nine month contract. This has both a downside and an upside.

The downside is you only get paid for nine months work.

The upside is you get three months to engage in consulting engineering activities. In addition, most schools of engineering allow faculty members one day per week during the nine month academic year to engage in outside consulting.

In my case these freedoms (upon which I looked as opportunities) allowed me to develop a considerable consulting practice. This had four consequences:

1) It kept me involved in many airplane design and development projects;

2) It made me a much better teacher because I could relate on-going airplane design and development activities in my lectures to students;

3) My students received a better education because of the practical insights I could give them;

4) It increased my income.

I was fortunate that, when I left Boeing, the National Aeronautics and Space Administration (NASA) still had a reasonably well-funded program in aeronautics research and development. Therefore, a significant number of NASA funds were available for university professors to pursue aircraft related research and development activities.

However, by 2002 the NASA budget for aeronautics had eroded to the point where hardly any aeronautics research was being done. In certain political think tanks, aeronautics had been branded a mature technology with the implication that industry could take over the function of the taxpayers in funding research. One wonders whether these think tank people were aware of the fact, that while the United States was turning off aeronautics research funding, the Europeans opened the spigot. We are now killing the goose that laid the golden eggs (exports!!).

From an educator's viewpoint, an even worse consequence of stopping taxpayer funded aeronautics research was that universities lost precisely the funding that gave faculty and students the opportunity to stay on the leading edge of aeronautics technology.

My teaching, research, service and consulting activities are described in three sections:

6.1 Teaching and Related Activities from 1967 - 2002

My first appointment at The University of Kansas was in the rank of associate professor of Aerospace Engineering in August of 1967. I had three initial teaching assignments.

1) At the undergraduate level, one four-hour course in Airplane Flight Dynamics (AE 150 at the junior level) and two courses in Airplane Design (AE 121 for two hours and AE 122 for three hours at the senior level).

2) At the graduate level, one course in Advanced Dynamics of Flight (AE 251) and one in Aerodynamics of V/STOL flight (AE 247).

3) At the graduate level, develop and add courses in aircraft design.

From the start I taught the senior year aircraft design course sequence (AE 121 and 122) in the following manner.

In the first design course (fall semester) the students were taught the principles of preliminary airplane sizing and configuration design, assuming a mission specification is given. Each student had to design his/her own airplane and document the results in a pre-planned series of five design reports. Individual work was required.

In the second design course (spring semester), I used the team approach from the start. This allowed students to get some experience working together toward a common objective. It should be noted that I initiated this because I knew from my Aviolanda, Cessna and Boeing experiences how important this was. Three decades later (in 1998), team projects became an official Advisory Board for Engineering and Technology Programs (ABET) requirement for all aerospace engineering programs in the USA.

It did not take me long to discover that the time available to teach what I thought the students needed to know to be competitive in industry was grossly inadequate. Therefore, very soon, I proposed the following changes in the flight dynamics and design courses which were accepted by the faculty:

The four-hour AE 150 Flight Dynamics course was changed to a two-course sequence:

1) a three-hour course, AE 550 (Dynamics of Flight I) which deals with steady state stability and control and,

2) a four-hour course, AE 551 (Dynamics of Flight II) which deals with dynamic stability, control and response as well as with classical control theory methods for synthesizing automatic flight control systems.

With the extra hours I added a significant amount of flying quality theory, effects of the flight control system and regulatory aspects. Examples of how the material was used in industry to achieve certifiable flying qualities were included throughout both courses.

The two-hour AE 121 (Aerospace Systems Design I) and three-hour AE 122 (Aerospace Systems Design II), were changed to four-hour courses: AE 521 and AE 522 respectively.

This change allowed me to include important aspects of structural and systems layout design, including the design of the landing gear, the flight control system, the hydraulic system and the fuel system. Again, regulatory aspects were included in all topics. My experience in industry led me to believe that all undergraduate AE students should be exposed to a solid dose of design integration problems.

The course numbering change from 100 to 500 was done because the university rules for course numbering were also changed.

In the middle of my first semester, I started receiving complaints from several fellow faculty members. The complaints were that students were so busy working on assignments for my classes, that they could not get their work done for other courses.

During a faculty meeting on this subject, I pointed out that the problem was not that my expectations were too high, but that the student expectations of the complaining faculty members were too low. This seemed to settle the issue. I did not get any more complaints.

In later years two graduate courses in airplane design were added: AE 721 and AE 722. These were both courses in which team work was required.

In 1976 the American Institute of Aeronautics and Astronautics (AIAA), with sponsorship from Bendix Corporation, launched the first national team aircraft design competitions for students.

Several aircraft manufacturers also were interested in promoting such competitions. Therefore, in 1980, AIAA launched individual student aircraft design competitions. In 1986 they added undergraduate and graduate team aircraft design competitions, and in 1988, engine and spacecraft design competitions.

Participation in at least one of these competitions was a class requirement in my design classes. Table 1 shows how KU students fared in various aircraft design competitions.

In the classroom I always insisted that students:

1) Be on time for class;

2) Hand in assignments on time or, suffer significant grade penalties;

3) Deliver professional work in content and appearance;

4) Remove hats and/or baseball caps when they are in my class or office.

I have been known to send students home to “get dressed” properly before talking to them in my office. In dealing with students I have always tried to be fair, to be responsive to questions, and to help students overcome problems.

Table 1 Record of K.U. Students in National Aircraft Design Competitions

Individual Aircraft Design Competitions	Team Aircraft Design Competitions
	Bendix Team Aircraft Design Competition
	1976 1st
	1977 1st
AIAA Individual Aircraft Design Competition	
1980 1st, 2nd, 3rd, 4th and 5th	
1981 1st and 2nd	
1982 1st, 2nd and 3rd	
1983 1st, 2nd and 3rd	AIAA Team Aircraft Design or NASA FAA Team Aircraft Design Competition
1984 1st and 2nd	
1985 1st, 2nd and 5th	1985 no design entered
1986 1st	1986 1st (AIAA)
1987 2nd and 5th	1987 1st and 3rd (AIAA)
1988 3rd	1988 1st (AIAA)
1989 1st	1989 1st and 2nd (AIAA)
1990 no design entered	1990 2nd, 3rd and 4th (AIAA)
1992 1st	1992 2nd (AIAA)
1993 1st and 2nd	1993 2nd (AIAA)
1994 did not place	1994 1st (NASA/FAA), 3rd and 4th (AIAA)
1995 no design entered	1995 1st (NASA/FAA), 1st (AIAA)
1996 1st	1996 3rd (AIAA), 2nd (NASA/FAA)
1997 1st	1997 1st (NASA/FAA)
1998 no design entered	1998 1st (NASA/FAA)
2000 1st	2000 did not place
2001 1st	2001 1st (AIAA)

Although I believe that my teaching methods and experience as an airplane designer have had some influence on the excellent performance of KU students, the main reasons for their excellence in design are as follows:

a) The "vehicle orientation" of the AE curriculum at KU. Students in their sophomore and junior year must take all technical AE courses BEFORE they are eligible to take the design courses in their senior year. I therefore could concentrate on really teaching design. The students were already well versed in aerodynamics, performance, stability, control, propulsion and structures.

b) Other faculty members also injected "design" examples and applications in their AE classes.

When I started at KU, the AE department had an excellent pilot/technician, Norman Hoecker who doubled as the chancellor's pilot for several years. In addition, Norm (as we called him) was a licensed A&P mechanic. He was a genius at getting things done at extremely low cost. I had the good fortune to accompany him on many flights where he let me do the flying, under his supervision.

Typical airplanes I flew with Norm were the Beech D17 Staggerwing, the Beech D18S, the Ford[45] Trimotor and the Douglas DC-3. Figures 123-125 show renditions of the first three airplanes. The DC-3 was already shown in Figure 39.

The DC-3 was donated to KU by an alumnus. There were no strings attached to his donation. As a result, we did not have the airplane very long because it was expensive to operate, due to maintenance costs. One day Norm traded the airplane for a brand new weather radar set, a new feature for smaller airplanes in those days. He installed the weather radar set in the chancellor's D18S airplane making it a lot more mission reliable. Norm and I spent many hours flying the D18S on a variety of KU missions. The airplane was quite a challenge to land on a narrow runway with a little crosswind. It was also very noisy. Nevertheless, I always looked forward to flying it.

War Story 59

Flying the Ford Trimotor came about in a rather interesting manner. A gentleman in Kansas City owned one. During a return flight, he lost an engine flying over the Vinland Airport south of Lawrence. His landing at Vinland was successful and he had a new engine installed sometime later. Because the Vinland Airport had a rather short runway, he felt uneasy about flying the airplane out of there, so he called Norman Hoecker and asked if he would be willing to fly it to Lawrence. Norm said he would.

Norm had never flown a Ford Trimotor before and called me to find out if I had. I had not. So he said, "I'll get a copy of the flight manual, we'll study it, and fly the airplane out of Vinland together." That is how I made my first and only flight in a Ford Trimotor, which also was a test flight. As it turned out, the take-off distance, even with a failed engine, would have left plenty of runway margin, so there was no safety problem.

Lesson: Airplane Performance 101. With a low wing loading and a low power loading it does not take much of a run to get off the ground.

War Story 60

The designer of the Ford Tri-Motor, Bill Stout, had a standard admonishment for young, aspiring airplane designers in the form of a famous motto albeit in poor English:

"Simplicate and add lightness."

Bill certainly lived up to that with the Tri-Motor. Control cables to the rudder and elevator ran outside the fuselage for easy installation, inspection and maintenance. Never mind the drag. Also, the engine instruments for the two outboard engines were mounted on the side of each nacelle so that the pilot could see them through the side windows. A simple solution and a light solution: no additional wire bundles into the cockpit. Never mind the pilot's instrument scan.

Lesson: Sometimes considerations such as simplicity and low weight win out.

One of the goals I set for the AE Department was to develop a collection of airplanes to enhance student learning. Obviously, to do so one needs airplanes and adequate hangar space. We had neither.

One day Norm called and said that he could get a Grumman F11F fighter from the USNavy (for free!) to start our collection. The F11F was the USNavy's first carrier-based, supersonic jet fighter. A Navy pilot would fly the airplane into the Olathe Naval Air Station, now the Johnson County Airport. Figure 126 shows a three-view of the airplane. It was one of very few airplanes built with a fuel tank in the vertical tail!

I was dumbfounded at the news and thought that Norm was kidding. He wasn't, and even arranged for the USArmy to airlift the airplane from the former Olathe Naval Air Station to the Lawrence Airport with a Sikorsky Skycrane! Figure 127 depicts the Skycrane.

Our beautiful F11F, in Blue Angel colors, languished for years next to (what is now) the "silver hangar" while we tried in vain to get the money for a new airplane display hangar. I kept asking the chancellor (via our Dean) to request a line item in the state budget for the construction of a modest hangar. This never happened. Eventually we donated the airplane to the Combat Air Museum in Topeka.

Early in 1968 I was asked by NASA to organize a seminar on elastic airplane stability and control. This seminar was held at the Kansas Union, June 10-14, 1968.

Old-timers in the elastic airplane analysis and design business will recognize the names of Robert Johannes, Morey Ostgaard, Paul Burris, Gerald Rainey, James Arnold, A.P. Madsen,

John Wykes, J.H. Paterson, J. McBride, A.R. Dusto, C. Wolowicz and Carl Larkins. Just getting all these well-known people together was well worth the hard work needed to put this seminar together.

This also was my first opportunity to work with the KU Division of Continuing Education. Organizing conferences and institutes was one of its strong points and, at that time, in the hands of Dana Leibengood and Richard Treece. They were very helpful in getting the seminar organized and run smoothly.

Also in 1968 I began a long time involvement with the Lawrence Chamber of Commerce. I became a member of the Aviation Committee which was charged with promoting growth and better facilities at the Lawrence Airport. At that time, the airport actually belonged to the KU Endowment Association. Some years later it was donated to the city of Lawrence.

Most of my former students will find it hard to imagine that, at one time, I was the KU soccer coach. This happened as follows. In 1968 I was approached by several liberal arts students from South America. They asked me to be their soccer coach. They had heard from one of my students that I had an interest in soccer and had actually played on soccer teams. These students wanted to form a KU soccer team to play in an intercollegiate league. However, to play in a league they had to have a faculty sponsor and coach. In those days the KU Athletics Association was not interested in supporting soccer activities. So I agreed to help the students out. As a result, for two years I actually served as the pro-bono KU soccer coach. I even paid for the shoes and uniforms of the team because no support was forthcoming from the Athletics Association. I remember having quite a time keeping up with these much younger students, as they ran around the field to keep in condition.

In 1969 I received the School of Engineering Gould Award for Undergraduate Teaching. Recipients of this award are chosen by students. For a professor, it was really satisfying to be appreciated by one's students. Reversing the last two digits, in 1996 I again was awarded this honor.

In 1969 and 1974 the Secretary of the Navy invited a number of faculty members to spend time on board the aircraft carrier *Lexington*, operating in the Gulf of Mexico. I was lucky to be one of those invited. I was thrilled when I also was given the opportunity to copilot a Grumman S2F Tracker onto and off the carrier in 1969, and the same with a C2 Greyhound in 1974. This made me an "honorary tailhooker" in the USNavy. The piston-engined S2F ("Stoof") and the turboprop C2 are shown in Figures 128 and 129 respectively.

The USNavy can be proud of the professionalism of its naval aviators. They made getting on and off a carrier look like easy work.

The Vietnam War had political repercussions on campuses around the nation. KU was no exception. Let me say at the outset, that I believe it important for universities to allow and encourage wide differences of opinion on any topic. This includes holding demonstrations as long as they do not threaten the freedom and rights of other people.

Encouraged by a few faculty members, many students (apparently with little else to do) saw fit to engage in very disruptive behavior. It was sad to observe that some members of the KU top leadership displayed little backbone in protecting the rights of everyone.

During late spring of 1970 several bad incidents happened on campus, including the burning of the Kansas Union building. Things got so bad that the administration decided to allow students to be excused from class work during the last two weeks of the spring semester. It also cancelled the spring Reserve Officers Training Corps (ROTC) review and came close to terminating the entire ROTC program. Several faculty members and I worked on various committees to stave off some of the more ridiculous proposals to lower academic standards and even to get rid of ROTC.

At one point I was told that a group of rabble-rousers would disrupt my airplane design classes which dealt with the subject of weapons integration. None of my students had any sympathy for the dissenters and spread the word that such attempts would be met by force. None of my classes were ever disrupted.

It is my opinion that much of the blame of what went wrong that spring rests on the shoulders of former Chancellor Larry Chalmers. Many faculty members were glad to see him leave a year later. Chalmers did a lot of damage to the image of KU around the state. Many of my acquaintances in Wichita, for years afterwards, refused to send their children to KU.

What really galled me that spring was that many students in the aerospace engineering department used the "two-weeks-off" policy as an opportunity to get off easy that semester. These experiences formed the low point in my career as a professor.

While teaching the airplane design courses at KU I found it very difficult to get students to use a standard methodology in calculating drag polars and stability and control derivatives for their airplane designs. The reason was obvious: there was no "cookbook" covering these topics.

Therefore, I decided to write two "cookbooks": *Methods for Estimating Drag Polars of Subsonic Airplanes*[(46)] and *Methods for Estimating Stability and Control Derivatives of Subsonic Airplanes*[(47)].

I was pleased that these manuals turned out to be a success not just with my students, but with engineers in industry.

War Story 61

The first textbook I used in teaching flight dynamics was Bernard Etkin's well respected book *Dynamics of Flight* [(48)]. Being very "applications oriented" I found it, and all other books available at that time, much too theoretical. There was very little indication of how theory can actually be applied in the process of designing, developing and certifying airplanes. There were hardly any references to the all important airworthiness regulations. Also, any systematic discussion of how to design an airplane for certifiable flying qualities was lacking. Therefore, I decided to develop my own course notes and use them in teaching my flight dynamics classes.

By 1971 these notes had taken the form of a complete manuscript for a two-volume book. I decided to send the manuscript to several major textbook publishing houses. All agreed that it was a good manuscript. However, all declined to publish it because they felt that there was not a significant market. It should be recalled, that the early 1970's were very bad years for the aerospace industry. There were many layoffs and few aerospace engineering students.

The investment needed to publish a 947-page book was fairly significant. Nevertheless, I decided to take the plunge and publish the book through my own company, Roskam Aviation and Engineering Corporation (RAEC). Thus, in 1972, my first textbooks appeared on the market. They were soft-bound, yellow colored books. The title was *Flight Dynamics of Rigid and Elastic Airplanes, Volume I and Volume II* (References 49 and 50).

The books were an immediate success. They were shipped out of my basement. The investment paid off and I decided to print a larger number of books in a sturdier, hardbound format. These were brown-red colored and sold even better.

Lesson: Don't be discouraged when turned down by existing publishers. If you really believe in your product, start your own venture. This is the American way!

In 1968 the KU Aerospace Engineering Department brought in a young professor from New York University, Dr. Edward C.T. Lan. His expertise was aerodynamics, particularly advanced computational aerodynamics. Eddie and I collaborated on several research contracts for NASA. In 1980 we collaborated in writing the textbook, *Airplane Aerodynamics and Performance* [(51)].

For me, 1972 was an important year because I was promoted to the rank of full professor. I also became department chairman and served in that capacity for four years. In 1976 Professor Vincent Muirhead became the chairman. I remember feeling very relieved when the transition occurred. I never did like a management role and the chairmanship experience re-convinced me that this was not for me. Vince was a retired USNavy Commander who had served during the infamous Japanese attack on Pearl Harbor in 1941. He turned out to be an excellent chairman who served until his retirement.

Around 1973 I first met Burt Rutan[(28)]. Burt was working for Jim Bede at the latter's Newton, Kansas, facility, where the single-place BD-5 and BD-5J* airplanes were being developed and marketed. Figures 130 and 131 show these interesting airplanes.

---

* J stands for jet powered. The BD-5J still is the world's smallest, jet powered airplane.

Burt's responsibilities were manyfold and included the development of the BD-5J as well as the design, development and testing of a new type of simulator device for the BD-5.

Jim had agreed that Burt could continue with the development of the Rutan Vari-Viggen shown in Figure 132. The Vari-Viggen was a single engine, propeller driven canard-pusher machine, inspired by the Swedish SAAB(52) JAS-37 Viggen fighter of Figure 133.

At that time Burt already had quite a reputation as a visionary designer. I wanted to meet both him and Jim and perhaps even get some flying in. Therefore, I flew to Newton in our department Cessna 172.

War Story 62

When Burt offered to take me for a ride in his Vari-Viggen I was delighted. He demonstrated a range of maneuvers and even let me fly the airplane for awhile. What impressed me most about the Vari-Viggen was the excellent stability and the ability to perform full stick-aft turns without any tendency to stall. You just don't do that in most other airplanes.

Lesson: This experience certainly helped me appreciate the fact that canard airplanes can be both attractive and very safe to fly.

War Story 63

The BD-5 (Figure 130) was a really small airplane with very small moments of inertia, particularly in roll. Therefore, control sensitivity in roll was expected to be a feature that a pilot would have to get used to. To help familiarize pilots with the BD-5 flying qualities, Rutan and Bede had evolved a unique simulator.

This simulator consisted of a truck towing a BD-5 via a cleverly designed system of hinges which allowed a significant amount of motion in five degrees of freedom: vertical, lateral, pitch, roll and yaw. Forward motion was provided by the truck. This was a safe method of letting a novice pilot experience the BD-5 flight characteristics in a very realistic environment.

I jumped at the opportunity to get some simulator time in this contraption and made five simulated takeoffs and landings. The first three landings were rather hard, until I finally got "the hang of it" and made two credible takeoffs and landings.

Lesson: The BD-5 is the most control-sensitive airplane I ever had an opportunity to fly. The Rutan-Bede simulator device was an ingeniously designed system to familiarize pilots with that airplane without actually flying it.

In 1973 I organized and chaired the first KU Aerospace Engineering Advisory Board meeting. The board consisted of representatives from the aircraft industry, NASA, FAA and the KU aerospace engineering faculty. The main purpose of the meeting was to determine whether the AE curriculum met the needs of industry. One result was the addition of a new course (AE 21 Aerospace Design and Drafting) to the curriculum. For 30 years this advisory board (in annual or semi-annual meetings) has been of significant help in fine-tuning the educational programs of the department. Currently, many of the advisory board members are former KUAE students.

Also in 1973, NASA asked me to serve as a member of its Research and Technology Advisory Council (RTAC). For the next decade, I served on various sub-committees dealing with general aviation, aerodynamics and avionics technology issues. All this came about as a result of considerable airplane research activities conducted at the KU Flight Research Laboratory as described in Section 6.2.

Partly as a result of this advisership, I was asked by NASA to organize a national conference on aeronautics with the theme: *The Future of Aeronautics*. This conference was to be held under a NASA contract at KU in 1974.

The purpose of the conference was to bring together representatives from universities, industry and government to discuss and assess trends and opportunities in aeronautics and aeronautical education with the expectation of suggesting options and directions for future programs.

The conference was held in the Kansas Union on October 23 and 24, 1974. A summary document also was published (Reference 53).

This conference attracted more than 75 luminaries from all over the USA. Some of the most active participants were James Fletcher (NASA Administrator), John Brizendine (President of Douglas), Courtland Perkins (Professor at Princeton), Arthur Bryson (Professor at Stanford), Willard Hawkins (Vice President of Lockheed), Malcolm Harned (President of Cessna), Eugene Covert (Professor at MIT) and Larry Loftin (Associate Director of NASA Langley). As before, the KU Division of Continuing Education, represented by Richard Treece, had a major hand in making this conference a success.

Probably as a result of that conference, I was asked by NASA to put together yet another conference, this time a *National Workshop on Drag Reduction for General Aviation Airplanes*. KU again was given a contract to organize this meeting.

The Drag Reduction Workshop was held at KU in 1975 and attracted more than 60 national experts on airplane drag. I edited the proceedings document which is still used as a reference source for drag reduction by airplane designers (Reference 53 in Appendix A).

I stayed involved with various other advisory activities to NASA until about 1992 when NASA decided to abandon its advisory panel structure. This was part of a trend which came out of the Reagan administration. Aeronautics was seen as a mature technology thus, taxpayer support of aeronautics research was no longer needed. Industry would take care of it. This very shortsighted decision has saved the taxpayers very little money and eventually will cost the US its dominance in civil aeronautics.

Senator Nancy Kassebaum of Kansas invited me to give testimony before the House Committee on Science and Technology in 1974 and 1989. My testimonies are in the congressional records of those years.

In 1974 I received another promotion. I was appointed to a Distinguished Professorship and became the first Ackers Distinguished Professor of Aerospace Engineering. This represented a great honor.

I am thankful to Ed Polhamus (Branch Chief at NASA Langley), Bill Thompson (Head of Aerodynamics and Flight Test at Cessna), Mal Harned (Senior Vice President at Cessna), Don Grommesh (Vice President of Engineering at Learjet), Richard Holloway (Head of Aerodynamics at Boeing, Wichita) and Beverly Hodges (Director of Engineering at Boeing, Wichita) for writing letters of recommendation.

The following war story illustrates that connections with the right people can really help.

War Story 64

The AE Department was operating a very old, straight tailed, Cessna 172, primarily for transportation (Figure 86). The airplane needed to be replaced, but no funds were available. Because of my consulting activities at Gates Learjet Corporation I had come to know its President, Mal Harned, rather well. By 1973, Mal had left Learjet and joined Cessna as the Senior Vice President in charge of operations. Because of my acquaintance with Mal, I felt it appropriate to call and ask if Cessna could donate a new Model 172 to the KU Aero Department to replace the old one. His reaction surprised me. He asked, "When do you want the airplane?"

Two months later we received a brand new, swept tailed, Cessna 172 which still serves the department transportation needs. A swept, tailed Cessna 172 was shown in Figure 87.

Lesson: If you don't ask, you don't get.

Mal Harned, an alumnus of the KU aero department, turned out to be a staunch supporter. He later was instrumental in helping put private funding together for a new hangar facility. We named the Malcolm Harned Propulsion Laboratory in his honor.

In December of 1976 I taught my first short course* in Wichita, Kansas. The subject matter was *General Aviation Feedback Control Technology*. This course was actually financially sponsored by the NASA-Dryden Flight Research Center. The purpose of the course was to start a process of technology transfer to the general aviation industry from the research done

---

* A typical short course lasts 4-5 days. Also typically, six one-hour lectures are presented each day.

at KU under NASA sponsorship (See Section 6.2). The course was attended by 21 engineers from Cessna, Beech, Boeing and Gates-Learjet.

As a result of the surrounding publicity, KU received requests from various parts of the country to hold similar courses on a regular basis. Consequently, in 1977 I taught my first short course as part of the newly established Aerospace Engineering Short Course Program for the KU Division of Continuing Education. It was a four-day short course called *Airplane Dynamic Stability, Control and Synthesis of Automatic Flight Control Systems*. The course was held at KU and attracted 51 engineers.

One thing led to another and before I knew it, I was teaching six or more, one-week short courses per year in the areas of stability, control, automatic flight controls, airplane design and performance.

In 1981, this short course program came under the very able leadership of Jan Thomas Barron, Senior Program Manager of Continuing Education.

Under her leadership, first nationally and then internationally, the program has grown to more than 60 short courses per year conducted by more than 25 different instructors. Annually, more than 1,600 engineers attend these short courses. The program is nationally and internationally recognized as a model for other universities to follow.

At the time of publication of this book, I have taught more than 144 short courses on *Airplane Design*, *Airplane Flight Dynamics*, and *Airplane Performance*. These courses were taught in England, France, Germany, Switzerland, Italy, The Netherlands, Singapore, Australia, Canada, Brazil and at many, many locations in the United States. A summary of short courses which I have taught is contained in Appendix E.

During the mid 70's, while teaching aircraft design classes, I once more became unhappy with the textbooks available. As before, I started to develop very extensive class notes on the process of airplane design decision making. To translate these notes into a publishable format, I needed time away from KU. In 1983 I asked for, and was granted, a second* sabbatical leave to transform these notes into an eight-volume-textbook series on aircraft design.

I envisioned developing a systematic approach to teaching the airplane design-decision making process (emphasis on process!) to inexperienced students. The approach I wanted was to present that process in the form of a series of step-by-step procedures with the intent of not leaving a stone unturned. The resulting procedures also clearly illustrated the iterative nature of the design-decision making process.

In the real world, airplane designers evolve their own sequence of decision making. There is nothing unique about any particular sequence. The important thing is not to omit any step. In airplane design, everything depends on everything else.

---

* My first sabbatical is discussed in Section 6.3.

My proposed sequence of design decision making was meant to help inexperienced students through the maze of airplane design decisions.

I had come to believe that teaching airplane design decision making was a vitally important last link in the chain of subjects taught as part of an aerospace engineering curriculum. This last link is often called a capstone course. That terminology is correct. It shows students how all the previous subjects that they were taught can be brought to bear on the problem of designing a brand new airplane.

That effort resulted in the encyclopaedic, best selling, rainbow colored, eight volume textbooks: *Airplane Design, Parts I through VIII*, (References 54- 61). First printing of Part I was in 1985. It took me five years to complete the entire eight-volume-set. The last volume was published in 1990. In 2002 these books were still being published, most in their fourth printing.

The color scheme I selected for these books is noteworthy. The first seven volumes had the seven rainbow colors. The eighth, and last volume dealing with cost predictions, was white: the combination of the rainbow colors. The books have been found on the shelves of airplane designers all over the world. I have been told by several Chinese and Korean students that the books have been reprinted (without my permission) in China.

In late 1974 I received a call from Dr. Jay Pinson (at that time Associate Dean of Engineering at the University of Dayton, Ohio). He invited me to participate in a new type of aircraft design short course to be held during the summer of 1975 at the Bergamo Center, a Roman Catholic retreat just outside Dayton.

The course was to be co-taught by several top people in the field: Dr. Leland Nicolai (from the Air Force Institute of Technology and later the Lockheed Skunk Works), Daniel Raymer (from Rockwell and later an independent consultant), Bud D. Nelson (from Boeing and later from Northrop), Jay Pinson (now Dean of Engineering at San Jose State) and me.

We formed an interesting and congenial team. Together we covered virtually every aspect of modern military aircraft design. The participants in the course were mostly USAF engineers working at Wright-Patterson Air Force Base (WPAFB). As part of the course, students had to design their own airplanes and report on their work to the instructors. I remember many lively discussions on the relative merits or de-merits of their designs.

Except for those who lived in Dayton, everyone stayed at the Bergamo retreat where we also had all our meals. It was a very nice place and I looked forward to that course every year. I participated in these short courses through 1991.

War Story 65

On Monday evening the Bergamo short course attendees and the instructors were treated to an airshow staged by the Dayton Radio-Controlled Model Club.

The members of that club went all out to provide a fantastic demonstration of their skills in building and flying RC models. It is hard to forget the dogfights between Snoopy on his Doghouse, a Flying Iron and a Flying Kitchen Stove.

Lesson: The Dayton RC modelers proved that you can make anything fly, provided there is enough power behind it, and provided you know how to control it.

On Thursday night we always had a banquet with well-known speakers such as Paul Garber from the National Aerospace Museum, Sir Frank Whittle and Dr. Hans Pabst von Ohain.

Sir Frank[62, 63] and Dr. Pabst von Ohain[63, 64] were the famous co-inventors of the jet engine. Both lived in the United States.

I remember many interesting conversations with Hans about his WWII experiences working for Professor Ernst Heinkel on his early jet engines. Von Ohain became a scientific advisor to the USAF after WWII. He was very helpful to several of my KU students when they were doing research projects on the origin of the jet engine.

It was a very motivating experience for the mostly young short course attendees to be able to talk to giants like Garber, Whittle and Von Ohain.

From 1982-1984 I served as vice president for education of the American Institute of Aeronautics and Astronautics (AIAA).

From 1985 to 1988 I also served as a member of the Aerospace Engineering Board (AEB) of the National Research Council. The AEB membership was briefed on many advanced research programs in aeronautics and astronautics and then asked for advice. We had many very interesting and informative meetings. The next two war stories deal with that.

War Story: 66

During one meeting of the AEB, we were briefed by NASA engineers on plans for a future space station. We were shown impressive color presentations of the yet to be international space station and how it would be assembled in space.

After the briefing we were asked for questions. I asked, "How many shuttle missions are going to be required to carry out the planned assembly, and how many shuttle missions are planned over the next 10 years?"

It turned out that the NASA leadership had not given any thought to that issue. When pondering the question it became clear that there were not nearly enough shuttle missions available to assemble the station as designed at that time.

Lesson: When planning a new project, sometimes it is the logistics which render a design invalid. This question should be confronted during early preliminary design.

War Story: 67

During another meeting the Board was briefed about the then secret Copper Canyon project. This was part of the National Aero-Space Plane (NASP) project mentioned by President Reagan as the "Orient Express" in one of his State of the Union addresses. It turned out that the whole project hinged upon the feasibility of developing positive thrust-minus-drag, over a very wide range of hypersonic Mach numbers. The feasibility of doing this with air-breathing propulsion had never been demonstrated in any test.

After the briefing the AEB members again were asked for questions. I asked, "What level of technology validation and what funding level is being contemplated to assure that positive thrust-minus-drag can be guaranteed with, say, 99.5% probability?"

The answer given by NASA managers was totally unsatisfactory, particularly in terms of the proposed funding which was much less than the certification cost of a medium sized, commercial jet transport. I severely criticized NASA management for proposing a very high risk project with totally inadequate funding, and not providing credible technology validation.

Lesson: When planning a new, high risk technology program, make sure adequate funding is available or being requested. To propose a taxpayer supported project with demonstrably inadequate funding borders on the unethical.

I still believe that these two meetings resulted in me being removed nicely, and with thanks for services rendered, from the AEB.

Since those early meetings, the space station has undergone major redesign and has been scaled down and delayed. Even at that it is significantly over budget. The "Orient Express" project was eventually reduced to a meager research effort and ultimately cancelled. I did not get any satisfaction out of these sad developments.

As a result of my involvement with the forward swept wing X-29 (described in Section 6.3) I served four years (1990-1993) on the Laboratory Advisory Group of the USAF Flight Dynamics Laboratory, WPAFB, Dayton, Ohio. That group was dissolved in 1993 as a result of a re-organization of USAF laboratories.

In 1990 I was asked to write an overview article for the *Journal of Guidance and Control* on the influence of stability and control on airplane design. It is an honor bestowed on people with lots of gray hair!

The resulting article turned out to be 12 pages long with 101 references (Reference 123 in Appendix A). It appeared in the *Journal* in 1991. It is probably good reading and reference material for any engineer aspiring to become an airplane designer. Over the years I have become convinced that for one to really understand airplane design you need a sound knowledge of stability and control theory, regulations and applications.

In 1990 NASA initiated a series of Aerospace Engineering Design Grants through an organization called the University Space Research Association (USRA). Many universities competed for these grants and KU, as a result of several grant proposals I wrote, was one of those selected.

With the help of these grants a number of airplane design projects were carried out as part of our regular senior aircraft design courses. At the end of the spring semester, faculty and students of the participating universities got together and presented the results of their work. This was a very useful activity for the students. It gave them the opportunity to share their results with many other groups.

I well remember the first of these conferences. I was appalled at the lack of depth and professionalism exhibited by the work of students at many other universities.

I emphasize that this was not the fault of the students. There clearly was a lack of design experience and knowledge among the faculty. In my view, their faculty was also setting very low standards for the students to meet.

In many discussions which followed I pointed out where the design education deficiencies were and what should be done to correct them. I must not always have been very tactful in my comments. The person in charge of the USRA program was Carol Hopf. She always attended the annual discussions and, on several occasions, pointed out to me that I definitely would not win the Mr. Congeniality contest. Carol did a great job managing that difficult program. When Carol left the program she was replaced by Dr. Vicki Johnson, one of my former students.

I must say that most of the faculty at the affected universities responded positively during the following years. This resulted in a significant improvement in the quality and professionalism of design education throughout the country.

In 1991, I was invited to Pretoria, South Africa as the guest of the South African government for two reasons:

1) To deliver the inaugural address at the Third South African Aeronautical Engineering Conference.

2) To consult with government officials about certain proposed reforms in their air safety and accident investigation methods.

I had some misgivings about going to South Africa because of its apartheid policies of discriminating against non-whites. However, there were genuine efforts to end the oppressive actions of the white government and to move towards what was called the New South Africa. They also asked me to somehow integrate that theme into my keynote address.

I consulted with several black faculty and staff members at KU about the desirability of accepting the invitation. They all urged me to go. In their view it could only help. Therefore I decided to make the trip.

My keynote address, *Commercial Aircraft Design Opportunities in the New South Africa*, was delivered August 14, 1991 at The University of Witwatersrand in Pretoria (listed as Reference 124 in Appendix A). It was well received and I had several extremely interesting and positive discussions with South African faculty members, government officials, and industry leaders. During all my discussions with South Africans they expressed their support for ending the era of apartheid.

It was exciting to make a side trip to a small national park and see prides of lions in their natural environment. I also remember thinking that the countryside around Johannesburg was very much like some areas of southern California.

At the time of publication of this autobiography, the new South African government is in place, and there seems to be hope that South Africa will become a leader in the development of better economic conditions and democracy among other African countries. I wish them well; they sure have a beautiful country with truly enormous potential.

War Story 68

During an airplane design short course at Airbus in Toulouse I was invited to tour the mock-up of the new Airbus 340 (Figure 134). This was in 1991 when the A340 had not yet made its first flight. The chief test pilot invited me to take the flight commander's seat while he took the right seat (Figure 135). He then proceeded to explain many aspects of the Airbus cockpit control and flight control design philosophy. Building on their experience with the Airbus 320 they were using a fly-by-wire, joy-stick controlled system.

When he finished with his explanations, he looked at me and asked, "Now, Professor Roskam, would you like to know the real reason for selecting a joy-stick to control this airplane?"

I must have looked a bit flabbergasted and answered, "Sure." He then pulled out a tray in front of me and said, "So that we can serve the pilot dinner during flight."

Lesson: A bit of humor never hurts.

After the course at Airbus in Toulouse, I was scheduled to teach a similar course on airplane design at British Aerospace, in the old DeHavilland[(2)] plant in Hatfield, England. Much to my surprise and delight, the course was being held in the former private dining room of Sir Geoffrey DeHavilland. Sir Geoffrey was the founder and CEO of that famous company.

In one of the hangars, DH employees had restored to flying condition, the red-painted, DH Comet racer of 1934, named *Grosvenor House*. Figures 136 and 137 show pictures of the author standing in front that famous airplane which won the McRobertson speed air-race from London to Melbourne in 1932 (this took me back to the KLM *Uiver* days mentioned on page 3 in Chapter 1). Spending the week at the former DeHavilland facilities was an exciting reminder of early aviation history. That entire week I felt like I was walking on holy ground with all the DH memorabilia all around me. The street names were all familiar to me. They were named after the people who guided the DeHavilland Company in its halcyon days: Bishop, Geoffrey DeHavilland (son of the founder and chief test pilot), John Derry, Arthur Hagg, John Cunningham, etc.

In 1992 I was asked to teach a short course on airplane design at DASA in Hamburg, Germany. Today, that plant is part of Airbus, actually the European Aeronautics, Defense and Space Company (EADS).

War Story 69

Most of the attendees of this DASA course were fairly young German aeronautical engineers. One of the things I always did in short courses was use a lot of historical examples of things tried by airplane designers of the past. Some of those examples deal with the development of early jet fighters and bombers manufactured in Germany during WWII from 1939 to 1945. In particular, I liked to discuss airplanes like the Messerschmitt 262 and 163, Arado[(65)] 234 and Junkers 287. Figures 138 - 141 show renditions of these WWII airplanes.

I was amazed that not one of the German engineers in my audience had even heard of these projects. When I asked for the reason, the answer I received was interesting. "Professor Roskam, we were drilled into forgetting what happened during WWII. The topics you bring up were not discussed at our universities or in our high schools."

Lesson: It is very important to learn from past experiences, right or wrong. Pretending bad things did not happen is like sticking one's head in the sand.

War Story 70

In Chapters 1 and 2, I discussed several events and experiences during WWII. For about one and one half years my family and I lived in Bramfeld, near Hamburg.

I could not resist visiting some of these places since I was in Hamburg anyway. Therefore, on a Sunday morning I stepped out of the hotel and flagged a cab. The driver turned out to be a lady roughly my age. Since I still speak German, I told her that I wanted to visit several places that were familiar to me when I was a 12 year old boy during WWII. It turned out that she remembered vividly what had gone on during those days and also was familiar with the areas I described. As a result, I had a delightful tour of Bramfeld and Hamburg. It was amazing how much had changed during these many years but also, how much was still the same. One big difference: all was peaceful and prosperous.

Lesson: It is a good thing that time heals most wounds.

In 1992 after the course in Hamburg, I had the opportunity to conduct another short course on airplane design, again for British Aerospace Corporation, but this time in Woodford near Manchester. This course was held at the old AVRO[8] plant, where during WWII the famous Lancaster bomber was built (Figure 14). This, to me, was another almost holy site.

AVRO's chief designer, Roy Chadwick, and his design team hatched the Lancaster at this location. The Lancaster, together with the Boeing B-17 (Figure 18), made the ultimate allied victory in Europe possible.

In 1994, AVRO was building various models of the Regional Jet (RJ) series. Figure 142 shows all three RJ types. This airplane is actually a derivative of the DeHavilland DH146 which was the last airplane designed by the former DeHavilland company at Hatfield. Sadly, in late 2001 British Aerospace management saw fit to terminate the production of this remarkable airplane. I believe that was a very short sighted decision.

War Story 71

One evening I was invited to tour the factory where the RJ series of airplanes was being assembled. I noticed that the floors in the final assembly and systems checkout areas were rather dirty; dust, metal shavings and other debris were everywhere. After the tour the factory manager asked for comments. Never being a good example of diplomacy, I told him that I was impressed with the airplane, but that his customers must be unhappy about the dirty environment in which their airplanes were being assembled and checked. More or less red-faced, he agreed and said that something would me done about it.

I well remember that the next year I was invited to teach the same course at the same facility. One evening they proudly showed me their "super clean" final assembly area.

Lesson: It is important to keep final assembly and system checkout areas very clean. This promotes safety, pride in workmanship and keeps customers happy.

Several of the employees at AVRO were volunteering their time to work on a AVRO Vulcan[66] jet bomber which was parked outside the engineering building (Figure 143). In my lectures on airplane design I like to point out the fact that the Vulcan was a slightly more efficient airplane than its American contemporary, the Boeing B-47 (Figure 92). This has to do with wetted area and span-loading. However, the reason the B-47 became the granddaddy of most modern jet transports is easier engine accessibility. I had an opportunity to verify this by looking into the engine bays of the Vulcan.

In 1992 I received a grant from the National Science Foundation (NSF) to transfer my experience as an airplane designer and airplane design teacher to faculty members of other universities. What motivated me was the experience with the NASA/USRA program.

As part of this grant, 20 faculty members involved in airplane design teaching at American universities were given stipends to attend a two-week short course on airplane design and design teaching at The University of Kansas.

The course was over-subscribed and therefore, NSF asked me to repeat it the next year, 1993. I thoroughly enjoyed the contacts with so many design teaching colleagues around the country. It was a lot of fun working with these professors.

In the fall of 1993 I applied for, and was granted, my third sabbatical for the spring of 1994. I used this time to completely overhaul my textbooks on flight dynamics. I voluntarily taught AE521 and AE621 during that semester as well.

In 1994 the KU Department of Aerospace Engineering celebrated its 50th anniversary. As part of the festivities a conference was held with papers presented by several former students who had achieved notable positions in industry. It was wonderful to see so many former students return to their alma mater for this event. I was asked to give the keynote address, *Commercial Transport Evolution and the Role of Technology* (Reference 136, Appendix A).

One of our former students, Doug Shane, was head of flight operations at Scaled Composites. He had flown into Lawrence in his own, self-built, Rutan Longeze airplane (Figure 144). He offered me a ride and let me handle the controls during our flight.

War Story 72

Another former student who attended was James (Jim) Thiele, President and CEO of American Blimp Corporation.

When Jim was a student he came into my office one day to show me pictures of a giant advertising balloon he had built and sold to Dairy Queen. That balloon was shaped like a very large ice cream cone. I was impressed and asked what else he was planning to do. He said that upon graduation he was going to start a company to build advertising blimps. His idea was to make the hull transparent so that internally mounted lights could be used to give the whole machine a translucent appearance. As it turned out, this is exactly what Jim did. His company now is the largest airship manufacturer in the world.

Lesson: This is a lesson for future students. With knowledge, imagination, and hard work, it is amazing what can be accomplished.

War Story 73

In September of 1995 I received a call from James Thiele informing me that one of his airships (he calls them light-ships) would be in Lawrence under an advertising contract with Blockbuster Video.

He asked if I would like a ride. Needless to say, I jumped at the suggestion. On a beautiful sunny Friday the lightship, painted in the Blockbuster colors, showed up (Figure 145).

After boarding the ship the pilot called "up ship." The ground handlers had positioned themselves underneath the gondola and, following that command, pushed up. Full throttle and slightly back stick, and away we went. Ten minutes into the flight I was asked to take over the controls and do some gentle maneuvering.

Flying this airship was a wonderful experience. The landing was performed by the pilot and, of course, with the help of several ground handlers.

Lesson: Because an airship is literally lighter than air, not much pushup is required to launch it. Also, dynamic lift (lift due to angle of attack and airspeed) is an important ingredient in maneuvering an airship.

Sometime in 1997, I was called by Crispin Muncaster from Elsevier, a British publisher of scholarly journals. His idea was to start a new, international aircraft design journal dedicated specifically to aircraft design topics. He proposed to ask Egbert Torenbeek of Delft University of Technology in The Netherlands, and me to be the co-editors of this new journal. Egbert and I accepted, and the first issue of this quarterly journal, *Aircraft Design*, was published in 1998. Sadly, after a three year run, Elsevier decided to stop publishing this journal at the end of 2001. They were losing too much money on this venture.

In 1999 a German student, Freiherr Christian von Strombeck conducted a design study for a very long range, small jet transport. One of his conclusions was that, to avoid the Extended Range Twin Jet Operations (ETOPS) certification and associated operational expenses, a tri-jet would have lower cost. However, a problem with previous tri-jets was the center engine installation, which invariably led to higher engine maintenance costs. I suggested to Von Strombeck that perhaps all three engines belonged under the wing. That would make the airplane asymmetrical. He found this idea to be workable.

In a follow-up class during the fall semester of 2000, a group of KU students built an RC version of such an asymmetric tri-jet. Figure 146 shows that model which is a modified Airbus 310 model. The trick is to place the engines so that the inherent yawing and rolling moments due to engine placement are zero. In that model we were constrained by structural considerations. This resulted in the number 2 engine being closer to the fuselage than would be desirable in an actual airplane.

In January of 2001 I announced to the KU Department of Aerospace Engineering that I would retire from teaching at The University of Kansas on December 31, 2003.

In February of 2002 I taught my first distance course using compressed video as the enabling technology. The course was arranged by KU Continuing Education and sponsored by Embraer of Brazil. I believe that long distance education will be the direction to go with both short courses and graduate courses.

In the next section my experiences with various research projects are summarized.

Figure 123 Beech D17, Staggerwing (Courtesy Beech Aircraft)

Figure 124 Beech D18S (Courtesy Beech Aircraft)

Figure 125 Model of the Ford Trimotor

Figure 126 Grumman F11F, Tigercat

Figure 127 Model of the Sikorsky CH-54A, Skycrane (Jolly Green Giant)

Figure 128 Grumman S2F, Tracker (Courtesy Grumman)

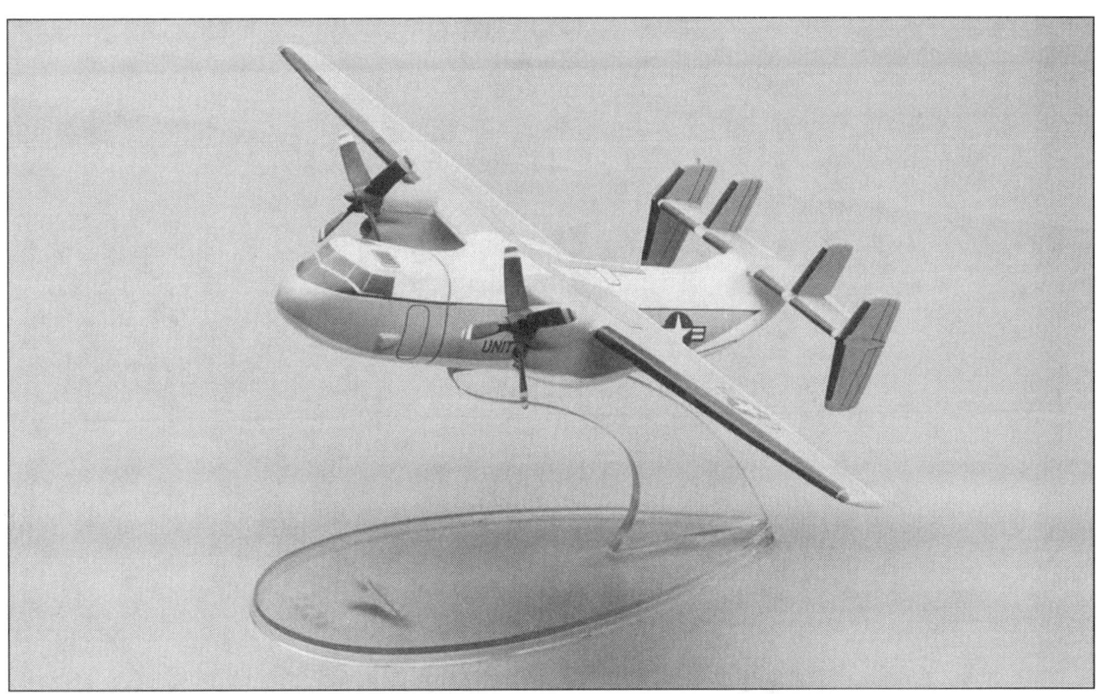

Figure 129 Model of the Grumman C2, Greyhound

Figure 130 BD-5 with James S. Bede in the Cockpit (Courtesy James S. Bede)

Figure 131 BD-5J (Courtesy James S. Bede)

Figure 132 Rutan Vari-Viggen (© 1999, EAA, Mark Schaible)

Figure 133 SAAB JAS-37, Viggen (Courtesy SAAB)

Figure 134 Airbus 340 (With Permission from the Royal Aeronautical Society Library)

Figure 135 The Author in the Driver's Seat of the Airbus A-340

Figure 136 DeHavilland Comet, *Grosvenor House*

Figure 137 DeHavilland Comet, *Grosvenor House*

Figure 138 Model of the Messerschmitt 262, Sturmvogel

Figure 139 Messerschmitt 163, Komet (With Permission from the Royal Aeronautical Society Library)

Figure 140 Model of the Arado 234

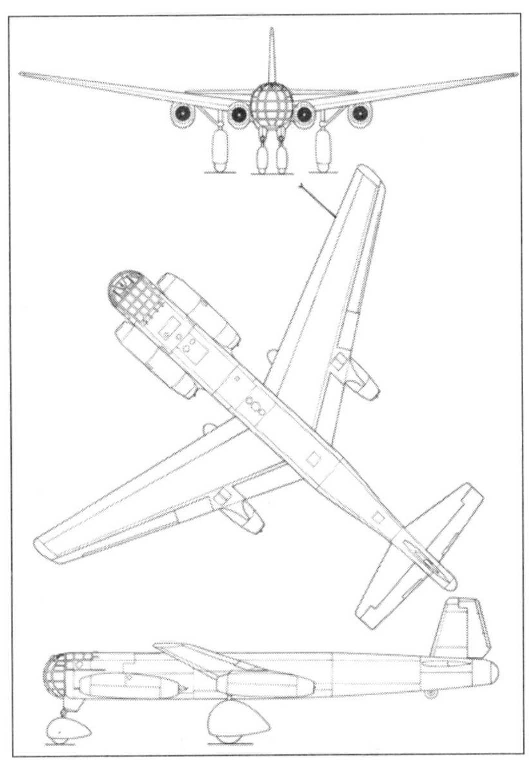

Figure 141 Three-view of the Junkers 287 (Copied from: Jet Planes of the Third Reich; Smith & Creek; with Permission from Monogram Aviation Publications; Sturbridge, MA, USA)

Figure 142 AVRO RJ 70, RJ85 and RJ 100 (Courtesy British Aerospace)

Figure 143 AVRO Vulcan (Courtesy British Aerospace)

Figure 144 Rutan Longeze (© 1999, EAA, Mark Schaible)

Figure 145 Lightship by American Blimp Corporation

Figure 146 RC Model of an Asymmetric Trijet

6.2 Research at the Flight Research Laboratory from 1968-1999

One condition I had set forth for coming to KU was that I be given the opportunity to organize a flight research laboratory. The purpose I had in mind for this flight research laboratory was to conduct research in aerospace engineering, and involve graduate and undergraduate students in this pursuit. Dean William P. Smith and the AE Chairman Dr. David (Dave) Kohlman, were in agreement with me on those points.

To set up such a laboratory required the approval of the director of the KU Center for Research in the Engineering Sciences, Inc. (called CRES). The Dean of the Graduate School, Dr. Bill Argersinger, was the CRES director and a hard nut to crack. At first he did not like the idea of another separate entity. However, with Dave, Bill and I all pushing, he came around and the KU Flight Research Laboratory (FRL) was officially organized in 1968.

I became the first FRL director. I even designed its logo (Figure 147) and assigned its motto, *Avigare Necesse Est* (Latin for aviation is necessary).

Over the years, all AE faculty members brought research contracts into the FRL. I only will describe the work done under contracts for which I was primarily, or partially, responsible.

The first two contracts which I secured for the FRL were from Boeing, Seattle, and from Beech Aircraft Corporation, Wichita.

The purpose of the Boeing contract ($20,200) was to collect, study and document methods for predicting roll damping characteristics of airplanes. This contract came through the office of Harry Higgins, my former boss at Boeing.

The Beech contract ($5,350) was for a proprietary design study of a light, pusher propeller airplane. Beech did not think the various configurations we evolved would sell.

Dave Kohlman and I served as co-principal investigators on both contracts. This was the beginning of many cooperative research efforts between Dave and me. More importantly, these research projects became extremely effective means to improve undergraduate and graduate education of our students. One of the students who worked with us on these first contracts was Alan R. Mulally who later became the CEO of The Boeing Commercial Airplane Company.

The University of Kansas has a research development fund out of which young professors are funded (on a competitive basis) to pursue research in specific areas. This was looked upon as "seed" money. I proposed two small efforts: one dealing with light airplane response to turbulence, the other with spoilers for roll control. Both projects were funded, $3,167 and $3,000 respectively.

The bulk of all research money awarded to the FRL is spent paying students for being part-time research assistants. Some of the money is used to acquire equipment needed to carry out the research work.

Dave Kohlman and I also participated in a flight evaluation of an idea to increase airport/runway productivity. The idea was called the Brandt Drift-off Runway. It was patented by a Mr. Brandt who was the father of one of our students. Figure 148 shows a schematic of this type of runway. As seen, there are essentially two runways next to each other with no separation in between.

The idea was to allow a landing airplane to drift over to the right for further slowdown as soon as the pilot deems it safe. Once the airplane has drifted off another airplane is cleared to land. This way the productivity per runway could be very significantly increased.

Dave and I both were intrigued by the idea and agreed to work on it pro bono.

War Story 74

To test the efficacy of the Drift-off Runway idea Dave contacted the commander of Forbes Air Force Base (now, Forbes Field) in Topeka. Forbes had an extremely long and wide concrete ramp used for parking B-52 bombers. This ramp was large enough to simulate two adjacent runways. Dave also contacted the FAA which agreed to send several observers.

On the day of the test the ramp was cleared of all military aircraft. A horde of light, single and twin engine airplanes descended upon Forbes to test how well the "drift-off" idea would work. The control tower guys had been briefed and did a superb job keeping us all in line. I flew the AE department Cessna 172 in between two big twins, being careful to touch down beyond the contact point of the twin ahead of me to avoid wake turbulence.

We all thought that the idea was very workable. Even the FAA people were impressed. Sadly, the idea never got any further.

Lesson: Good ideas, particularly those which require an agreement between many government agencies, are hard to get accepted.

Eventually, several large airports installed high-speed turn-offs to expedite the process of getting airplanes off the runway. These high speed turn-offs, in essence, are a less concrete-intensive version of the Brandt Drift-off Runway.

In 1968 the AE department hired Dr. Edward C.T. Lan as a professor in theoretical and applied aerodynamics. Together with Eddie, a \$41,290 NASA contract was secured to explore and devise rapid, preliminary design type methods for aeroelastic analysis of wing planforms. This work resulted in several NASA contractor reports (Appendix A, Items 29-33). In 1976 I received a Certificate of Recognition and cash award from NASA for these pioneering efforts.

In 1968 I also received a \$2,700 KU seed grant to study low cost high lift devices for light airplanes.

Based on work done on our various seed grants, Dave Kohlman and I both felt that it should be possible to achieve significant improvements in the performance of light, general aviation airplanes by incorporating a low-cost, scaled-down version of Boeing jet transport, high lift technology, higher wing loadings and spoilers for roll control.

We decided to submit a proposal to NASA Langley for a research contract to establish the feasibility of doing this. Our first proposal to NASA Langley was for $57,000 to study improved control methods for light aircraft.

One student who worked as my first graduate student on these studies was, again, Alan Mulally. Alan, as always, did a truly superb job.

Our NASA contact was Joe Stickle who ran the Langley General Aviation Branch. Joe used to say "Every time I see Jan Roskam, he hands me a research proposal." For many years I did. Other well known NASA engineers with whom we dealt were Joe Chambers and Joe Johnson. For some reason there were a lot of people called Joe at NASA Langley.

In 1969 the FRL received a $57,000 grant from NASA Langley to perform this work. In collaboration with Cessna, we decided to use the Cessna Cardinal as our baseline vehicle. The Cardinal is shown in Figure 149.

The Cardinal was evolved from the Cessna 172 by removing the wing struts and giving the wing a conventional carry-through structure. We decided to leave that carry-through structure alone and attach our new outer wing panels to that carry through. The resulting bulky root fairing was something we did not like but had to live with.

Thus evolved the KU/NASA/Cessna Redhawk* airplane N1910F (see Figure 150).

At Cessna, the Vice President of Engineering Harvey Nay, and the Head of Aerodynamics Bill Thompson, were very helpful in getting this project off the ground. Cessna "sold" the Cardinal prototype to KU for the princely sum of $1.00.

NASA increased its support of the Redhawk project with another grant for $94,000, also in 1969. With the help of a large group of students, Dave Kohlman and I redesigned the Cardinal wing roughly in the following manner:

a) Reduced the wing chord by about 50%, keeping the span the same

b) Used very simple Fowler flaps at the trailing edge, using simple external flap-tracks

c) Used Krueger flaps at the leading edge

d) Drooped the ailerons for added high lift

e) Added spoilers for roll control

f) Controlled ailerons through the left control wheel only

g) Controlled spoilers through the right control wheel only.

---

* A Cardinal is a red bird. The Jayhawk is the KU mascot. Hence the name Redhawk.

Features f) and g) were incorporated for safety reasons: we did not quite trust the force-feel characteristics of our spoilers. As it turned out, these were perfectly acceptable.

Dave and I only did the preliminary design work. There were a lot of details, particularly in the structural design and analysis area. The high lift and the roll control system design also commanded a lot of detail attention. It was in these areas where several graduate students had an opportunity to work on a real life project.

To validate the flying characteristics of the Redhawk with its spoilers, Dave came up with the idea to develop a fixed-base simulator with a visual display, driven by a moving terrain belt, and viewed with the help of a Fresnel Lensing system.

We got a Beechcraft Duke prototype from Beech (free) and used the fuselage as our simulator cab. Norman Hoecker and Dave Nelson helped in taking the airplane apart. A Beech Duke production airplane is shown in Figure 151.

The moving terrain and associated visual system were developed with the help of several undergraduate and graduate students. Jerry Hanson, who had joined the AE Department in 1970, also was of immense help in getting these projects off and running. Figure 152 shows that simulation facility. It all worked amazingly well and was very realistic. We even had an inflatable cushion in the pilot seat to simulate changes in vertical acceleration.

The simulator work showed that the Redhawk would handle very well.

It is important to re-emphasize, that many students were able to get significant hands-on work as well as valuable educational experiences as a result of this simulator development.

I talked Don Collins, formerly from Learjet, into coming to KU to earn an advanced degree. He got his DE degree on this project by supervising a staff of graduate and undergraduate students in the detailed design and analysis of the new wing and its high lift system. Don later became an engineering project manager at Aviation Engineering Consultants, and later yet at Beech Aircraft Company, both in Wichita.

Next, we negotiated a contract with Robinson Aircraft Company of Bellevue, Washington, to actually build the wing with the new high lift devices. The gentleman who ran Robinson at that time was Jim Raisbeck, an engineer whom I had first met at Boeing. Jim later formed Raisbeck Engineering, a company that makes a wide variety of successful modification kits for airplanes of all types.

The Redhawk airplane was test flown successfully and ferried to Lawrence by Dave Kohlman. A thorough flight test program followed which demonstrated all that we had predicted. The airplane was later donated to the Wichita Air Museum where it can still be seen. Again, several students got hands-on experience, this time with actual flight test preparation and flight test data analysis.

The Redhawk project turned out to be of seminal value to the general aviation aircraft industry. The Fowler flaps with their simple, external tracks were later used on a number of products by Cessna, Mooney(67) and Sud Aviation (now, SOCATA) in France. The spoilers also found application in several airplanes.

Dave and I wrote an article called *The Grudging Progress of Lightplane Design*, which appeared five years later (Reference 40 in Appendix A).

By 1969, Beech Aircraft also had become interested in spoilers and, as a result, the FRL was given a $25,000 contract to conduct a study of manually controlled spoilers for light airplanes.

That same year I also received a KU grant for $3,000 to study an upper surface, vortex augmented wing. The idea for such a wing came to me via Boeing, Seattle. A former Boeing engineer and sailplane enthusiast, B.M. Gladych, had tried this on a sailplane and claimed significant lift performance advantages at low speed.

I was encouraged by my former boss at Boeing, Harry Higgins, to check this out. A graduate student, Mark Gleason, ran an extensive series of tunnel tests on a Cessna 210 model and showed that, at least under the conditions tested, the lift improvement was small and the drag increase (as expected) was huge. Figure 153 depicts an example of one vortex augmented configuration.

Mark went on to head the aerodynamic development group of Ford Motor Company.

Also in 1969, Bell[(68)] Helicopter Company contracted with the FRL for a $10,000 project to study flying qualities of the Bell Model 300 tiltrotor airplane which later evolved into the Bell Model 301. Figure 154 shows a mock-up of this airplane.

War Story 75

Sometime in early 1970 I received a call from Harvey Nay, vice president of engineering for Cessna Aircraft Company. Our telephone conversation went something like this:

“Jan, I hold in my hand an electric car window actuator which I bought at our local Chrysler dealer for $25. I would like to use this in a low cost autopilot for the aileron controls. What I need to know is, will it work?”

I answered, “Harvey, first we would have to perform a closed loop analysis to determine the workability. Second, an endurance test will be needed to determine whether the actuator will hold up when operating under continuous loading. In a car the actuator is only used intermittently. However, in an airplane it would be in a continuous load situation.”

Harvey said, “ Name your price and we will give the FRL a contract to do that work.” We got the contract for $10,000.

In my naivety I called the Chrysler engineer responsible for that actuator, and asked him to please give me the transfer function of the actuator. I remember it being very quiet on the other side of the line. Finally he asked: “Will you run that by me again?” I did. He then said, “What in the world is a transfer function?”

I knew it was time for a different approach.

With the help of Jerry Hanson, who was quick in coming up with experimental setups, we ended up using the inverse Bode-plot method to determine the transfer function of the actuator. A closed loop analysis revealed that Harvey's idea would work fine in a Cessna 172 type autopilot.

With Jerry's help we next rigged up a system for testing the actuator under a simulated load with temperature probes to keep track of heating tendencies. After about two hours of operation the actuator went up in smoke. That was the end of another seemingly good idea.

Lesson: Always check the real world performance of new equipment. Something unexpected, which turns out to be a show-stopper, may crop up.

In 1971 I submitted a proposal to NASA Langley and NASA Dryden for the design and testing of a new type of stability augmentation system to be used with airplanes with purely mechanical flight control systems. We called it SSSA for Separate Surface Stability Augmentation.

The basic idea was to split any control surface into two pieces. One large piece was controlled directly by the pilot via the conventional mechanical controls. The other smaller piece was controlled by an actuator, via the automatic stability augmentation system as well as by a position transducer located at the cockpit controls.

With this system it was possible to achieve virtually any level of damping of airplane motions without hingemoment feedback to the cockpit controls. It also was possible to use the system as an attitude command system. The system was to be demonstrated on a Beechcraft Model 99, a 19 passenger, twin turboprop airliner shown in Figure 155.

Key to the feasibility of the system was the absence of hingemoment feedback to the pilot controls. To establish this, a wind tunnel test program was run on a Cessna 210 model equipped with separate surface rudders and ailerons. The tests showed that hingemoment feedback was well within the friction bandwidth of the mechanical flight controls.

The first SSSA grant from NASA was for \$146,000. The NASA manager to whom I reported was Shu Gee at NASA Dryden, Edwards Air Force Base.

As part of the SSSA proposal I obtained agreement from Beech (with considerable support from James Lew, Vice President of Engineering) to "lease" a Model 99 to KU as part of this NASA sponsored work. KU was to be responsible for all levels of system design (including all the electronics) and Beechcraft would modify the airplane in accordance with the KU design. Test flying was a combined responsibility with Bob Stone, chief test pilot at Beech, in charge.

This turned out to be a very large project for the KU FRL (eventually it exceeded \$1,000,000) and could not have been taken on without help from experienced engineers. As luck would have it, I was able to convince Gerald Jenks from Cessna Aircraft and Mac Ashburn from NASA (Kennedy Space Flight Center) to come to KU, enroll in our MSAE program and take the lead roles in this program. Both did an excellent job of getting this program off the ground. Gerald (we called him Jerry) also served as co-pilot during the flight test program. Jerry later became a program manager at McDonnell-Douglas (now also Boeing) and presently serves on the University of Kansas Aerospace Engineering Department Industrial Advisory Board. Mac took a teaching position at the Salina Technical Institute.

One of the things we had to do was to ground test the entire system with a simulator and an iron bird. We used the Duke simulator (from the Redhawk program) and built an iron bird of the entire SSSA control system. Thus, the system was extensively "flown" on the ground for months before committing to the final design.

Jerry Hanson was a great help in getting things done in the laboratory. As usual, many undergraduate and graduate students worked on this project with him and derived real world educational benefits from doing so.

Boeing, Wichita was helpful in conducting the required flutter analyses under a sub-contract.

First flight of the SSSA Model 99 occurred in 1972 and the program was successful in demonstrating the potential of such a system. Figure 156 shows the test airplane in flight.

Figure 157 shows Bob Stone and Jerry Jenks with the airplane. Bob was an excellent test pilot. It was a tragic loss when we heard some years later that he had been killed in a flutter flight test involving the Beech T-34C. A picture of the T-34C is shown in Figure 158.

War Story 76

One of the first flights of the SSSA M99 airplane was conducted from Beech Field. I and two research assistants had briefed the flight test crew (Jerry Jenks and Bob Stone) about the test cards that needed to be completed that day.

We also emphasized that there was a large hole in the concrete ramp, duly marked with red flags, but fairly close to where the M99 was parked. We joked that they should not taxi the airplane into that hole.

Well, "Murphy" struck again that day. After completing the engine checks and other pre-flight checks, the test crew promptly taxied the airplane into that hole. This caused about $250,000 worth of damage and a significant program delay. Figure 159 is a picture of a memento of part of the broken propeller from that mishap. I kept this memento on a wall outside my office as a reminder to engineering students that Murphy's Law is for real!

Lesson: Don't count on briefings and red flag markers as adequate warnings. Go the extra mile and place a person with a big red flag near the hole if an airplane needs to ground maneuver in close proximity. Also make sure that this person can be seen from the cockpit.

Early in 1973 I purchased my first and only airplane, a Cessna Skyhawk (Figure 160). Actually, my company, Roskam Aviation and Engineering Corporation (RAEC), owned the airplane. My intent was to commercialize the SSSA idea in the form of a simple wing leveler which was to be offered on an STC (Supplemental Type Certificate) basis.

With the help of Jerry Hanson (working on weekends because this was not part of his regular job) and some students, we designed a Separate Surface Aileron System (Wing Leveler) for my airplane which I flew for several years. The airplane bore the "Experimental" designation, but I continued using it on consulting trips to Wichita. The system worked very well and never gave me any trouble.

As part of the flight test program I had to show that if the separate surface aileron failed in a hardover-down or hardover-up condition, the airplane was still easily controllable. I conducted these flight tests myself after having Jerry bolt the surface fixed in these hardover modes. I could not detect any significant differences in handling, other than having to carry a small amount of aileron deflection. Figure 161 shows the separate aileron surface in a simulated "hard-over failure" condition.

Another series of tests which had to be conducted were high speed dives to make sure that flutter would not occur. For these tests one of my students, Bruce Holmes, an experienced pilot already, was hired as the test pilot. We constructed a very careful flight test matrix to gradually sneak up on the design dive speed of the airplane. Bruce could not detect any vibration tendency.

At that point, in 1974, I was faced with a fairly large investment to get the system finally certified and in production. I chickened out and decided to stop further development.

Bruce Holmes went on the get his doctorate at KU and is currently the director of NASA general aviation programs.

About a year after the SSSA program was finished the FRL could no longer afford the upkeep costs associated with our wonderful simulator facility and it had to be scrapped. As a result, future generations of students were deprived of this useful learning tool.

Shortly after the Redhawk program was finished, NASA Langley became interested in the possibility of applying advanced airfoil and high lift technology to multi-engine light airplanes.

Dave Kohlman and I submitted another proposal to Joe Stickle at NASA Langley for the design, construction and flight testing of such an airplane. That airplane became known as the Advanced Technology Light Twin (ATLIT). The first grant was for $410,000. Dave was the principal investigator on that program.

A twin engine Piper Seneca was donated to the program by Piper Aircraft and a modified wing (built by Cessna Aircraft) was built.

The ATLIT airplane, shown in Figure 162, was successfully flight tested in 1976.

As usual, many students had an opportunity to learn about real world problems and get advanced degrees on this research program.

From an educational viewpoint, it is sad that NASA has completely gotten out of this type of research. The best we can do today is simulate the real world in radio-controlled (RC) model design-build-fly competitions. RC models are nice, however, they do not even come close to simulating real world problems.

During the latter part of the ATLIT program I became eligible for my first sabbatical leave from KU. I decided to spend half a year at The University of Delft in The Netherlands.

My first sabbatical took place from December 1976 to May of 1977. My counterpart in Delft, Professor Egbert Torenbeek, also was on sabbatical. Therefore, with his kind permission, I used his office during that period.

I had the opportunity to work with a large group of Dutch students who wanted to design an airplane under my supervision. That design became the known as the VATLIT, for Very Advanced Technology Light Twin (Figure 163).

The VATLIT design was a very fast, twin turboprop, tractor, high wing airplane aimed at the King Air Market. The cruise speed was predicted to be around 400 kts, at 40,000 ft altitude. The airplane had a supercritical, zero sweep wing, with winglets. The project was fairly widely written about (for example, Reference 60 in Appendix A). Although the VATLIT was never built, it had two significant consequences.

1) During 1978, I was contacted by Tom Harris (former Vice President of Aero Commander of Bethany, Oklahoma), President of Management Enterprises, Inc., and the US representative of the Piaggio Aircraft Company of Finale Ligure, Italy. Tom indicated that the VATLIT project had come to the attention of Dr. Piaggio, CEO and owner of Piaggio Aircraft Company, and he invited me to come to Italy for a discussion.

Many readers may not know that Piaggio is one of the oldest airplane companies in the world. Just before WWII, Piaggio built a streamlined, four-engined bomber, the P-108 which looked very much like the Boeing B-17 or vice versa. My first visit to Piaggio resulted in a lot of engineering work which my company, RAEC, did for Piaggio. This is summarized in Section 6.3.

2) Several of the Dutch students who worked with me on the VATLIT design, decided to continue their studies toward a doctoral degree at The University of Kansas. The following names and their jobs in 2002 come to mind:

* Kees van Dam, Professor of Aerospace Engineering at The University of California at Davis. Kees is an expert on high lift design. He teaches short courses for KU.

* Paul Vijgen, Senior Group Engineer at Boeing. He also teaches short courses for KU.

* Ton Peschier, vice president engineering for the De Schelde Shipbuilding Company in The Netherlands.

* Bob van Keppel, Senior Group Engineer at Boeing.

These students plus many other students from Holland became known at KU as "Roskam's Dutch Maffia." Many of our research projects could simply not have been conducted without the very significant help from the Delft students. There were, and still are, not enough American born students to carry out the research function of the university.

One problem is the poor mathematics and science preparation of US born students compared with almost any European or Asian born students. In my view the real problem is the poor quality of US elementary and high school education. This was true in the 1960's and was still true in the 2002's. We Americans do not seem to want to improve our education system. As I write this in 2002, more than 90% of our graduate students are foreign.

From 1965 through 1975 NASA conducted a considerable amount of work in the development of an aspect of flight testing referred to as Parameter Identification. Similar work had been conducted at Delft University by my colleague Otto Gerlach. Both approaches had led to the development of measurement, recording and software systems which allowed the determination of airplane stability and control derivatives from dynamic flight test maneuvers. Later developments also enabled the determination of airplane performance parameters and drag polars from dynamic flight test maneuvers.

War Story 77

It occurred to Dave Kohlman and me that it should be possible to develop a low cost version of these systems for use in general aviation type airplanes. Consequently, we wrote a proposal to NASA Dryden to develop and flight test such a system. We were successful in landing a large research grant. The result was a low cost system which was relatively easy to use and did not require major airframe modifications. Publication 81 in Appendix A describes the system in more detail. Ron Renz, one of our top graduate students, worked on this project. Figure 164 shows what the system finally looked like.

This work had two consequences:

1) Dave Kohlman and Bill Schweikard (who was teaching propulsion classes at KU) together with Ron Renz set up a company, Kohlman Systems Research (KSR) in Lawrence, Kansas. This company specialized in flight testing of airplanes using techniques similar (but considerably refined and developed) to the KU system. These flight test results could be used in the design of FAA approved simulators. Companies and armed forces from all over the world use KSR to develop flight test validated simulator models.

2) Ron later left KSR to form his own company, Alligator Inc., which engages in flight testing and airplane modification activities.

Lesson: Much of the research work performed at universities has commercial applicability. In some cases this can drive faculty members away from teaching because of the relatively low salaries professors make at most state universities.

In 1977 NASA Langley became interested in noise transmission problems in general aviation airplanes. I managed to obtain several research grants which allowed us to construct a Beranek tube in the FRL (Figure 165). With the help of that Beranek tube we were able to do a lot of systematic testing of noise transmission losses through various types of materials used in airplanes. Most of that testing was done under contract to Cessna, Beech and Learjet.

As usual, our Director of Aero Laboratories, Jerry Hanson was instrumental in helping us with that project. Several years after completing this NASA grant work we had to dismantle this research tool as well: the cost of upkeep did it again.

In 1984 I decided that the time had come to relinquish my directorship of the FRL. I felt that my increased consulting activities also did not allow me do justice to that post. Dr. Dave Downing was the logical person to take over.

My next KU research project was a logical consequence of the step-by-step airplane design procedures which I laid down in my eight-volume series *Airplane Design*. How these books came about was described in Section 6.1.

During the 1980's several computer manufacturers came up with so-called engineering workstations. Companies like Apollo, Silicon Graphics and IBM had come to market with the first generation of desktop engineering work-stations. These were fairly powerful desk-size computers which had the capability to handle engineering calculations (which were previously done as batch jobs on mainframe computers) at one's desk, with only seconds of turnaround time. Therefore, it became possible to automate the step-by-step design procedures. Ultimately, this led to the Advanced Aircraft Analysis (AAA) software.

To describe the manner in which the AAA program came about, I need to start in 1987. That year I was asked by Ed Petrushka, Vice President of Engineering of General Dynamics (GD), Forth Worth Division, to come to Fort Worth to discuss preliminary design procedures. Ed Petruska told me that General Dynamics had a significant turn-around problem in its preliminary design department.

Standard procedure in industry was for any aerodynamics, weight and balance, stability, control and propulsion calculations to be performed by specialized engineering groups. Because each department often had its own agenda (Peter's Principle), the result was long delays in getting new design ideas evaluated. I could relate to this, because that was exactly what I had found in other companies.

At that time, General Dynamics was using large numbers of the afore-mentioned work-stations in particular for design and drafting purposes. Early versions of CAD were installed on these stations.

Ed wondered if my step-by-step design methodology (as described in *Airplane Design*) could be programmed in such a way that his designers could do all the initial calculations themselves on one platform. This would allow them to save a considerable amount of calendar time and make them independent of the engineering specialists.

As it turned out, I had been having some thoughts along the same lines, and so I suggested that he give the FRL a contract to try this out. He did and we got started on what became known as the AAA code. Several graduate and undergraduate students were involved in the development of the project. Four graduate students, notably William Anemaat, Seyed Malaek, Todd Lawson and Donna Gerren, were instrumental in creating the architecture of this very user-friendly computer code. I never developed the skills required for modern computer programming. However, I did clearly visualize what I wanted the new software to be able to do for an airplane designer.

I made several coordination trips to GD during the code development. During one of those trips Ed Petrushka introduced me to the famous Harry Hillaker, the "father" of the F-16 fighter. Figure 166 shows Harry and me by an example of the F-16.

The AAA code allows a design engineer to start with an airplane mission specification and rapidly determine the size of the airplane, the thrust required and the weight. Weight and balance, installed thrust, stability and control calculations, performance and even cost calculations are all part of this program. The result was that any new airplane configuration could be very rapidly analyzed in one code, without having to consult the "experts".

It was agreed that GD and KU would be co-owners of the code, but that KU had the sole marketing rights. The code began to attract attention outside KU because of my use of this code in several airplane design and flight dynamics short courses. Attendees wanted to know how they could acquire this code. The answer was that KU was not a commercial institution and therefore this was next to impossible to do. After discussions between myself, Aerospace Engineering Department Chairman Dave Downing, and Dean of the School of Engineering Carl Locke, it was decided that the best way to proceed would be for me to start a new company and pay a license fee to KU. That was the start of DARcorporation (Design, Analysis and Research Corporation) in 1991. How DARcorporation developed the AAA code and a CAD code, is discussed in Chapter 7.

In 1991 Cessna Aircraft Company was interested in looking at different ways to portray speed/altitude information in the cockpit. The FRL received a contract to look at various such ways and report on pros and cons. This work was done with two students, one of whom was an experienced pilot with IFR and instructor ratings. As a side task we also performed a study to add a third attitude indicator to the displays of the Cessna 208, Caravan. This airplane is a fairly large, single engine, single pilot airplane that is also used for passenger transportation. The third attitude indicator study was aimed at improving redundancy during IFR operations.

In the early 1980's it had become clear to some of us in the aircraft industry, that it might be possible to make the task of flying easier. The first thought was to enable what was called Single-Pilot-IFR (SPIFR). The SPIFR program gradually led to the AGATE (Advanced General Aviation Transport Experiment) project. The NASA engineer who pioneered these concepts was Dr. Bruce Holmes, one of my former students. Bruce formed an effective industry consortium which led to flight test demonstrations on several airplanes. In 2000 this program became the Small Airplane Transportation System (SATS) program. In 2002 the funding of this program is at a dangerously low level and it may not succeed because of this.

In 1992 graduate students Todd Lawson, Ab Dirkzwager, Charles Gomer and Ron Barrett evolved a novel airplane design with de-coupled flight controls. This particular airplane design was used by NASA in its public relations work on behalf of the AGATE program. Figure 167 shows a rendition of that design.

In 1994 I led a group of students from KU, Kansas State University (KSU) and Wichita State University (WSU) in the design study of a family of new, general aviation airplanes which we called Shrike. The Shrike airplanes were to have completely de-coupled flight controls and automated displays with the primary objective to make flying as easy as driving a car. My students won the first NASA AGATE design competition with their effort.

In 1995 I led a similar student group (this time including Pittsburg State University) which won the second AGATE competition with the design of a four-place, single engine, jet powered airplane. A feature in this airplane design was our proposal to use RC model servos to control tabs which in turn controlled the de-coupled flight control system. My students built and flew an RC model of this airplane. It is shown in Figure 168.

As a partner in the AGATE program, Beech Aircraft (which had become Raytheon Aircraft) became interested in this idea. The FRL was given a contract to look into various types of actuators to determine the real life (i.e. certifiable) potential. The results of our work showed that a range of problems needed a solution, before FAR 23 certification could be considered.

The Beech/Raytheon research work was the last funded research I brought into the FRL.

The fact that I started DARcorporation (see Chapter 7) meant I had to make sure that a payroll was being met each and every month. Therefore, I no longer had the time to devote to getting research for KU. I compensated by increasing my teaching commitments at KU.

DARcorporation provides a significant amount of work for students on a wide variety of aerospace engineering projects. Therefore, several students work at DARcorporation instead of at the FRL. There is a lesson in this for academia in general. It is OK to encourage professors to get into the entrepreneurial arena. However, a likely consequence is that much research effort will be lost for the university.

In the next section I describe some of my consulting experiences while at KU.

Figure 147 Logo of the Flight Research Laboratory of The University of Kansas

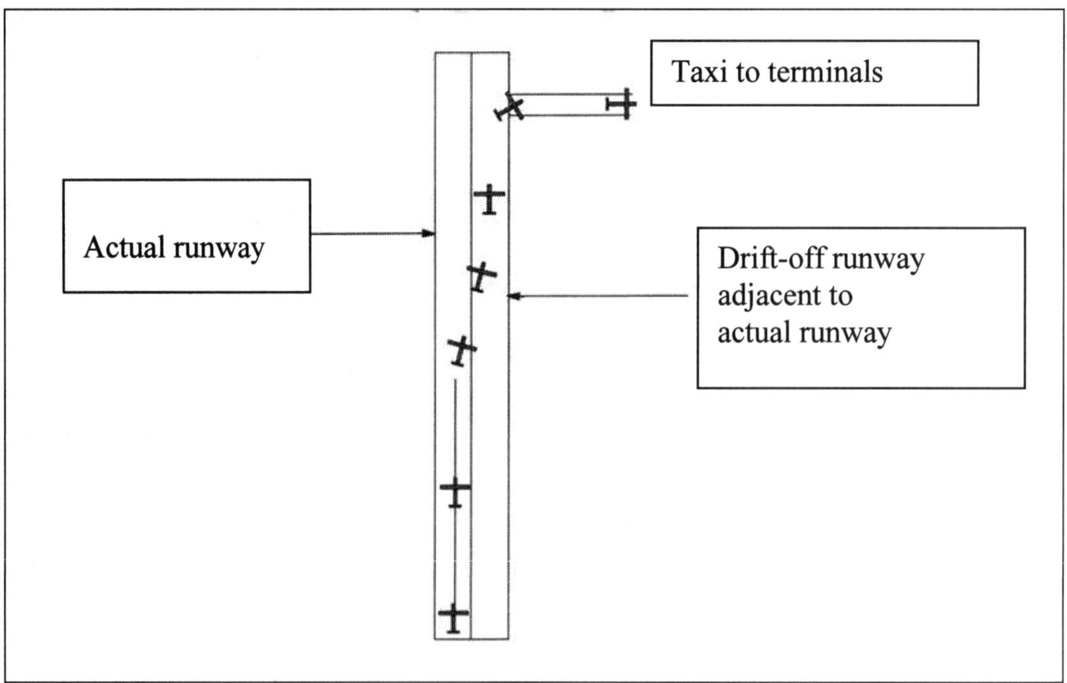

Figure 148 Sketch of the Brandt Drift-off Runway

Figure 149 Cessna Cardinal (Courtesy Cessna)

Figure 150 KU/NASA/Cessna Redhawk

Figure 151 Beechcraft Duke (Courtesy Beech Aircraft)

Figure 152 Simulation Facility of the Flight Research Laboratory in 1972

Figure 153 Example Test Configuration of a Vortex Augmented Wing

Figure 154 Mock-up of the Bell Model 301 (Courtesy Bell Helicopter)

Figure 155 Beechcraft Model 99 Regional Transport (Courtesy Beech Aircraft)

Figure 156 NASA/KU/Beech/Boeing/SSSA Model 99 Experimental Airplane

Figure 157 Test Pilots Stone and Jenks with the SSSA Model 99

Figure 158 Beechcraft T-34C (Courtesy Beech Aircraft)

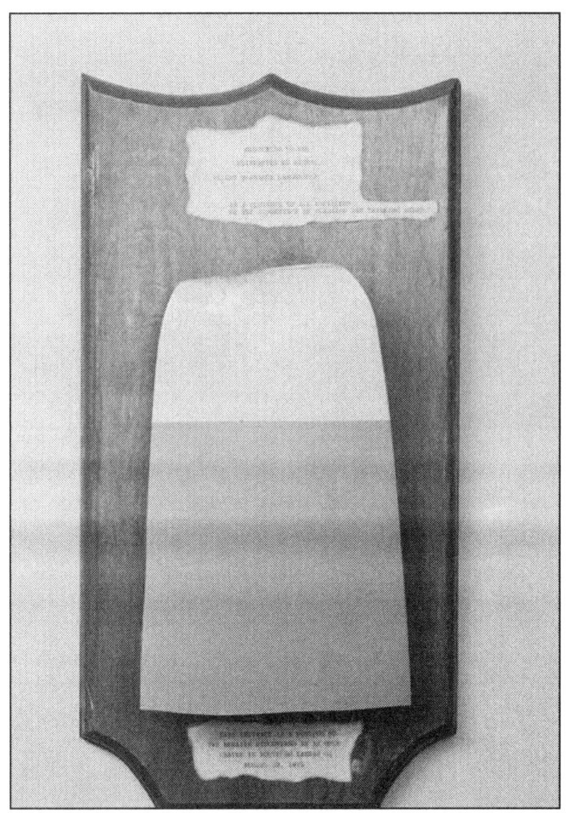

Figure 159 Memento of Broken Propeller of the Airplane of Figure 156

Figure 160 Cessna Skyhawk Registered to Roskam Aviation and Engineering Corporation

Figure 161 Separate Surface Aileron (Bolted Hard-Over) on the Airplane of Figure 160

Figure 162 KU/Piper/NASA ATLIT (Advanced Technology Light Twin) (Courtesy NASA)

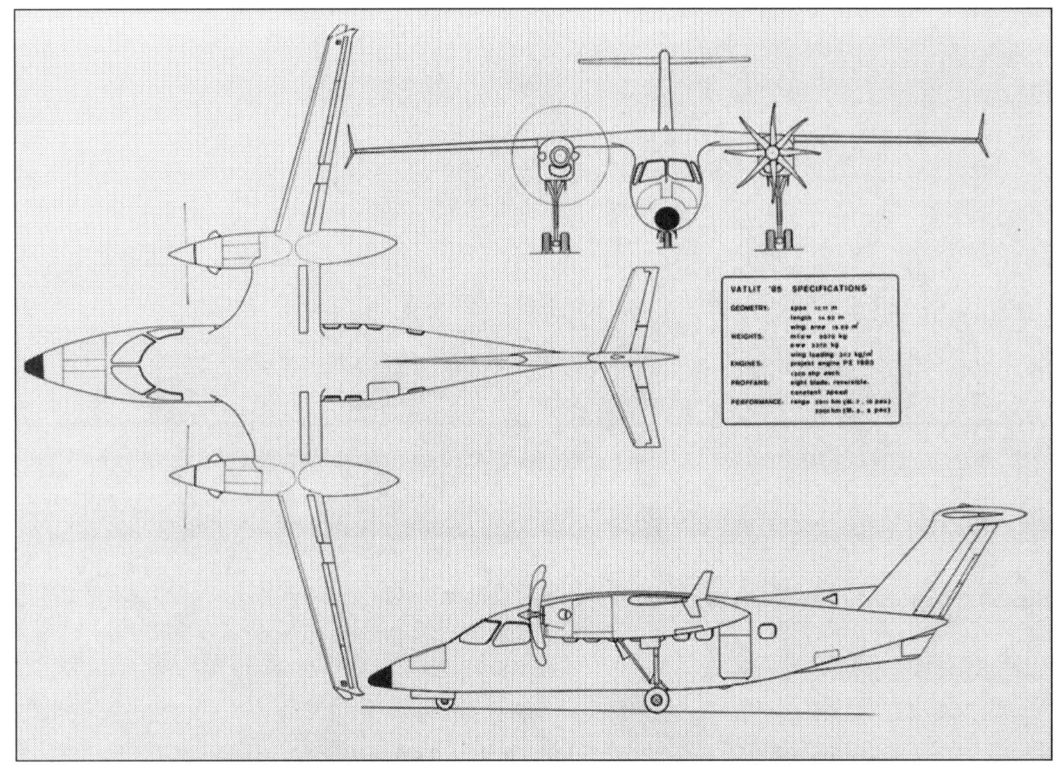

Figure 163 Three-view of the VATLIT (Very Advanced Technology Light Twin)

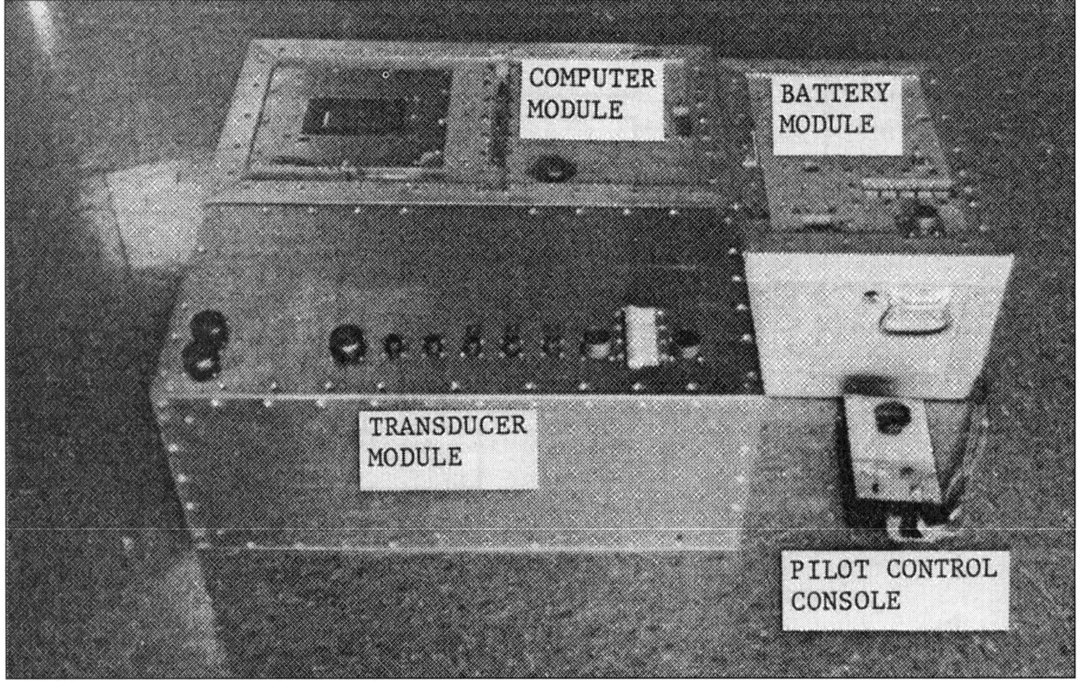

Figure 164 Low Cost Parameter Identification Flight Test System

Figure 165 Beranek Acoustical Test Tube at the Flight Research Laboratory in 1980

Figure 166 Harry Hillaker, Designer of the F-16, with the Author
(Courtesy General Dynamics)

Figure 167 Artist Impression of an Advanced KU Design (Courtesy NASA)

Figure 168 Jet Powered RC Model Built and Flown by KU/KSU/WSU/PSU Students

6.3 Aircraft Design Consulting from 1969 - 2002

Beech Aircraft Company: 1968-1969

During the summer of 1968 I was invited to be a design-review consultant at Beech Aircraft Corporation in Wichita, Kansas. My job was to critically review several existing and projected new airplanes and come up with recommendations for cost-effective improvements.

I worked with James Lew (Vice President of Engineering), Dick Tumlinson (head of aerodynamics) and James Terry (head of advanced design).

One result of that work was the change in the King Air line to a T-tail and the addition of a sharp-edged dorsal fin. The T-tail eliminated a tail buffeting problem due to the propeller slipstream. The dorsal fin helped the pedal-free directional stability and eliminated any tendency toward rudder-lock. Figure 169 and 170 show the old and new King Air airplanes respectively.

Roskam Aviation and Engineering Corporation (RAEC): 1971-2001

In 1971, with the help of my accountant, Blue Barrand, I formed Roskam Aviation and Engineering Corporation (RAEC). My growing consulting and book-publishing activities made this step necessary.

There was another reason: preliminary work done at the FRL indicated that the separate surface stability augmentation system had fallout potential for a simple, SSSA wing-leveler autopilot for light airplanes. To test this out, I needed an airplane. For various legal and tax reasons it was better for a company to own an airplane rather than an individual. Thus, in 1971, I bought the Cessna Skyhawk shown in Figure 160.

Until the formation of DARcorporation in 1991 all my consulting activities were carried out through RAEC.

Bell Helicopter Company: 1970

In 1970 I was contacted by the chief technical engineer at Bell[(68)] Helicopter Company in Fort Worth, Jan Meyer Drees. I had known him in Holland when I worked at Aviolanda and he ran the Netherlands Helicopter Industries.

Jan called me to help with the flying quality analysis of the Bell Model 300 (which evolved into the Model 301) in the airplane mode of operation (Figure 154).

This revolutionary new aircraft was a tilt-rotor (the original granddaddy of the V-22 Osprey) and Bell wanted me to analyze the flying qualities in wing supported flight.

Professor Dave Kohlman and I collaborated on this work, some of which was done through the KU FRL. Three students assisted us on that project. Our analyses indicated that, in wing supported flight, no significant flying quality problems were anticipated. Needless to say, Bell was happy with the results of our work.

War Story 78

During one trip to Bell, I was given some dual time in a Bell UH-1 Huey helicopter by a Bell test pilot. Figure 171 shows a model of this machine which was equipped with a stability augmentation system. I had never flown a helicopter. However, I did know how the basic controls in a helicopter worked. To my amazement, I did not have any trouble controlling the machine with the stability augmentation system on, including hovering in place.

Lest I become too smug about my ability to control a helicopter, the test pilot inquired whether I would like to try it without stability augmentation. I said yes, whereupon he switched the stab-aug system off. In forward flight I had no problems. However, in slowing down to hover I promptly lost control. The Bell test pilot had to take over!

Lesson:

Helicopters are much more difficult to control than airplanes.

Teledyne Brown Engineering: 1978

RAEC also received a contract from Teledyne Brown Engineering in Huntsville, Alabama, for the design, development and testing of three simple, bottled-gas-gyro driven attitude control autopilots for an experimental supersonic missile, the STAB target missile.

Much of that work was carried out in the KU FRL (RAEC paid rental fees to KU for this work). Jerry Hanson acted as a consultant to RAEC and, with his help, we finished that task and delivered the autopilots. All worked flawlessly.

Gates Learjet Corporation: 1969-1990

In 1969 I also became a design consultant to Gates Learjet Corporation, at first on the Learjet Models 24 and 25. Figures 172 and 173 show these wonderful airplanes.

I knew the vice president of engineering, Donald Grommesh, because we had worked together on the Cessna T-37 program. Don called to see if I would be interested in working as a consultant to Learjet.

Most of my work at Learjet was done in close collaboration with Dan Coen, director of engineering; Dick Etherington, director of advanced design; and Ronald Neal, lead engineer (later, head) of aerodynamics. Dick Etherington, a KU aerospace engineering graduate, later served on the KU AE department advisory board.

At first, I also worked with Jim Wilcox, a flight test engineer whom I had first met at Cessna, and with Hank Beard, chief test pilot. Hank was a really interesting guy. He flew many high performance fighters before coming to Learjet. It was quite a treat to hear him talk about his experiences.

At that time Learjet was looking for ways to improve the payload-range performance of the Model 24 and 25 airplanes. They also were looking for ways to improve the flying qualities. One problem was the lack of wind tunnel data. That was helped to some extent by NASA putting an actual Model 23 (see Figure 174) in the full scale wind tunnel at NASA Ames. It certainly is an unusual luxury for an engineer to have full Reynolds Number tunnel data available.

William P. Lear ,[(69)] who started Learjet and later sold his company to Charles Gates, was an amazing individual. Reference 69 is a "must read" book about Bill Lear and his many accomplishments. The following war stories deal with amusing events which really happened in the early Learjet days.

War Story 79

Bill Lear had a well-known aerodynamics designer working for him, Gordon Israel, whom he reportedly had hired away from Grumman[(15)] Aviation and Engineering Corporation.

No wind tunnel tests were performed on the first Model 23 airplane and Gordon became worried that the vertical tail was too small to provide adequate directional stability and one-engine-inoperative control. Gordon kept insisting that the vertical tail was too small and tried to talk Bill into letting him change that tail. The prototype assembly had advanced to the point where the vertical tail and the T-tail were already installed on the airplane.

About four months before first flight, Bill started to worry that Gordon might be correct and thus he signed a shop order to build the larger vertical tail. This was done expeditiously and one day the new tail had been installed on the prototype.

Gordon proudly went to Bill Lear's office and invited him to come see the new tail. Bill looked at this newly installed tail, turned to Gordon and said, " That tail looks like hell. Take the damn thing off, put the other one back on, and that is the way we will fly it."

This was done and it turned out that Bill Lear had been right! The larger tail was never flown and, as far as I know, still resides in the "bone-yard" behind the original Learjet plant (now Bombardier Aerospace) in Wichita.

Lesson: Aerodynamics is (still) not an exact science. There is something to be said for the intuitive feel certain people develop for what an airplane should look like. Bill Lear certainly was one of those people.

War Story 80

The Model 23 Learjet wing was only 9% thick because of its Swiss P-16* fighter heritage. Therefore, vertical space in the vicinity of the rear spar was at a premium. To actuate ailerons with a mechanical, cable driven control system it was necessary to translate cable motion along the rear spar into linear motion at the aileron, but perpendicular to that spar. The detail designers at Learjet tried to convince Bill Lear that the only way to do that was with a mechanism which required some type of fairing external to the wing contour. Bill wanted it all to fit inside the wing contours for reasons of drag and good looks. One day the designer in charge told Bill that his way of doing it was impossible.

One never told Bill that something he wanted was impossible. He had a very well equipped workshop in his house. He locked himself in the workshop and two days later emerged with a device that did what he wanted. He brought it to the gentleman in charge of system design, dropped it on his desk and said, "Do it this way." The device worked and was affectionately called the "pork chop" because it resembled one.

Lesson: Designers should be very careful in proclaiming something to be impossible. Someone may just outsmart them and prove them wrong.

War Story 81

Bill Lear was also a jet-rated pilot and often flew demonstration flights for potential customers. One day he and a customer boarded a Model 23 demonstrator. It happened to be lunch hour and there was nobody around to help with ground start. Bill connected the ground power cart with a plug which went (in perpendicular fashion) into the tail cone. Following a quick walk-around he and his passenger boarded the airplane, closed the door, started the engines, and requested permission to taxi to the active runway. They forgot about the power cart.

Permission was granted and off they went, trailing the power cart behind them. When Bill got to the end of the runway this problem was noticed by the control tower operator. He promptly notified Bill, who stopped the left engine, disembarked, disconnected the plug leaving the cart where it was, and re-boarded the airplane. He asked the tower operator to notify the Learjet plant to pick up the power cart and then he took off.

After completing the demonstration flight and bidding farewell to his passenger, Bill stormed into the design department and demanded to speak to the "clown" who had designed the ground power plug installation. This hapless gentleman was told in no uncertain terms that he should have installed that plug at an angle sufficient for an automatic disconnect to occur. That is how early Learjets ended up with an angled, self-disconnecting ground power plug!

Lesson: It does not hurt to design for eventualities which are not supposed to occur.

---

* Bill Lear had bought the rights to the wing of the cancelled P-16 ground attack fighter which was to be built in Switzerland.

At Learjet, I had several interesting flights in Models 24 and 25 with Hank Beard, the chief test pilot. Hank actually gave me some dual time on the Model 24 and let me do landings and takeoffs albeit under his very close scrutiny.

In 1967 a controlling interest in Learjet was sold to Charles Gates of Gates Rubber Company. In 1970 the company was renamed Gates Learjet Corporation (GLC).

Mr. Gates brought in Mal Harned, a KU aero engineering graduate, to run the company. Mal was a propulsion and helicopter specialist and a very dynamic individual. He ran the Hughes Helicopter Company before coming to Learjet.

Mal convinced his board of directors that GLC needed to offer executives a "total transportation solution." That meant the development of a helicopter which was to be sold, together with a Learjet, to allow true door-to-door transportation.

To run the helicopter effort Mal brought in Cornell Slivinsky, a well known helicopter designer, also from Hughes. The machine which emerged from those design efforts was the Gates Twinjet Helicopter (Figure 175). This helicopter was to pioneer the use of two turboshaft engines in a commercial helicopter.

As Figure 175 clearly shows, the front end of the Gates Learjet Model 112 looked just like that of a regular Learjet. That was an important trade-mark issue with the marketing department.

Certainly one of Mal's major accomplishments was getting Garrett Airresearch Corporation in Los Angeles to develop the TFE-731 turbofan engine. This engine was to be married to a growth version of the Model 25, to be called the Model 35/36. Largely due to the much better cruise s.f.c. and a slightly enlarged wing, the payload-range performance improved significantly. Eventually, the 35/36 became a big sales success for GLC, and the TFE-731 program a similar success for Garrett.

Mal brought in Harry Johnson (also from Hughes and also a KUAE graduate) to run the GLC engineering organization. Under the guidance of Harry and Dick Etherington, Ron Neal and I evolved several new wing designs all of which were judged too expensive to use.

Then, at the end of 1972, we hit upon the simple extended wing concept for the Model 36. This consisted of a two feet constant chord extension of the M25 wing. This moved the tip tanks outboard, also by two feet. It is interesting why such a simple idea took so long to evolve!

Figure 176 shows the Model 36. Figure 177 shows a comparison of the M25 and 36 wings which shows the high degree of commonality between the two wings.

War Story 82

Nowadays, when designing a new airplane, it is often a good idea to design "growth capability" into the airplane. It should be noted that this is exactly what Bill Lear had in mind when he purchased the rights to the Swiss AFU P16 strike fighter before starting the

Swiss-American Aircraft Company in Switzerland. This company was the predecessor of Learjet of Wichita.

The Model 23 wing was essentially the P16 fighter wing. Since fighters are commonly designed to much higher load factors than commercial airplanes, this provided built-in growth potential. It is remarkable that the Model 35/36 with a takeoff weight of 17,000 lbs has basically the same inboard wing structure as the Model 23 with a takeoff weight of 12,500 lbs.

Lesson: An airplane program tends to have long term success if it has growth capability designed into it from day one.

An interesting problem with the M35/36 was that the rolling moment of inertia was significantly increased (compared with the Model 25) so that more roll control power was required.

Extending the existing ailerons violated the idea of a low cost wing tip extension.

It was at this point that I hit upon the idea of using the existing inboard wing spoilers for roll control. By signaling these spoilers with a fly-by-wire system, via a position transducer on the control wheel, the airplane had plenty of roll control power. If the fly-by-wire system were to fail, the roll control still met the so-called Level II flying qualities requirement. Therefore, the system could be designed and certified without redundancy.

Another interesting problem which arose during the development of the Model 36 had to do with the yaw damper.

War Story 83

At one point, the M36 certification was being held up because the yaw damper (designed by a subcontractor) did not properly damp the Dutch roll of the airplane. I was asked to look into this problem.

After quite a bit of root-locus work I discovered that by tilting the sensitive axis of the rate gyro aft, significant improvement in damping could be obtained. When I briefed the bosses on my proposed solution they asked me to draw up a bracket which allowed for aft tilt of the gyro and get it made by the experimental shop. The modification would then be flight tested the next morning, a Saturday. Figure 178 shows a sketch of that bracket.

I went home to Lawrence late Friday night, figuring that the problem had been solved. Saturday midmorning I received a call from our test pilot, Bob Berry. "Jan, your yaw damper does not work. Things are worse than before. Please come to Wichita to help us straighten this out."

I asked Bob whether they had reversed the wiring but he assured me that they had verified the wiring polarity.

So, back to Wichita I went, racking my brain to figure out what might have gone wrong. Along the way it occurred to me that perhaps someone had installed the tilting bracket backwards which, according to our root-locus studies, would indeed un-damp the Dutch roll. Therefore, as soon as I arrived at the plant I went to the experimental shop to check the bracket. Sure enough, it had been installed backwards.

I remember Bob Berry, asking me, "Jan, you mean just turning that bracket around will solve the problem?" I said, "Bob, count on it." Bob came back with, "OK you go with me when I fly it again!" I did, everything went as predicted, and the airplane was certified.

Lesson: Always assume that if something can be installed the wrong way, it will be. In this case, the designer (me!) should have designed the bracket so that it could have been installed only one way. Again, when possible, design for a one-way fit.

The next war story made me feel humble about my flying abilities.

War Story 84

Bob Berry, several Learjet engineers and I were on a return flight in a Model 36 from Oklahoma City, where we had conducted FAA business. Bob was in command of the flight and I acted as copilot. We had a curtain partition between the cockpit and the cabin and the curtain was closed. The engineers in the back were enjoying cups of coffee.

When we were flying level at 25,000 feet Bob asked if I had ever barrel rolled a Learjet. I said no, and that I did not think it would be a good idea. He informed me that barrel rolls were very easy to perform in any Learjet and I was welcome to try. I said that I was not that good a pilot and that I probably would mess things up for the guys in the back.

Bob smiled and said, "Let me show you how." He then performed a perfect barrel roll. There was not a peep out of the guys in the back. Then he said, "Now, you try it." At that point I should have refused but I decided, against my better judgment, to give it a try. Naturally I messed it up and there was plenty of coffee spilled in the back. They never let me forget it!

Lesson: Always stay within your competence. Don't try to show off, particularly with passengers on board.

The Model 112 helicopter program at GLC ran into major financial (cost overrun) problems and the board of directors decided to terminate the program.

Mal Harned left the company to become the senior vice president of Cessna, and was replaced by Harry Combs. Harry had been the guiding light behind Combs Aviation, a major force in general aviation fixed-base operations. He also authored a significant book about the Wright Brothers, *Kill Devil Hill* (Reference 70). I highly recommend that aero engineers read that book.

At that time, the KU aerospace engineering department was operating a very old Cessna 172. The airplane needed major repairs and it did not look like this would be financially possible. I therefore tried a different approach which was the subject of War Story 64 in Section 6.1.

By now the reader may wonder how I could reconcile, from an ethics viewpoint, working for several different aircraft manufacturers at the same time. The answer is simple: You always tell any new customer which companies you are currently doing work for, and you lay out any potential conflict of interest that might conceivably exist.

It is then up to the customer to decide whether there is a conflict of interest. The really important thing is to lay everything out in the open, before agreeing to do new work.

I have found that the reasons I have been approached by so many companies are three-fold:

1) Companies prefer to consult with someone who has broad experience and, in fact, is working for several clients, as long as they are being informed;

2) Companies know that a reliable consultant keeps work proprietary;

3) I had the reputation of getting things done well and fast.

My work at Learjet turned into a long term arrangement which was fun, as well as educational.

After the M36 work I was asked to lay out detail design plans (hardware and software) for an engineering flight simulator. Although that work was completed, the company decided not to build it.

I also was involved in several early design studies which eventually led to a bigger airplane, the Learjet Model 55, shown in Figure 179.

Cessna: 1969

Early in 1969 I was approached by Milt Sills (at that time chief test pilot of Cessna) to assist with a handling qualities analysis of the new Cessna Model 500, which eventually was named the Citation I. I reviewed quite a bit of wind tunnel and predicted data, and came to the conclusion that the airplane should be very easy to fly.

Despite this, I thought it would be wise for Milt to fly the Learjet 25 before flying the 500. Milt, who at that time had never flown a jet, took me up on my suggestion to get checked out in the Learjet 25.

The Model 500 (Figure 180) turned out to be a delightfully easy airplane to fly.

Milt later became Vice President for Product Development at Cessna and also serves on the AE department advisory board.

Canadair: 1977-1978

War Story 85

Some time after the M36 was certified, Ron Neal left Gates Learjet to become vice president of engineering for Canadair in Montreal. His job was to get the new Challenger 600 business jet program going. Canadair had bought the design rights to this airplane from Bill Lear.

Bill had not been successful in getting the financial community interested in this first, wide-body business jet. Figure 181 shows that airplane. Here was another case of Lear being way ahead of everyone else. The Challenger program at Canadair (now Bombardier Aerospace) has become immensely successful, spawning a whole family of business jets and regional jetliners.

One day in 1977, I received a call from Ron. He indicated that his engineering department was trying to convince him that the horizontal tail of the Challenger was too small by about 30%. The reason given was that according to engineering calculations, the airplane would not be able to rotate within the advertised fieldlength constraints. Ron felt that the tail was probably sized properly and that a mistake had been made somewhere, but, he did not know where. So he asked what I might be able to do to help.

I suggested that he send me a copy of the tail-sizing report and include the work done on the take-off rotation. When the report arrived, I noticed that it contained a sideview of the airplane with all forces and moments which act on the airplane drawn in. Nice work! Except for one little thing. The so-called Newtonian reaction force (airplane mass times forward acceleration), which acts through the c.g. and helps in the rotation process, had been left off. I checked the equations and, sure enough, this force was absent.

I called Ron and suggested that upon putting that force into the equation it would be my guess that the tail was indeed adequately sized. This turned out to be the case. Canadair received only a very small bill for my consultation services on that one.

Lesson: Engineers should understand Newton's Laws before tackling problems relating to airplane dynamics.

Since that event I have done other work relating to low speed flying qualities on the Canadair Challenger 600.

SIAI Marchetti: 1976-1978

By 1975 Bill Thompson, Cessna's head of aerodynamics and flight test, had retired. Bill had quite a career as a test pilot and engineer, mostly at Cessna. Reference 71 contains a very entertaining autobiography filled with noteworthy experiences. In addition, he authored References 31-33 which are very good references on the development of Cessna airplanes.

Bill's retirement did not last long. He was hired as a design consultant by SIAI-Marchetti in Sesto Calende, Italy. SIAI-Marchetti was interested in developing a new, two-place, tandem, military jet trainer with a supercritical wing which would become the S-211. This really good looking, small jet trainer is shown in Figure 182.

However, SIAI-Marchetti had a problem. They did not have enough engineers to pull off this project in a reasonable time frame. At the recommendation of Bill, it was decided to bring me in as a consultant to help with design, wind tunnel testing and various other engineering assignments. To start things off, I was invited to Italy to meet Dr. Alessandro Brena, the director of engineering at SIAI Marchetti. I found Dr. Brena to be an extremely competent, and very personable individual, with whom I got along very well.

Dr. Brena proudly showed me the wind tunnel model gallery at the Sesto Calende facility. I cannot remember having seen that many different tunnel models at any other company. Data on SIAI-Marchetti aircraft going back to WWI can be found in older issues of *Jane's All The World's Aircraft*.

After several meetings with Bill and Dr. Brena, RAEC got a contract to

a) develop suitable supercritical wing airfoils;

b) arrange for the construction of a wind tunnel model;

c) arrange for testing of this model and the analysis of data;

d) assist in detailed structural design of the airplane.

The work on the supercritical airfoils was carried out by Dr. Eddie Lan at KU using the Garebedian-Korn Code developed at NYU. When Dr. Lan was finished with his work, I made a trip to NASA Langley on behalf of SIAI-Marchetti. The purpose of the visit was to discuss the airfoil with Dr. Richard Whitcomb, the famous NASA engineer who developed the "area rule process" for supersonic airplanes, and who also developed the basic idea of supercritical airfoils. I was very happy when Dr. Whitcomb put his stamp of approval on our work.

Because RAEC also did not have an adequate number of engineers, the structural design and analysis work on the S-211 was carried out by Aviation Engineering and Consultants of Wichita, Kansas. This company, started by Dan Coen, Kent Bauer and Don Bruss, did the work under subcontract to RAEC, with full approval from SIAI-Marchetti. Many experienced engineers who were working full time at either Cessna, Beech, Learjet or Boeing-Wichita did part-time work on the S-211. We rented the fourth floor of a bank building in downtown Wichita for a period of 18 months.

Boeing-Seattle got the contract for design and construction of the model, and all tunnel tests were conducted by RAEC in the Boeing Transonic Wind Tunnel (BTWT) in Seattle. The wind tunnel model of the S-211 is shown in Figure 183.

Carmen Pecarero with whom I had worked on the elastic SST model years before (see Chapter 5), was very helpful in steering this project through the Boeing system. Several KU students held part-time jobs during this contract which helped them gain valuable real-world experience.

War Story 86

The contract to design the lateral flight control system of the S-211 was given to a small company in Vergiate, Italy. This company had never designed a flight control system for a high performance airplane. SIAI-M asked me to visit them and conduct a one-day short course with do's and don'ts of flight control system design. I did, but some of it must not have sunk in.

After the first flight of the airplane, the test pilot (Commandante Ghisleni) called me in the US to inform me that the roll performance of the S-211 was totally inadequate and that my help was needed in getting it fixed ASAP.

I asked him to have the ailerons loaded up with a simulated loading apparatus and to deflect the stick in the cockpit to the stop and measure the aileron deflection. The next day he called and said that he got only about 9 degrees of aileron deflection. At that point I knew that the cause of the problem was control system compliance.

I suspected that one or more of the lateral control pulley brackets had not been mounted stiffly in the airframe and that the ensuing deformation limited the aileron deflection. My Italian friends checked and found that one pulley had been installed right in the middle of the rear pressure bulkhead. In the S-211 that pressure bulkhead is a rather thin membrane made of 0.06 inch aluminum. By stiffening that bulkhead the problem was solved.

Lesson: Avoid control system compliance. Check all pulley and quadrant attachment for stiffness before passing a design to manufacturing. Even then, it is desirable to simulate control surface loading and check deflections on the ground before first flight.

During my consulting work for SIAI-Marchetti and later for Piaggio, I had the opportunity to make two flights on an Air France Concorde (Figure 184 shows a prototype of the Concorde). Many of my fellow passengers were Wall Street bankers on one- or two-day business trips. However, on my first trip I happened to sit right behind Robert Six (then president of Continental Airlines) and his wife, actress Audrey Meadows. They were delightful people.

I also made many trips to Italy per conventional jet transports.

I always stayed at the Tre Re (Three Kings) Hotel in Sesto Calende. The hotel management got used to the fact that many times we had to arrange engineering meetings at the hotel. The reason was the frequent strikes which were unpredictably called by the local labor unions. These strikes closed down the SIAI-Marchetti plant thereby causing us to move our meetings to the Tre Re Hotel.

Foxjet: 1979

In 1979 I was invited by Tony Fox to come to Minneapolis, Minnesota, to discuss a new, small, business jet. Tony ran a successful company which was in the industrial equipment business. He had started another company, called Foxjet International, to develop and build the Foxjet (Figure 185). The airplane looked like a small Learjet.

War Story 87

When I arrived at the plant I was given a tour of the mock-up and then shown to Tony's office. This turned out to be a most interesting experience. The office consisted of two parts, one elevated above the other. On the elevated part was a huge desk with a chair, which can best be described as a throne. Everything had rather gaudy colors.

Tony Fox was seated on his "throne" and motioned me to a chair by a conference table in the lower part of his office. He wanted to know how much the certification program of the Foxjet might cost. I gave him a ballpark estimate which he did not like. Our discussion did not last very long. The airplane was never built and he never paid the bill I sent him.

Lesson: Starting a new business jet program takes a lot of upfront money. Some people don't like to hear that bad news.

Piaggio: 1979-1986

At the end of the VATLIT design episode (Section 6.2) I was contacted by Tom Harris, the US representative for the Piaggio Aircraft Company of Italy. He indicated that Piaggio executives would like me to travel to their plant for technical discussions on a new airplane. Therefore, I went to Finale Ligure, Italy, the headquarters of Piaggio.

In Italy I met Dr. Rinaldo Piaggio, the CEO; Dr. Alexandro Mazzoni, the Vice President of Engineering; and Franco Morelli, the head of aerodynamics.

As it turned out, they had a preliminary design (patented by Dr. Mazzoni) of a twin turboprop pusher, but with a three-surface configuration. They predicted better than VATLIT-like performance for their design and wanted my comments in regard to the VATLIT design: Which was better?

After several days of back and forth discussions we arrived at the conclusion that RAEC would be given a contract to verify the three-surface concept. My assignment was to generate, independent of Piaggio, the stability, control and performance characteristics of the new Piaggio design, the P-180, shown in Figure 186. The Piaggio people were particularly interested in bettering the Beech King Air.

I took all the geometric P-180 data back to the USA and, together with KU Professor Dave Kohlman and several graduate students, conducted the analysis. Our report was finished in

November of 1979. The conclusion was that the proposed P-180 had several advantages over the VATLIT design and would very definitely outperform the Beech King Air in all areas of performance. I went back to Italy for a briefing on our findings. Our report was well received. As a result RAEC got a new series of contracts to assist with the detail design and development of the airplane.

The first contract was to run a low speed wind tunnel test on a model built by Piaggio in the Wichita State University (WSU) wind tunnel. That model did not have the correct airfoils but served to develop the stability and control characteristics of the airplane. This led to the incorporation of negative dihedral in the canard, as well as in rear fuselage fins, to help in high angle of attack stability.

The staff at the WSU tunnel did a good job keeping the test proprietary. I remember that the Italian engineers who also helped with these tests were astonished at the hours that were put in each day. They also were a bit nonplussed by the fact that we did not take out time for lunch. We just ordered in hamburgers and kept on going.

The second contract was to develop supercritical airfoils appropriate to the P-180 mission. To carry out that contract I contacted Professor Gerald Gregorek at Ohio State University (OSU). He and his research staff were experts in the numerical design of new airfoils. He also had access to a 2-D pressure wind tunnel at OSU to check the airfoils in the tunnel at the correct Reynolds numbers.

At that time the technology of designing supercritical airfoils was still considered "export-sensitive" and, therefore, required special permission. I negotiated that permission with NASA management on behalf of Piaggio.

The airfoil design, development and testing work took about one and a half years and resulted in proprietary Piaggio airfoils which were used in the final design.

The third contract given to RAEC was to design, develop and test a high speed model in the Boeing transonic wind tunnel in Seattle. RAEC in turn (with permission from Piaggio) subcontracted much of this work to Boeing Technology Services (BTS). Again, I had the pleasure of working with Carmen Pecarero at BTWT. Figure 187 shows a model of the airplane in the Boeing wind tunnel.

The goal of these wind tunnel tests was to make sure that the new configuration was certifiable, had generally gentle flying qualities, and was recoverable from high angle of attack excursions. We also needed to verify the drag predictions. The BTWT tests resulted in three airplane changes: negative dihedral in the horizontal tail, area ruling of the wing-nacelle intersection, and the addition of larger, rear fuselage mounted, dorsal fins. The latter helped to generate longitudinal and directional stability at extreme angles of attack. These fins were to become a hallmark of later Learjet designs. How that came about is explained later in War Story 91.

War Story 88

The marketing department of Piaggio wanted a catchy name for the airplane. During one meeting in Italy I suggested the name Avanti. This was seriously frowned upon by Dr. Piaggio because Avanti was also the name of the communist party newspaper in Italy.

After much argument, Tom Harris was asked to organize a worldwide name-giving contest among potential customers for the airplane. The name that rolled out of that contest (which I had nothing to do with) was Avanti.

Thus, the airplane was dubbed the Piaggio P-180 Avanti. Figure 188 shows the production version of this very beautiful airplane.

Lesson: Sometimes the first choice turns out OK.

War Story 89

I also got involved in some of the decision making with regard to the manufacturing of the airplane. It was essential to maintain large runs of laminar flow over the wing and fuselage to make true the predicted performance of the airplane.

My Italian friends wanted to make the entire airplane out of carbon-fiber composites to assure tight surface tolerances. I predicted that this would be too expensive and also would result in higher weight.

In the end we evolved a new "outside-in" tooling method to make the fuselage out of aluminum and yet do this to very tight tolerances. Figure 189 is a sketch comparing the "outside-in" with the conventional "inside-out" method of tooling.

We machined the wing torque-box out of two pieces, using a numerically controlled machine which Piaggio had acquired to manufacture the wings of the European Tornado fighter. As a result, the P-180 has a very smooth wing and fuselage. The airplane achieves 60% laminar flow runs over the wing upper and lower surfaces and fuselage laminar flow up to the front door. The P-180 is the world's fastest commercial turboprop.

I could not convince my Italian friends to use similar techniques on the canard, the vertical tail and the horizontal tail. These were indeed made from carbon-fiber composites and the contract to manufacture those components was given to Sikorsky. Many years later the company decided to also make these components from aluminum. This not only saved weight, but was a lot cheaper in manufacturing.

Lesson: Be very careful, particularly with small airplanes, about the choice of materials. In many cases one is better off with conventional aluminum.

I had the good fortune to have several eyeball-to-eyeball meetings with Dr. Piaggio. I found him to be a very competent and likable individual who certainly knew when and how to ask the right questions. He also had a strong social conscience.

War Story 90

During one meeting with Dr. Piaggio he told me that he believed one of his most important tasks in life was "to see to it that my people are gainfully employed for the rest of their lives."

Lesson: I have not met many managers who felt that strongly about the welfare of their employees. Many CEO's in the USA would do well to keep that in mind, instead of always being concerned about their "fiduciary responsibility" to the share holders.

Dr. Piaggio also showed me his personal jet, the Piaggio-Douglas PD-108, a twin-jet business airplane designed by Douglas and Piaggio. This nice looking airplane was certified, but achieved limited series production status. Only 29 of these airplanes were built, all by Piaggio. Figure 190 shows this really neat and interesting airplane.

War Story 91

It was clear to Piaggio management that for the P-180 to be successful, solid sales and support were required in the United States. Dr. Piaggio asked me which US company he should team with to assure the future of the P-180 program in the USA. I did not hesitate and suggested he get in touch with Gates Learjet.

Since I knew Harry Combs, the President and CEO of Learjet rather well, Dr. Piaggio asked me to set up a meeting between the two of them at the Paris Airshow in 1983. This I did, with considerable help from Tom Harris. The result was a sort of marriage between the two companies (no name changes) and a name change for the airplane, which was to be known as the Gates-Piaggio GP-180 Avanti.

The fuselage and empennage were to be built in Wichita, Kansas and shipped to Genova, Italy for final assembly. Gates-Learjet also was to take a major role in the certification and flight testing of the airplane.

Because of these arrangements Learjet gained insight into various aerodynamic characteristics of the Avanti, in particular, the benefits associated with the ventral fins. These ventral fins contribute to longitudinal and directional stability at very high angles of attack. The fins are oriented on the fuselage so that in the design cruise condition they do not generate any forces, except some friction drag. Much of the development work leading to the P-180 fins was done at BTWT in Seattle. Similar fins later showed up in many Learjet designs. They also were widely copied by other companies.

As things turned out, the cooperation between the companies did not last long. Two events turned the cards against this venture.

Event 1: GLC landed a major sale of the Model 36, as the C-21 for the USAF. This required an increase in production and, therefore, a sizable investment in production tooling. At that time the US Government made interest-free loans available to companies with government contracts and the need to increase production.

One has to understand that Harry Combs was a fierce champion of private enterprise and the idea of "keeping the government off my back." He also was quite consistent about his feelings. He therefore turned down the interest-free loans and used GLC cash-flow for the required tooling investment. That would have been fine, except for Event 2.

Event 2: The commercial market for business jets took an unexpected, severe downturn. This did not leave adequate cash-flow to cover the commitments on the GP-180 program. Harry therefore decided to sever the link with Piaggio in 1986. This decision hurt Piaggio financially, since it now had to go it alone.

Lesson: It ain't over until its over! When striking a deal with another company it is best to look at worst case scenarios in terms of market developments.

The airplane made a first flight in 1986. The P-180 program suffered many delays because of various financial problems. However, in 2002 the P-180 was still in production and selling well in the US after the Ferrari family took over Piaggio. The P-180 is the world's fastest turboprop and even outperforms several business jets. Happily, the name Piaggio still endures.

Piper Aircraft Corporation: 1979

In 1979 I also was involved in some configuration, stability and control analyses for the Piper Model 41, which later became the Model 46 Malibu. A side view of the Malibu is shown in Figure 191.

At that time the chief designer of the Malibu was Jim Griswold with whom I had done work on the T-37 program at Cessna. After Piper, Jim went on to found Venture Aircraft Company. His son and nephew, Doug and Mike Griswold both were students of mine at KU.

The Grumman X-29 Project: 1978-1988

Aviation is full of myths and sometimes downright wrong conceptions. A classical example is what happened to the forward swept wing.

In 1978 I was invited by Harvey Album of the Stanford Research Institute (SRI) to participate in an evaluation of a new project dealing with an experimental, forward swept wing fighter airplane. The project was sponsored by the Defense Advanced Research Projects Agency (DARPA), and eventually led to the X-29 (see Figures 192 and 193). The contract to build two X-29 airplanes was given to Grumman in 1981. The airplane first flew in 1984.

It is of interest to review a bit of forward swept wing history to put all this in perspective. The following lengthy war story is my attempt to do so.

War Story 92

In 1943, during WWII, the German Luftwaffe flew a four-engine, 35 degree, forward swept wing, jet bomber named the Junkers Model 287. Figure 141 shows a three-view of this airplane. This jet bomber could out-fly any Allied fighter, including the up and coming British jet, the Gloster Meteor (Figure 26). Luckily for the Allied war effort, the Ju-287 never achieved operational status although it was extensively test flown.

Following the German surrender in 1945, teams of US and British aircraft experts (military and civilian) were rapidly deployed to various German aircraft design and development facilities to retrieve as much information about the state of German aircraft technology as possible.

The American teams were under the leadership of Colonel Watson and referred to as Watson's Raiders. As a result, several US manufacturers became familiar with the Ju-287 technology.

Shortly after WWII it became clear that the Soviet Union had sinister designs on Europe. As coined by Winston Churchill, an Iron Curtain descended over Eastern Europe. It became necessary for the USA to start re-arming.

Consequently, the USAF received many design proposals from aircraft manufacturers for forward swept wing fighters and bombers. The phenomenon of structural wing divergence was known to be a potential problem. It was feared that to overcome the divergence issue, large increases in wing weight would be inevitable. To allow for a rational evaluation of the proposed weights for these new airplanes, the USAF enlisted the help of NACA Langley.

Two very bright, young engineers were given the task of coming up with a series of design graphs from which airplane designers could quickly determine the weight penalties involved in either aft or forward wing sweep. The names of these two engineers were F.W. Diederich and B. Budiansky. Their truly, brilliant work was published in NACA TN 1680 in 1948 (Reference 72). Some of the design charts that resulted from this work showed that there was a large weight penalty to be paid for forward sweep, compared to aft sweep.

It turned out that this report put the nail in the coffin of the forward swept wing.

Professors at universities around the world basically taught students that forward swept wings were not a reasonable design option because of the weight penalty associated with avoiding structural divergence inside the flight envelope.

This situation persisted until about 1974 when Colonel Norris Krone of the USAF finished his PhD dissertation, *Divergence Elimination with Advanced Composites*, at Purdue University under the guidance of Professor Terry Weisshaar.

Before continuing with this war story, it is of interest to review some of the carefully documented assumptions made by Diederich and Budiansky in their TN 1680:

1. Wings are made of aluminum, a homogeneous, isotropic material.

2. Wings consist of two spars with caps and shear-webs and an upper and lower skin supported by stringers which run along constant percentage chord lines. This is the classical semi-monocoque arrangement found in many wings, even today.

3. From an aeroelastic viewpoint it is assumed that the wing is rigidly clamped at the centerline.

Based on these assumptions they produced a methodology for arriving at trade studies, showing the effect of wing aspect ratio and sweep angle on wing weight. The results were dramatic, and showed that very large weight penalties were associated with forward swept wings. In view of this, it is reasonable to ask whether or not there are any advantages to the forward swept wing? The answer is yes there are four:

1. A forward swept wing tends to have inboard flow which, at high angle of attack, promotes root stall. An aft swept wing produces tip stall and requires large negative twist to alleviate the effect of roll-off at the stall so typical for aft swept wings. The negative twist in turn causes an induced drag penalty in cruise.

2. For the same reason, ailerons on a forward swept wing retain their effectiveness to high angles of attack. Ailerons on an aft swept wing when used close to the stall tend to aggravate the tendency toward roll-off.

3. At high Mach numbers the shock sweep line on a forward swept wing has a larger sweep angle than on an aft swept wing. This allows a forward swept wing to be designed with a smaller sweep angle.

4. From a cross-sectional area distribution point of view, a forward swept wing has a lower wave drag than an aft swept wing. This effect becomes important in fighter aircraft.

A common problem with many engineers who read technical reports, is that they do not question the underlying assumptions. Krone questioned all three assumptions with the following back-up rationale:

1. By using composite materials the homogeneous, isotropic assumption is no longer correct. This allows the tailoring of material properties to any particular requirement. In a forward swept wing, one would orient the fibers in such a manner that torsional stiffness is enhanced while sacrificing some bending stiffness. This method was used in the X-29.

2. It turns out that by machining a wing skin so that the rib-cap and stringers are located in a geodetic fashion a trade in favor of torsion stiffness also can be made.

3. If a forward swept wing airplane in a given flight condition would tend to diverge, the vertical load on the wing increases. This would accelerate the airplane upward. It then depends on how the spanwise mass distribution of the wing is arranged as to whether the divergence is enhanced or suppressed.

In other words, an airplane in flight does not behave like the "rigid clamping model." On the X-29 it was found that at some point the wing divergence couples into the rigid body freedom mode to produce a new type of flutter mode.

Lesson: When dealing with analyses of new technology, make sure all assumptions are carefully understood and justified.

We now know that for certain types of airplanes the forward swept wing is definitely a suitable candidate in configuration design decision making.

A side technology which was incorporated in the X-29 design, was that of digital-fly-by-wire (DFBW) and large, inherent instability. In fact, the X-29 had a 35% unstable static margin (by design) at aft c.g. The thought was to demonstrate that even this amount of instability could be handled with available DFBW technology. Therefore, there would be no question about the ability to handle less severe instabilities.

I must emphasize the fact that the addition of DFBW had nothing to do with the forward swept wing. One can design any airplane to be either inherently stable or unstable. The forward-swept-winged Ju-287 was an inherently stable airplane.

I served on the USAF X-29 oversight committee for many years. It was very interesting to participate in the discussions of the relative merits of the three proposed designs by General Dynamics, Rockwell and Grumman. I was very impressed with the engineering expertise of Grumman's Glenn Spatz and Rockwell's Mike Robinson. Both had a real knack to explain difficult matters in simple, clearly understandable terms.

The X-29 committee had the good fortune also to have the services of William (Bill) Lamar who made his mark on American military aviation by his many years of service as the civilian head of the USAF Flight Dynamics Laboratories at Wright-Patterson Air Force Base. Bill was a real gentleman and an expert on almost any subject dealing with military aircraft.

As indicated before, Grumman was the eventual winner and built two X-29 vehicles. The airplane was an astounding success, particularly in view of the very aggressive use of advanced technology.

As part of the forward swept wing work I was asked to participate in a NATO sponsored conference on forward swept wing aircraft. This conference was held at Bristol University in England. One of the speakers was Captain Eric Brown, a famous British test pilot who actually flew the Junkers Ju-287. I highly recommend his book, Reference 73.

Buehler Aviation: 1979

In 1979 I was approached by Bill Barnhouse, a consultant to Buehler Aviation in Florida, to do some stability and control work on the Buehler Model 103. This was a canard-pusher airplane and is shown in Figure 194.

Doug Griswold was one of the KU students who assisted me on that project. Our work showed that the airplane should be certifiable. My guess is that the company ran out of money, because it never was certified.

Mike Smith Aircraft: 1980

In 1980 I performed some configuration analysis work for Mike Smith on his Model 400 Lightning. This good looking airplane is shown in Figure 195. As far as I know, this airplane was never certified either.

The X-29, Buehler and Smith airplane projects were the last consulting projects I was involved in before the creation of DARcorporation. How and why this corporation came about was discussed in Section 6.2. Some of the airplane project activities I was associated with at DARcorporation are summarized in Chapter 7.

Figure 169 Beech King Air, Old Empennage Configuration (Courtesy Beech Aircraft)

Figure 170 Beech King Air, New Empennage Configuration (Courtesy Beech Aircraft)

Figure 171 Model of the Bell Huey Helicopter

Figure 172 Learjet Model 24 (Courtesy Gates Learjet)

Figure 173 Learjet Model 25 (Courtesy Gates Learjet)

Figure 174 Learjet Model 23 (Courtesy Gates Learjet)

Figure 175 Model of the Proposed Gates Learjet Model 112

Figure 176 Gates Learjet Model 36 (Courtesy Gates Learjet)

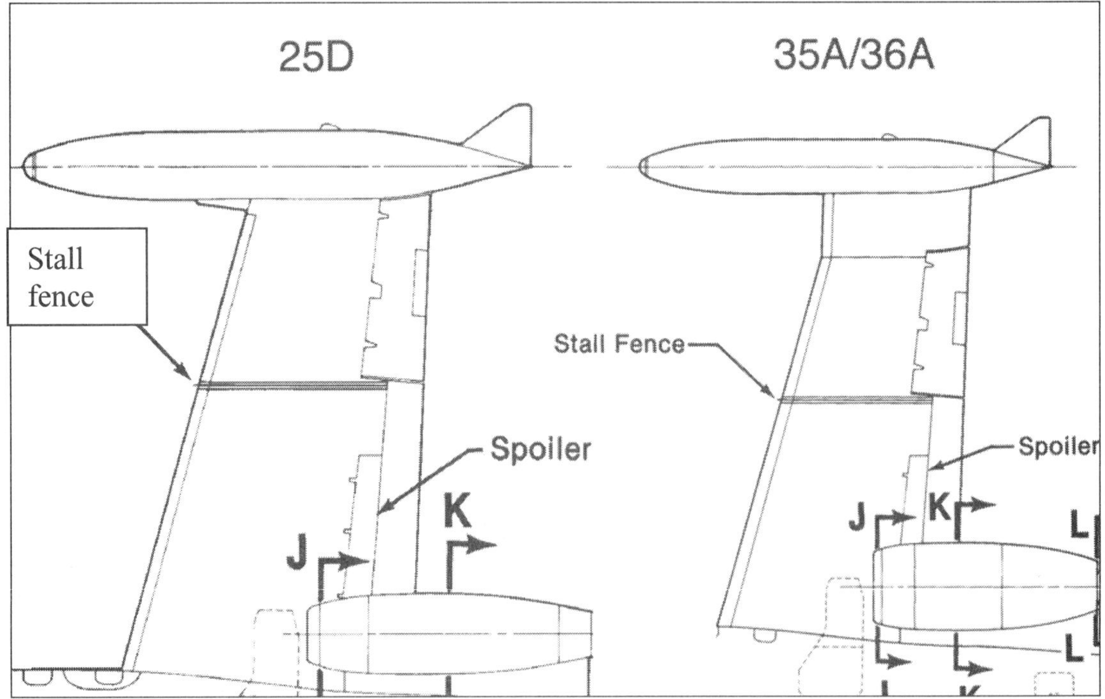

Figure 177 Comparison of Gates Learjet Model 25 and 36 Wings (Courtesy Gates Learjet)

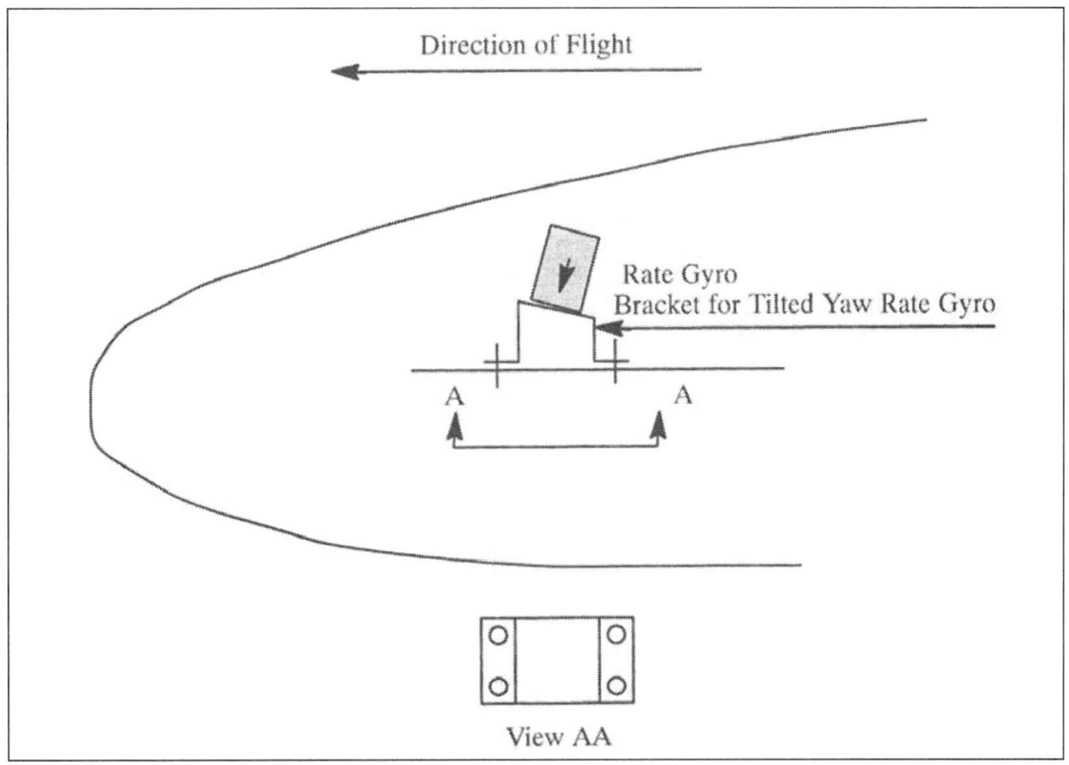

Figure 178 Experimental Bracket for Tilted Yaw Rate Gyro

Figure 179 Gates Learjet Model 55 (Courtesy Gates Learjet)

Figure 180 Cessna Model 500 (Courtesy Cessna)

Figure 181 Canadair Model 600, Challenger (Courtesy Canadair)

Figure 182 SIAI-Marchetti S-211 (Courtesy SIAI-Marchetti)

Figure 183 S-211 Model in the Checkout Area of the Boeing Transonic Wind Tunnel (Courtesy SIAI-Marchetti)

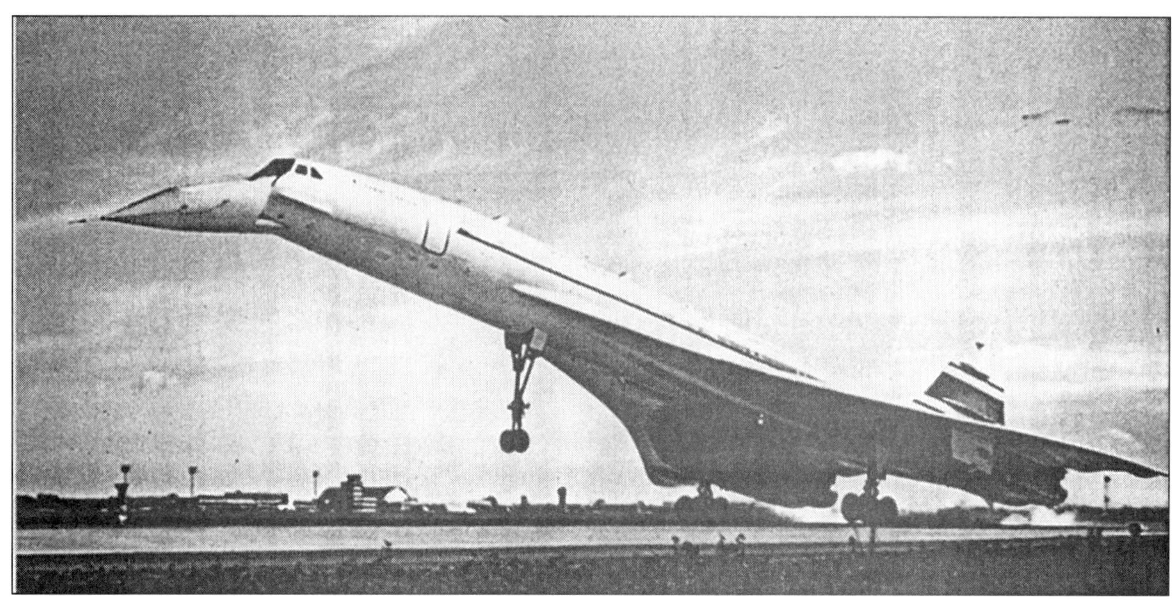

Figure 184 BAC/Aerospatiale Concorde (Courtesy British Aerospace)

Figure 185 Mock-Up of the Foxjet (Courtesy Foxjet International)

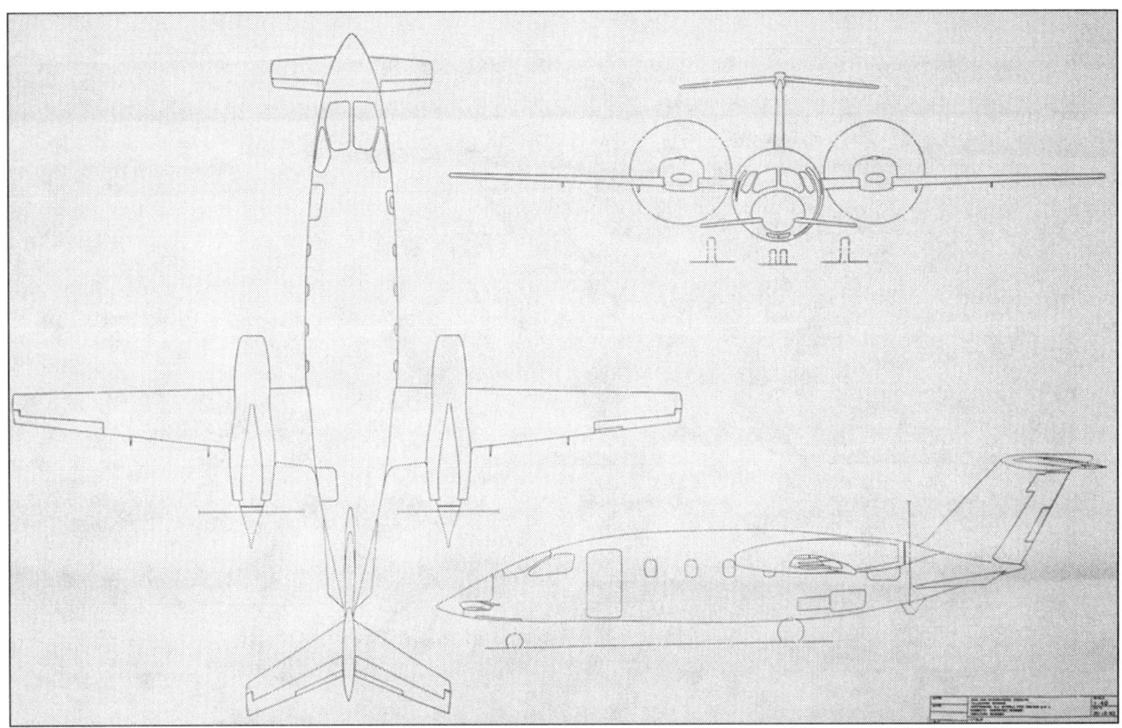

Figure 186 Preliminary Three-View of the Piaggio P-180 (Courtesy Piaggio)

Figure 187 Model of the Piaggio P-180 in the Boeing Transonic Wind Tunnel (Courtesy Piaggio)

Figure 188 Production Version of the Piaggio P-180, Avanti (Courtesy Piaggio)

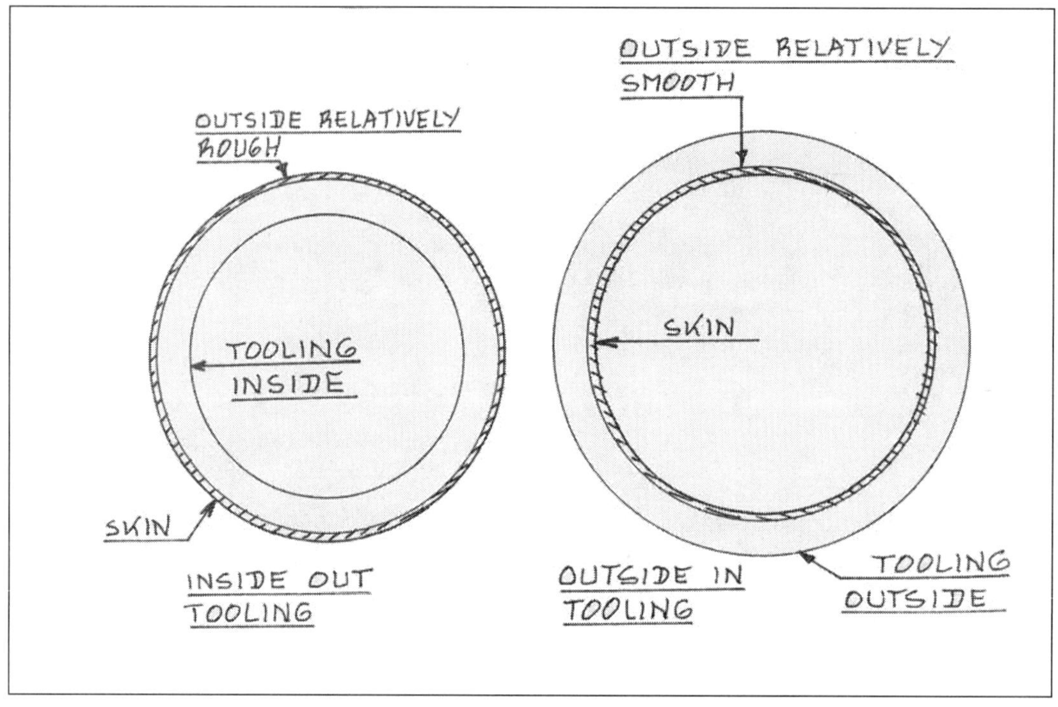

Figure 189 Example of “Inside-Out” and “Outside-In” Tooling

Figure 190 Piaggio/Douglas PD-108 (Courtesy Piaggio)

Figure 191 Piper Malibu (Courtesy Skytech, Inc.)

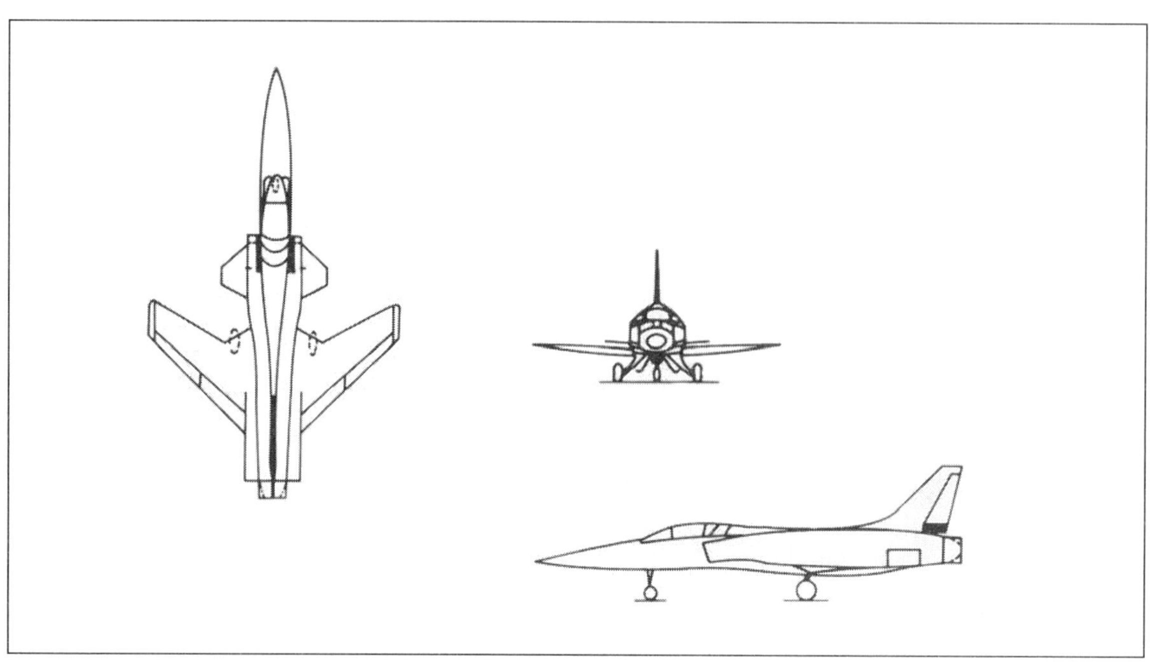

Figure 192 Three-view of the Grumman X-29 (Courtesy Grumman)

Figure 193 Grumman X-29 (Courtesy Grumman)

Figure 194 Buehler Model 103 (Courtesy Buehler Aviation)

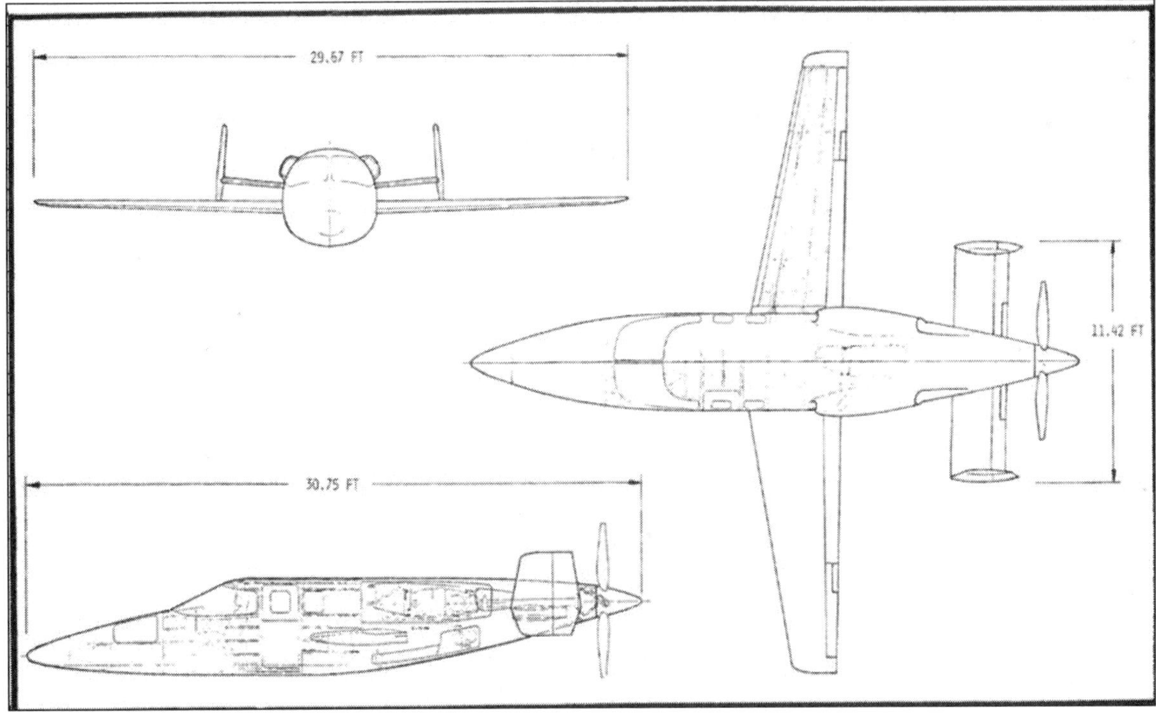

Figure 195 Mike Smith Model 400, Lightning (Courtesy Mike Smith Aircraft)

Chapter 7: Design, Analysis and Research Corporation from 1991 - 2002

How and why DARcorporation was formed was discussed in Chapter 6, Section 6.2. As stated there, the company came about as a so-called "spin-off" from The University of Kansas to market, develop and support the AAA (Advanced Aircraft Analysis) software.

The name DARcorporation was picked because my plan was for the company to expand into consulting engineering work. To give the new company a more flexible income basis it was decided to also take over all marketing of my textbooks from RAEC. My intent was to gradually phase out and liquidate RAEC. The latter happened in December of 2001.

I provided the start-up capital and bought a building from my accountants Blue Barrand and James Eagan. They wanted to sell their building at 120 East Ninth Street, Lawrence, Kansas, because they had joined the Mize-Houser accounting firm. Owning the building could be perceived as a conflict of interest. It was a happy circumstance for all involved that I was in a position to buy it. Since DARcorporation did not need the entire building, I back-leased the first floor to Mize-Houser and leased the second floor to DARcorporation.

My former student William Anemaat became chief engineer and later vice president of engineering. Our first AAA software sale was to SAAB of Sweden in 1991.

At first DARcorporation was to develop the AAA code while Kohlman Systems Research (KSR) of Lawrence, Kansas was to take care of the marketing aspects. This mode of operating turned out to be unsatisfactory for both companies. Therefore it was agreed by all parties concerned that DARcorporation would also take over the marketing function.

In 1994, under a NASA Small Business Innovative Research (SBIR Phase II) contract, the AAA code was rewritten and modernized to run on personal computers (PC's) in a Microsoft Windows environment. Also, the code had to be made attractive to designers of general aviation airplanes.

In addition, a user-friendly CAD program was developed called Aero-CADD. It is of interest to note how this came about.

Back in 1987, General Dynamics developed an internal CAD code, called ACADS (Airplane Computer Aided Design System). This code was developed under the guidance of one of its engineers, Tim Olson. This ACADS code allowed for the creation of very complicated geometries, typical of those arising in the design of fighter aircraft. It also was relatively easy to learn.

By 1987, I had become convinced that at The University of Kansas we should get with it and convert our manual drafting classes to CAD. To that end I selected the promising CATIA software (developed by Dassault in France) and gotten Cessna Aircraft Company to donate its first generation computer system, including 25 terminals. This offer was turned down by the KU powers that be; they did not want to afford the maintenance fees. Back to square one.

I discussed this problem with Ed Petrushka at General Dynamics who had been instrumental in getting the KU FRL the contract to develop the original AAA software code.

Mr. Petrushka came to our rescue by offering unlimited (no fees) use of the GD ACADS program. That is how the ACADS became integrated into the AE department and installed in the first School of Engineering computer lab on the third floor of Learned Hall. This all happened in 1988.

During the mid 90's Lockheed bought the F-16 Division of General Dynamics and the future of the ACADS program was in doubt. Tim Olson quit his job at what was now Lockheed, and formed his own company, CADDSoft Solutions in Fort Worth, Texas. There, he developed a new and much more capable code, called CADpro which eventually became Vellum Solids, marketed by Ashlar.

At DAR we decided to integrate that code into our Aero-CADD program rather than reinvent the wheel. Therefore, a deal was struck between CADDSoft Solutions and DAR to develop, market and support the Aero-CADD program.

Another version of the new code, called GA-CAD, became available in 1996. Two years later, a complete CAD code was added to the DARcorp software suite. In both instances, the CAD portion of the code and some of the aero-special features were developed by Tim Olson under contract to DARcorporation.

Today, in 2002, DARcorp still markets and develops the AAA and Aero-CADD codes. Both codes can be rented by students on a semester basis and many around the world do. Downloading from the internet has helped make this feasible.

At the time of publication of this book, the AAA software is in use with 232 universities and companies all over the world.

In the following, I will briefly describe some of the consulting engineering work in which DAR has been involved.

Fairchild Aircraft Corporation: 1992

For Fairchild Corporation of San Antonio Texas, DARcorporation performed design and analytical studies for modifications to the flight control system of an advanced version of its popular Model 23, Metroliner shown in Figure 196.

3X-jet: 1993 - present

In 1993 I was contacted by Richard (Dick) Bacon of Colorado Springs, Colorado. Dick had patented a novel engine arrangement for business jets. His idea was to take a twin engine business jet and make the engines different. One engine would be sized only to deliver the required cruise thrust: the cruise engine. The other engine would be sized to give the airplane proper single engine performance during take-off, in case the cruise engine fails. Normally the airplane would take off and climb with both engines running. Once at cruise, the takeoff engine would be shut down. Bacon called this approach the 3X-jet. Obvious benefits are lower cruise fuel consumption (because of better engine-to-cruise matching) and lower engine maintenance costs.

An important side benefit of the 3X-jet concept is that it results in rather spectacular climb and fieldlength performance with both engines operating.

I was asked to verify the economic benefits from such an engine arrangement. I did and found that Dick was correct. This led to publications 138 and 145 in Appendix A. Dick Bacon is currently pursuing his idea under the name 3X-jet Corporation. Figure 197 shows a proposed layout for a 3X-jet airplane.

Dick and I made a trip to the NBAA (National Business Aircraft Association) show in New Orleans in his Beechcraft Duke (Figure 151). Dick was kind enough to let me fly his beautiful airplane during the flights from Lawrence to New Orleans and back.

Sadly, the 3X-jet concept has, so far, failed to attract enough financial interest, to initiate its development. Time will tell whether this attractive idea will bear fruit.

AEL Industries (now BAE Systems): 1994-1995

In 1994 and 1995 DARcorporation carried out various water tunnel studies of a new type of refueling installation on a KC-135R and 707-320B airplane (Figures 198 and 199). To keep the cost of this program down, DARcorporation developed a method to modify commercially available plastic model kits for testing in a water tunnel. We were able to show that the proposed AEL system would not result in unfavorable interference with the basic KC-135R.

DAR also performed various stability and control analyses including stick forces and gradients for a KC-135R with a fuselage mounted external refueling system.

MDM Systems: 1996

For this company, the stability and control derivatives of a Beech Bonanza (Figure 200) were determined for several flight conditions.

Nexus Aircraft Corporation: 1996

For this company, preliminary design studies were conducted for a small, freighter/passenger airplane shown in Figure 201. This project was halted for lack of financing.

Air Tractor Inc.: 1996-present

Leland Snow, proprietor of Air Tractor, Inc., of Olney, Texas, and a well-known manufacturer of agricultural airplanes, contracted with DARcorporation to carry out preliminary design analyses for a range of new, single, twin and three-engined airplanes.

With one of these airplanes, the S-22 high wing, 10-seat, turboprop airplane, Air Tractor won a prototype construction contract from the Department of the Interior.

DAR also performed analyses of various other new airplane designs for Air Tractor.

Visionaire Corporation: 1998-2000

For Visionaire Corporation, Chesterfield, Missouri, DARcorporation carried out wind tunnel tests and flying quality studies to ensure the certifiability of the Visionaire Vantage, single-engine business jet. Figure 202 shows a picture of that wind tunnel model. Sadly, the test results indicated the need for several aerodynamic design changes to assure certifiability. This company also ran out of money and the future of the project is uncertain.

DreamWings: 1998-2001

In 1998 I helped John Hunter establish a light aircraft manufacturing facility at the Lawrence Municipal Airport. He called his company DreamWings.

DARcorporation received a contract to carry out configuration design studies which led to the two airplane designs shown in Figures 203 and 204.

DAR also performed detailed structural and systems design work on the Valkerie airplane until DreamWings ran into financial trouble in 2001 and ceased operations.

There is an important lesson in all this. In the airplane business, things usually take twice as much money and effort as first thought. Count on this in financial planning. Also, don't count on early return of profits. In a typical airplane program profitability is five to ten years in the future.

Kelly Space & Technology: 2000-2001

For Kelly Space & Technology, DARcorporation carried out configuration and performance analyses of its proposed K201 second generation Reusable Launch Vehicle (RLV).

This promising concept, along with several other concepts which were part of a new NASA space access initiative, was terminated in 2001 for lack of funding.

Safire Aircraft Company: 1999-2002

In 1999 DARcorporation received a contract from Safire Aircraft to perform configuration analysis work on its new Safire S-26 business jet shown in Figure 205. The current plan is for DARcorporation to begin a wind tunnel test program for this airplane in May of 2002.

SimCom: 1998-2002

Simulation models have been prepared for a wide variety of airplanes, including the Air Tractor 502 B, the Socata TBM-700, the Piper Malibu Mirage, and the Raytheon King Air 350. Renditions of these airplanes are shown in Figures 206 - 209.

In many ways, the preparation of simulation models of airplanes involves a process known as re-engineering. Using known flight manual performance, engine and geometric data as inputs it is possible to determine computationally the stability and control characteristics and performance characteristics of any airplane.

DARcorporation is engaged in several other projects which still are of a proprietary nature.

Figure 196 Fairchild Model 23, Metroliner (Courtesy Fairchild)

Figure 197 Model of a 3X-Jet Configuration (Courtesy Richard Bacon)

Figure 198 Water Tunnel Model of a KC-135R

Figure 199 Water Tunnel Model of a 707-320B with Refueling System under the Fuselage

Figure 200 Beechcraft Bonanza (Courtesy Beech Aircraft)

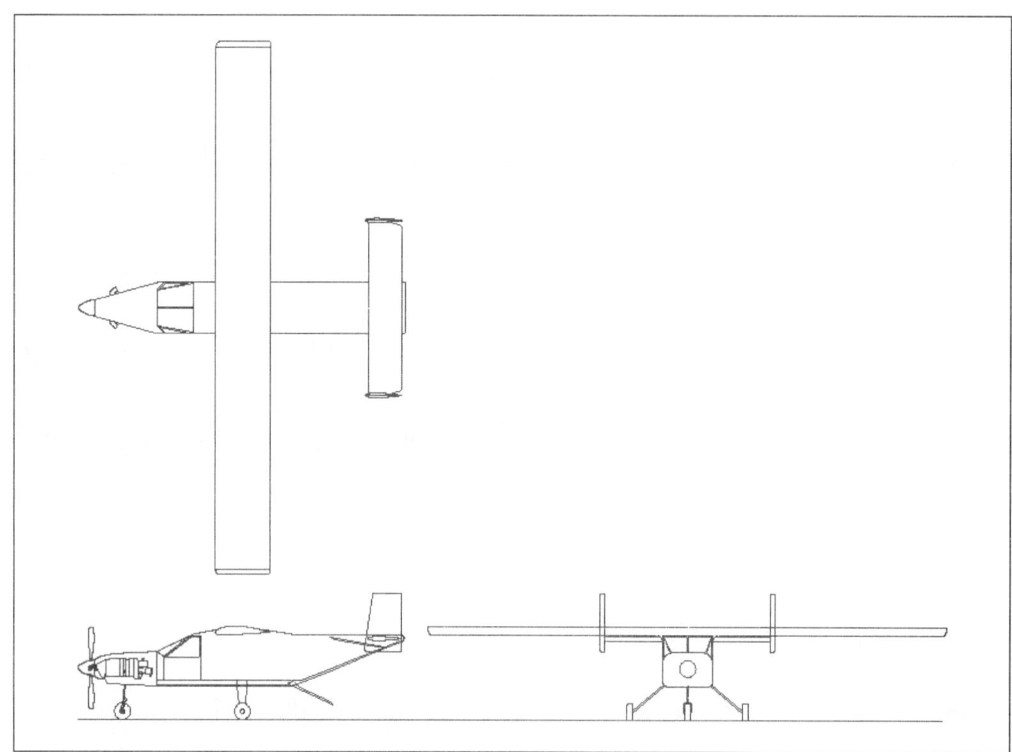

Figure 201 Three-view of the Nexus Airplane

Figure 202 Wind Tunnel Model of the Visionaire Vantage

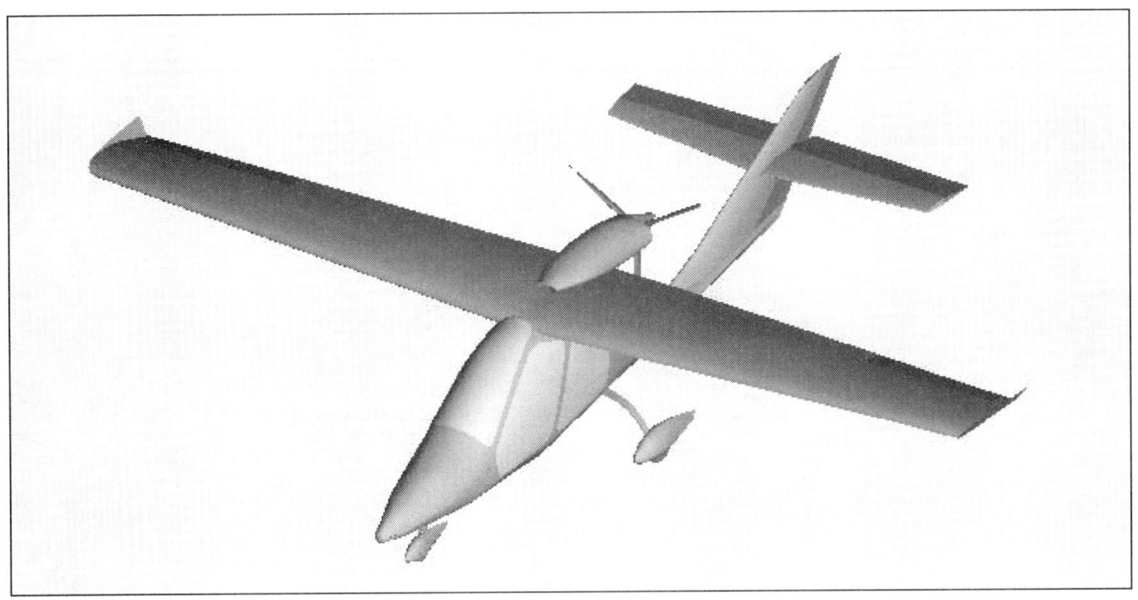

Figure 203 Aero-CADD Rendition of the DreamWings Hooligan

Figure 204 Aero-CADD Rendition of the DreamWings Valkyrie

Figure 205 Artist's Conception of the Safire S-26 (Courtesy Safire Aircraft)

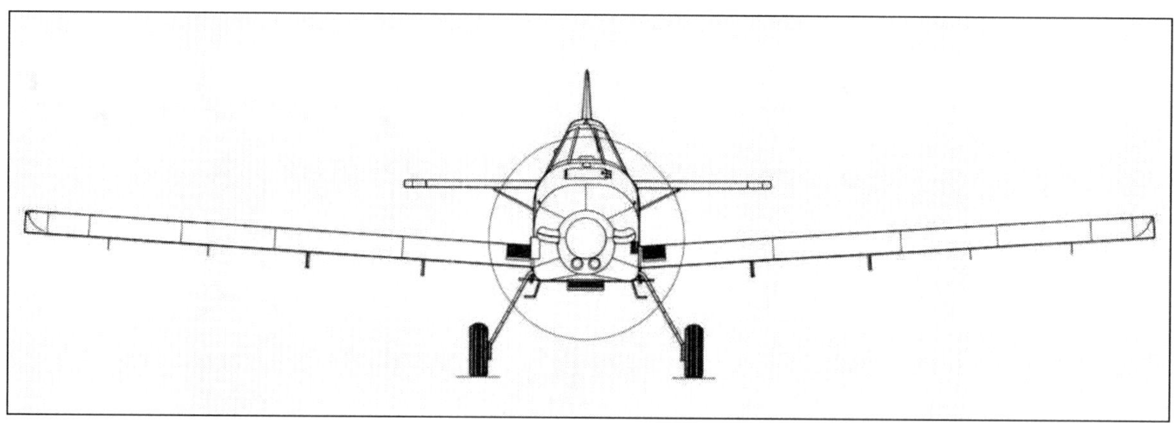

Figure 206 Air Tractor 502B (Courtesy Air Tractor)

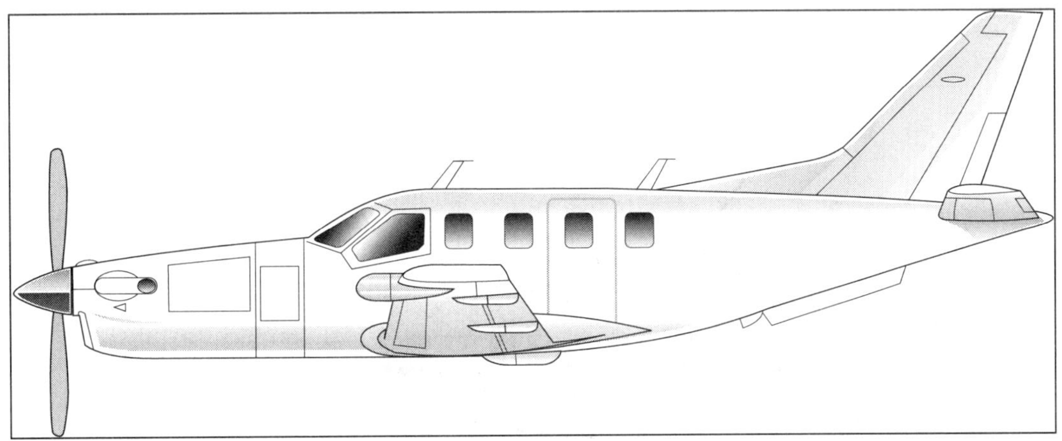

Figure 207 Socata TBM-700 (Courtesy Socata)

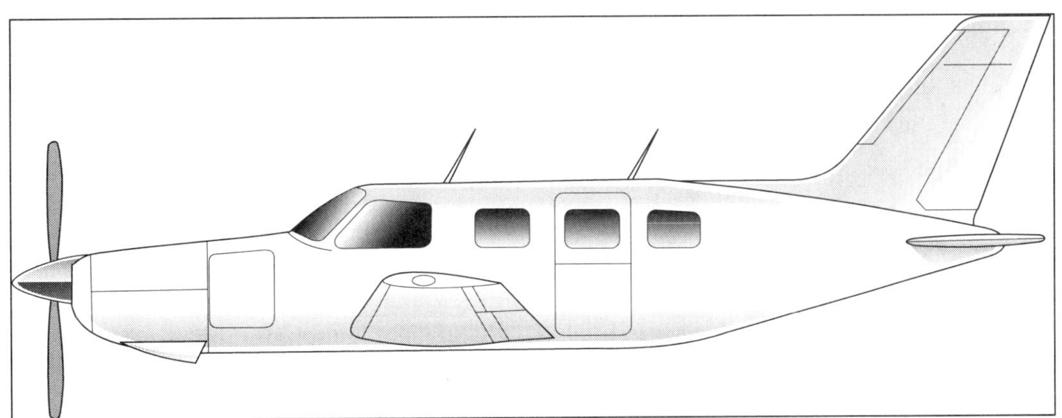

Figure 208 Piper Meridian (Courtesy Piper Aircraft)

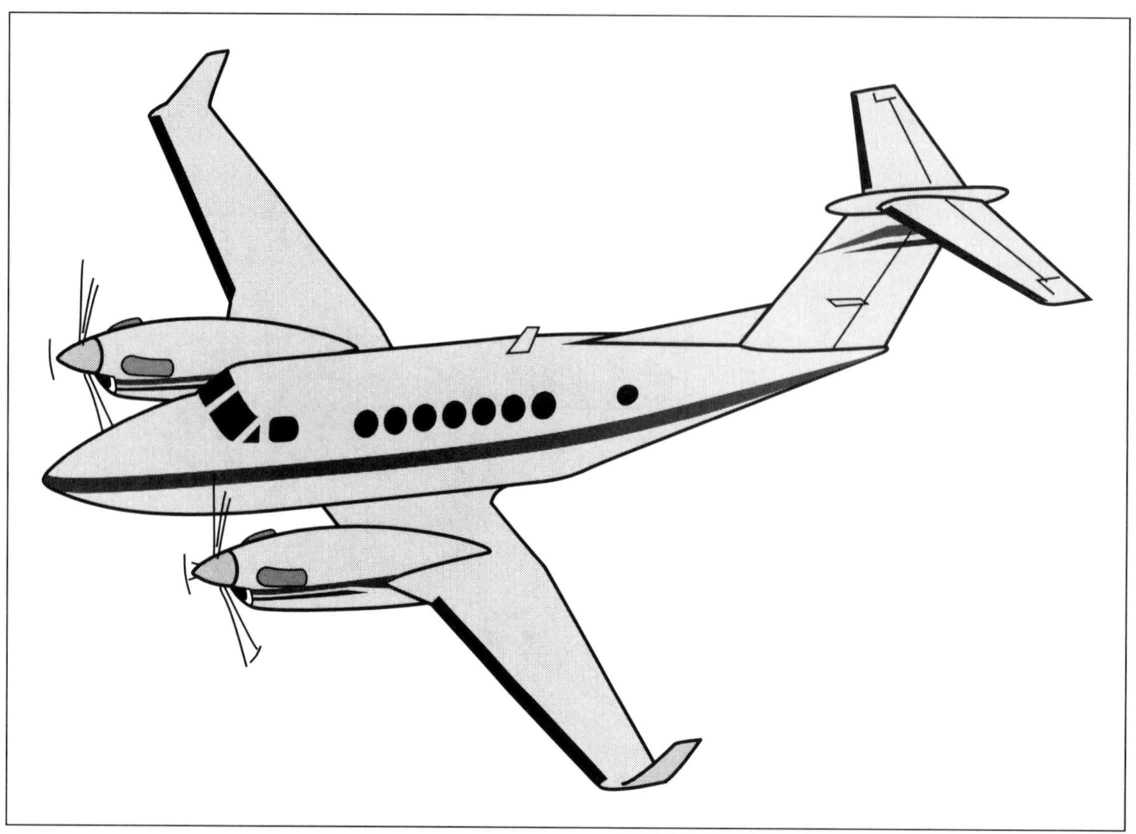

Figure 209 Raytheon King Air 350 (Courtesy Raytheon)

Chapter 8: Miscellaneous War Stories

In this chapter I have included a number of war stories about airplanes and events with which I had no direct, professional involvement. Some of these stories are based on my own observations and some on things I read, particularly in literature dealing with aircraft incidents and accidents. I believe these stories serve to make airplane and systems designers think about safety and cost when making design decisions. That is also why I use these stories in various lectures.

I wish to emphasize that it is definitely not my intent to assign blame to anyone or to any organization. To err is human. We all make mistakes. Aeronautical engineers always wrestle with the problem that seemingly little mistakes can lead to catastrophic consequences. That is the nature of our business. I like to equate flying airplanes with managing a very large pool of potential and kinetic energy. Managing that energy pool so that the energy does not destroy the airplane is a major responsibility.

The stories are presented based on my best recollection. In several instances I have intentionally omitted specific aircraft type identifications.

I have arranged these war stories to address the following generic topics which are vital to the creation of safe airplanes and, sometimes to maintaining secrecy:

1) Reliability and redundancy
2) Design with common sense
3) Design for expected occurrences
4) Conceptual flaws in design
5) Maintaining secrecy
6) Monitoring Structural Damage

1) Reliability and redundancy

The following war stories illustrate the fact that we airplane designers serve at the pleasure of the public. If our designs do not measure up to perceived safety levels many people will refuse to fly.

War Story 93

In 1984 my parents were visiting me. I picked them up at the Kansas City International Airport. They had arrived earlier in Chicago per KLM 747 (Figure 210). After my parents were settled in the car and we were on the way to Lawrence, my Dad said, "Jan, our KLM pilot informed us that the landing in Chicago had been automatic because of poor visibility. Does that mean that the pilot was not actually controlling the airplane down to the ground?"

I answered, "Yes Dad, that is what he meant." My Dad then asked, " How safe is such a system?"

I replied with, " How safe do you think such a system should be?"

My Dad was quiet for a little while and then came back with, “What exactly do you mean by that question?” I answered, “ Let me be perfectly blunt about this. What I mean is, once in how many landings would it be all right for the system to fail disastrously so that all passengers would be killed? As a designer I need a numerical answer to that question because that is the only way I can design adequate redundancy in the system.”

My Dad thought this over for awhile and then replied, “Well, once per one million landings would be safe enough for me.” I said, “Dad, you will be proud of us when I tell you that we design systems like that for a catastrophic failure probability of once per one-thousand-million landings.” My Dad was very impressed and asked how many such systems would be required to meet that level of safety. I told him that it would take three.

It turns out that KLM carries four such systems in its 747 airplanes. The reason is not to be safer yet. The reason is to give them the ability to dispatch the airplane back to Amsterdam with one system failed.

Lesson: This design criterion is referred to as the 10^9-criterion. Whether or not this provides an adequate level of safety depends on the public perception of that safety level. Designers better struggle with the following problem: if one believes the Boeing and Airbus predictions of growth in air travel over the next 15 years, keeping this design criterion at the 10^9 level will result in many more passengers losing their lives. The author believes that the time is past due for moving the design goal posts to a higher level of safety.

War Story 94

The aircraft industry is on the verge of producing very large airplanes. I mean large in the sense of the ability to carry a large number of passengers. What is very large? I believe numbers like 500-600 passengers qualify *. I have a serious problem with the very idea of very large passenger airplanes. Consider the question, “Is it ethically responsible to subject that many people to the possibility of a catastrophic accident?”

As an airplane designer and pilot I am well aware of airplane accident statistics and comparisons with other human activities. Flying is safer than almost everything we humans do. However...

The air transportation industry serves the public at its pleasure. Once the public *perceives* that flying is unsafe (note the use of the word perceive!) many people will cease flying and there will certainly be political activity aimed at restrictive regulations. The September 11, 2001, events certainly have taught us both. I do not **know** where the ethical, upper limit is for passenger-carrying airplanes. I do tend to **believe** that 500-600 is stepping over the limit.

Lesson: I would like to offer the following thought: Just because something is economically desirable and technologically feasible does not mean we as engineers should do it.

---

* Some 747’s in Japan are already being operated with more than 500 seats.

2) Design with common sense

The next war stories illustrate the fact that common sense in design is something that eludes even the best design teams.

War Story 95

Sometime in 1992 I was sitting in a new twin-jet Boeing 737-300 at Salt Lake City (see Figure 211). Through my window I could see the big cowl of the number one engine. There is a large cowl door which opens upward and is located between the nacelle and the fuselage. This door provides access to certain engine components.

When the airplane is parked at the gate and the hydraulic system is not operating, the inboard Krueger flaps tend to sag downward a bit. If the cowl door were opened in such a case it would interfere with (i.e. crunch into) the Krueger flap. Therefore, a large placard was painted on the cowl door. The placard read: "Do not open this cowl door unless the leading edge devices have been secured in the up position. For detailed instructions see inside of cowl door."

Lesson: It would help if people who compose placard instructions on airplanes would think about the consequences of their composition.

War Story 96

Early in January of 1993 I was awaiting push-back in a 747 at Schiphol Airport, near Amsterdam, The Netherlands. It was bitterly cold and snowing. The airplane had been duly de-iced.

Just before push-back the pilot announced that he wanted maintenance to check the oil in the number one engine. This would delay push-back a bit.

Pretty soon here came a blue KLM maintenance pick-up. A mechanic stepped out, dressed in full winter clothing including nice warm gloves. When he approached the nacelle cowl door he could not open it with his gloves on. So he took them off. When he touched the cowl his hand froze to it. It took awhile that day before we finally got going.

Lesson: Design all access covers for items requiring frequent ramp access so that people wearing winter clothing and gloves can open them.

3) Design for expected occurrences: If it can happen, it will happen (Murphy's Law)

The following war stories illustrate what can happen if designers fail to foresee the occurrence of certain events which can lead to trouble.

War Story 97

To celebrate the first flight of the F-111A, the management of the Fort Worth division of General Dynamics invited some top brass for a special demonstration. The brass and other guests were seated on a grandstand erected on the ramp. The idea was for the airplane after landing to taxi and park in front of this grandstand.

There were quite a number of high level guests who had arrived in squadron hacks. Those airplanes had been parked on the ramp as well.

The F-111A (Figure 104) made a successful demonstration flight and landed, as usual, with the wings swept forward and the big Fowler flaps deployed. In that configuration the airplane really looked impressive and the idea was to then park it in front of the grand stand. However, the test pilot thought that there was insufficient space between two of the parked airplanes for him to taxi through with the wings swept forward. Therefore, he engaged the wing-sweep system to sweep the wings aft. Crunch, crunch, crunch: the Fowler flaps were crushed against the side of the fuselage. All this in front of all the brass. Very embarrassing.

Lesson: The designers might have expected that, if it is possible to sweep the wings aft with the flaps deployed, someone would do it. The solution was simple: an interlocking device to prevent a pilot from sweeping the wings with the flaps down.

War Story 98

A Lockheed C-141 (Figure 212), military transport was climbing out of McCord Field, near Tacoma, Washington. Shortly after retracting the flaps the pilot engaged the pitch-damper. This is part of configuring the airplane for cruise operations. The airplane immediately began a series of diverging short period oscillations. After several oscillations, the g-level was building up to worrisome levels and the crew wondered what was going on. Luckily, at that point the pilot remembered what someone had taught him: If you ever get into trouble in an airplane, try undoing the last thing you did. The pilot disengaged the pitch damper and the oscillations subsided.

After landing it was discovered that, following an overnight repair of the rate gyro which drives the pitch damper, a mechanic had accidentally reversed the wiring. As a result the sign of the signals in the pitch-rate-to-elevator feedback loop was reversed and the damper was driving the airplane unstable.

Lesson: Murphy's Law strikes again! Prevent miswiring of flight crucial systems by designing for a one-way fit.

By the way, this particular lesson does not seem to get learned.

A similar, almost disastrous event happened to the experimental NASA QSRA airplane during its first flight. Figure 213 shows this rather interesting airplane. In this case a roll rate gyro was miswired.

In 2001, a Turkish Air Force CN-235 crashed because of a reversed aileron control system installation (again following a repair).

In 2001, an Airbus A320, after undergoing a repair to the control side-stick the night before, began rolling the wrong way following a pilot input right after take-off. Luckily the co-pilot realized the problem and by selecting priority for his stick, managed to recover the airplane. The wing tip came within two feet of the ground !!!

There have been a number of recent reports of wiring reversals in Airbus A300 transports leading to uncommanded rudder oscillations.

Ponder the following question, "How many accidents are needed before we design ALL flight crucial circuits for one-way fits?"

War Story 99

A brand new Fokker F-100 (Figure 214 shows a model of the prototype) was on final approach to the Geneva Airport in poor visibility conditions. In the F-100, a potable waterline to the front toilet had been installed close to the upper fuselage skin. Earlier in the flight this line had frozen and, of course, cracked. During the slow descent, the ice thawed and water poured into the main avionics bay which is located in the belly, below that toilet. The result was a complete shorting of electrical power to the flat panel displays and all cockpit displays went dark.

The pilots had a flashlight and three mechanical flight instruments that kept on working. With that help they were able to make a safe landing.

Lesson: This is an entirely predictable scenario. It should have been caught during an early design-safety review, but was not. Designers should remember the following law.

Every system in an airplane which carries a liquid WILL LEAK.

It is the responsibility of the designer to keep this in mind and ask the "what if" question, trace the likely path of the liquid, and take appropriate design action.

This particular lesson also does not seem to get learned.

In 2000, a similar incident happened to a brand new Boeing 717. The cause was leakage from the galley which penetrated the main avionics bay. Sound familiar? They were lucky that the incident occurred on a bright day with excellent visibility.

Some years ago, when teaching a short course at AVRO in Manchester, England, they proudly showed me the design solution applied in the AVRO RJ series of transports. In that airplane, the entire galley is mounted over a shallow bathtub. This tub in turn has several positive drainage paths, leading away from the avionics bay. That is one way to avoid such problems.

War Story 100

More than a decade ago, a Boeing 747 on its way to Hawai experienced a blowout of a cargo door located in the lower right belly. The airplane apparently took off with that door not properly latched. The door hinges were structurally integrated into the upper fuselage section wing skin. When the door opened in flight, the aerodynamic loads on the open door were so high that the hinges peeled the upper fuselage skin open (more or less like a sardine can). Several passengers were sucked out through the hole and fell to their deaths. The airplane landed safely.

Lesson: This failure scenario is entirely predictable and should not have been allowed to get past the various certification checks. Structural designers should be expected to think through any possible failure scenario. They should then ask the question: "What happens next?" This should be followed by appropriate design action.

I cannot overemphasize the importance of designers consistently playing the "what if" game while making design decisions. Doing this should be an every day drill!

War Story 101

A Boeing 767 (Figure 215 shows the prototype) experienced an in-flight, uncommanded reversal of the thrust reverser on the left engine. The airplane became uncontrollable in roll, and crashed, killing all on board.

Lesson: The failure mode which caused this might have been predicted. That being the case, the airplane should have remained controllable, or the thrust reverser actuation system should have been redesigned to include redundancy.

Consider the following a general design rule: Any hard-over failure of a control surface, throttle system, or thrust-reverser system, occurring anywhere within the operational flight envelope of an airplane, should be controllable.

When I worked at Boeing in the sixties, this rule was known as the Boeing Tameness Criterion. It is a good rule to remember and follow.

War Story 102

In 2000, an MD80 (Figure 216) passenger jet crashed as a result of a stabilizer jackscrew failure. Apparently there was a lack of lubrication in the jackscrew of this particular airplane which resulted in the screw-threads being stripped, allowing the stabilizer to deflect to an angle which made control of the airplane impossible.

There must be hard-stops designed into each control surface. In this case the hard-stop was designed to “catch” the drive nut. Such a hard-stop works as a hard-stop only as long as the screw threads are not stripped.

Lesson: The hard-stop was not really a hard-stop. Design engineers should not assume that anything but a true hard stop will be adequate when it comes to primary flight controls.

War Story 103

In many versions of the F4 fighter airplane (Figure 217) the Identification of Friend or Foe (IFF) receiver was located underneath the rear ejection seat. The failure rate of that IFF system was rather high and known to be high. As a result, the maintenance manhours associated with replacing the IFF were also very high.

Imagine the following maintenance sequence:

1) Disarm the rear ejection seat;
2) Remove the ejection seat;
3) Remove the IFF;
4) Install a new IFF;
5) Re-install the ejection seat;
6) Re-arm the seat.

Lesson: Items which require frequent replacement should be easily accessible. It should not be necessary to remove other equipment before access is possible. It is a good practice to write down maintenance sequences as soon as a decision is made to locate a component somewhere in the airplane. Doing that may give food for the thought that maybe the installation should be changed.

War Story 104

The category of ultralight aircraft has not been regulated. As a result some of the most obvious quality control measures taken in FAR 23 and FAR 25 certified airplanes are often omitted in ultralights. A tragic example was an ultralight (Figure 218) which was tested structurally by Dr. Howard Smith and his students at the KU FRL.

A major finding of the tests was that most of the flight control cables and structural support cables in that vehicle failed between limit and ultimate load.

The really bad thing was the failure mode: the swaged ends of the clevises would slip from the cable. This failure mode is specifically not allowed in FAR 23 and FAR 25 airplanes. It is avoided by very tight quality control during the manufacturing of cables.

Lesson: Lack of regulation can lead to dangerous situations.

4) Conceptual flaws in design thinking

The following war stories illustrate what flaws in design thinking can yield.

War Story 105

The certification of a business jet was significantly delayed as a result of problems uncovered while the airplane was in the last stages of certification test flying. The flight controls in the rear fuselage had to be rerouted to prevent rotor or disk bursting from putting all controls out of commission.

This potential problem was obvious from an early cutaway drawing of the airplane published by *Flight International*. It is amazing that this was not caught during critical design reviews.

Lesson: This was predictable. Management should hold regular critical design reviews during the detail design process of a new airplane. These reviews should be attended by experienced design people tasked to ask critical questions.

War Story 106

Another business jet had an AD (Airworthiness Directive) issued against it long after it was certified because of the potential of an aft c.g. shift of fuel from forward fuel cells to two saddle tanks located in the aft fuselage. Three test crew members died as a result of a crash which was caused by fuel shifting the rear tank during takeoff. Looking at a *Flight International* fuel system layout published before the airplane was certified, it is obvious that this scenario is possible unless one-way valving or baffling is part of the fuel system design.

Lesson: Here we go again! This was predictable. Management should hold regular critical design reviews during the detail design process of a new airplane. These reviews should be attended by experienced design people who are tasked to ask critical questions.

War Story 107

Many years ago the North American Columbus Division conceived a new idea for a supersonic, VSTOL fighter, the XFV-112. A contract was received for the construction and flight testing of two prototypes. Figure 219 shows the concept. It is of interest to observe that there is only one engine. In transitioning from the hovering mode to the flight mode, it is well to remember that the air which is drawn into the louvered wing and canard has all of its forward momentum stopped. This causes a rather large momentum drag. To accelerate to forward flight, the total installed thrust (from the vectoring louvers and from the engine inlet/exhaust system) must be able to overcome the total drag and provide a reasonable forward acceleration.

As it turned out, the system was not able to do this. The project was cancelled.

Lesson: Momentum drag can be significant. This is predictable and should not be forgotten.

War Story 108

When the first F-18 fighter (Figure 220) was flight tested at Patuxent River, it became evident that the airplane would not rotate at the predicted speed. This made the field performance of the airplane unacceptable. The problem was traced to an error in the calculation of aerodynamic forces in ground effect. This is particularly severe in case of a low placed horizontal stabilizer. As a result there was insufficient down-load capability to effect early rotation during the takeoff ground roll.

The problem was fixed by toe-in of the rudders. A squat-switch on the main gear biasses the rudders to deflect inward while on the ground. This creates enough positive pressure over the aft fuselage to effect early rotation.

This fix, although impressive, came at a price. All flight control software had to be re-validated. Also, the squat-switches represented additional system complexity.

Lesson: Engineers should not forget about ground effect.

War Story 109

The Piper Apache (Figure 221) was a fairly popular, low cost, twin-engined, propeller-driven airplane. The author got his multi-engine rating on this airplane. Interesting system design features were:

a) If the left engine failed, all electrical power was lost. As a result some of the flight instruments would no longer work.

b) If the right engine failed, all hydraulic power was lost and the landing gear had to be operated with a hand-driven pump.

My problem with this type of design is that the pilot is supposed to know the airplane and its systems well enough to be able to cope with engine failures. It is asking a lot of the human mind to assume that most pilots can cope with such complexities in an emergency.

Lesson: Engine failures should be non-events as far as airplane controllability is concerned.

War Story 110

This story concerns a post WWII era, four-engined turboprop. Early in its operational life there were two fatal crashes which, as a detailed accident investigation turned up, were caused by the following sequence of events.

Both airplanes had experienced hard landings before the crashes occurred. It was found, that a structural member in the landing-gear-to-engine-nacelle-attachment-structure had become weakened. As a result a flutter mode (called whirl-mode) became unstable at the design cruise speed of the airplane.

Lesson: Engineers should assume that, as a result of hard landings, certain areas of the structure can become weakened. As a result, certain flutter modes which are normally stable out to the design flutter speed of the airplane, may become unstable at speeds between the design cruise speed and the design dive speed. If that is the case, the structural design has to be changed.

War Story 111

An early four-engined jet transport, operated as a cargo airplane, crashed while on final approach to the Lusaka Airport in Africa. The five crew members died in the crash. From the pattern of the wreckage it was evident that the horizontal stabilizer had separated from the airplane. Detailed inspection of the wreckage revealed serious fatigue cracks in the spar structure of that stabilizer.

These cracks would not have been detectable by normal inspection procedures because of lack of access to the affected area. When other operators of this airplane type were alerted by the manufacturer, tear-down inspection revealed that several other stabilizers also were candidates for early fatigue failure. These stabilizers were repaired and put back in operation.

Lesson: Structural areas where high loads are predicted to occur are candidates for fatigue failures. Such areas should be easily inspectable. That means suitable covers must be designed into the structure to enable inspection, and therefore early detection, of fatigue cracks.

War Story 112

A large twin-jet transport was taking off on a dark night. After takeoff the pilot moved his hand to the flap handle to configure the airplane for initial climb. Both engines flamed out and the airplane crashed.

It turned out that the pilot's hand, on its way to the flap handle, had accidentally thrown the main fuel cut-off switch into its off position. The position of the fuel cut-off switch was changed in all airplanes of the same type.

Lesson: A study of cockpit ergonomics would have revealed this scenario as likely to occur. Designers working in concert with test pilots during the design phase of a new airplane should conduct detailed studies of actions likely to be taken by pilots and co-pilots.

War Story 113

A twin-jet transport was waiting for takeoff on a dark, rainy night. There were many airplanes in line and one of the passengers requested that a flight attendant ask the pilot when they would finally get airborne.

The flight attendant entered the cockpit, placed one of her feet on the edge of the center pedestal and asked the pilot how long it would be to takeoff. The pilot told her that it probably would be several minutes. Neither the flight attendant, nor the crew, noticed that her foot had set the rudder trim in motion to its stop.

After she had left the cockpit the airplane was suddenly cleared for an immediate takeoff. Directional control was lost during the takeoff run, the airplane ran off the runway and in the ensuing crash many people were killed.

Lessons: 1) Flight crews have detailed checks to perform before takeoff. One of these checks is to make sure that critical trim tabs are properly positioned. The pilots had indeed performed all required checks. However, when someone enters the cockpit, it must be assumed that a change may have occurred and the checklist must be re-visited. This was not done.

2) The scenario of a flight attendant placing a foot on the center pedestal and accidentally actuating a switch is predictable. This should have been foreseen during early design. Retroactively these switches were relocated to prevent reoccurrence.

War Story 114

A low altitude jet bomber was on an experimental flight when it hit a pelican. The impact severed all hydraulic lines which were located directly behind the leading edge. The airplane crashed, killing its crew.

Lesson: Don't locate flight crucial equipment behind the leading edge, certainly not in airplanes which are expected to fly at high speed and low altitude. Hitting large birds should be considered a likely occurrence.

War Story 115

An early wide-body tri-jet transport with a triple redundant, mechanically signaled, hydraulic flight control system had all three signal paths to the elevator actuators located close together right underneath the passenger cabin floor. Because of an improperly latched belly cargo door this door departed the airplane in flight. The airplane had a pressurized cabin and belly. As a result the air below the passenger floor evacuated rapidly. This caused a large pressure differential to act on the cabin floor which was not designed to withstand such a pressure differential The floor caved in locally and severed the three signal paths to the elevator. This rendered the airplane uncontrollable and it crashed killing all on board.

Lesson: If one occurrence can compromise an otherwise redundant design, the design is not redundant. In flight crucial systems ALL aspects of the design, including the signal paths, have to be redundant. That means separate locations for the signal paths.

Some of these war stories point to failures in the design decision making chain. Critical design reviews should be held during the design decision making process for any airplane, manned or unmanned. Design management should make sure that experts participate in these critical design reviews and be given plenty of opportunity to ask questions. These experts should be people with a lot of experience in the design, development and certification process of airplanes. There appears to be a real problem in not catching design snafu's until rather late in a program or until after serious incidents or accidents have occurred. Spending a little more money trying to catch these problems up front would be a lot more cost effective. It would also help improve air safety.

5) Maintaining Secrecy

Maintaining industrial or military secrecy is very difficult. The more people are involved in a project, the more problematic the maintenance of secrecy becomes. The following war story illustrates one way to avoid having to make comments.

War Story 116

While working at Boeing on the AMSA bomber project my boss and I had to conduct a briefing for some USAF brass at Edwards Air Force Base. The briefing was finished at lunch time and I was to be accompanied by a Brigadier General to a cafeteria across the ramp from where the briefing had been conducted. While walking across the ramp I saw parked on the ramp at some distance a black painted airplane. At Boeing we had heard some rumors about the Lockheed SR-71 (Figure 222) but, since the project was still a "black" program I did not know any details. I turned to my companion, pointed toward the airplane and said: "General, is that the SR-71 airplane?" The General looked in the direction I pointed and then turned to me and said: "I don't see anything!" I obviously did not ask any more questions.

Lesson: Keeping your mouth shut or pretending not to know is sometimes preferred.

6) Monitoring Structural Damage

In geriatric airplanes structural damage (usually in the form of fatigue cracks) will occur. To keep these airplanes safe requires a vigilant monitoring program.

War Story 117

Decades ago I was on a flight from Dayton, Ohio, to Kansas City with an intermediate stop in St. Louis. The airplane was a very old Boeing 707 which had been relegated to short range service. I was seated on the left, close to the wing trailing edge. During the takeoff run I noticed a substantial jet of fuel streaming aft over the wing, emanating from what was clearly a crack in the upper wing skin. After the flaps were retracted the leak disappeared, probably due to the changing root bending moment. When the fasten-seat-belt sign was turned off I asked the flight attendant to request that one of the pilots come see me about a potentially serious problem. Pretty soon a pilot, who had been occupying the jump seat in the cockpit, came over. After identifying myself I explained what I just saw. I suggested that someone from the crew sit next to me during landing because I believed that the phenomenon would repeat itself. I also suggested that the airplane be grounded following landing at St.Louis. Finally, I urged him to convince the pilot in command not to use reverse thrust on landing because that might result in a fire.

During the landing groundrun the crack dutifully opened up again and the fuel gusher began. The pilot said that at first he wasn't sure whether or not to believe me. Personally seeing the fuel stream aft convinced him that there was a problem. The airplane was grounded.

Lesson: This crack had been missed in previous inspections. Looking for cracks in a geriatric airplane requires vigilance on the part of the inspectors.

Figure 210 Prototype of the Boeing 747-400, Combi (Courtesy Boeing)

Figure 211 Boeing 737-300 (With Permission from the Royal Aeronautical Society Library)

Figure 212 Lockheed C-141, Starlifter (Courtesy Lockheed-Martin)

Figure 213 Artist Impression of the Experimental NASA QSRA Airplane (Courtesy NASA)

Figure 214 Model of the Prototype Fokker F-100

Figure 215 Prototype of the Boeing 767 (Courtesy Boeing)

Figure 216 McDonnell Douglas MD80 (Courtesy Boeing)

Figure 217 McDonnell Douglas F-4 (With Permission from the Royal Aeronautical Society Library)

Figure 218 Ultralight Built at KU

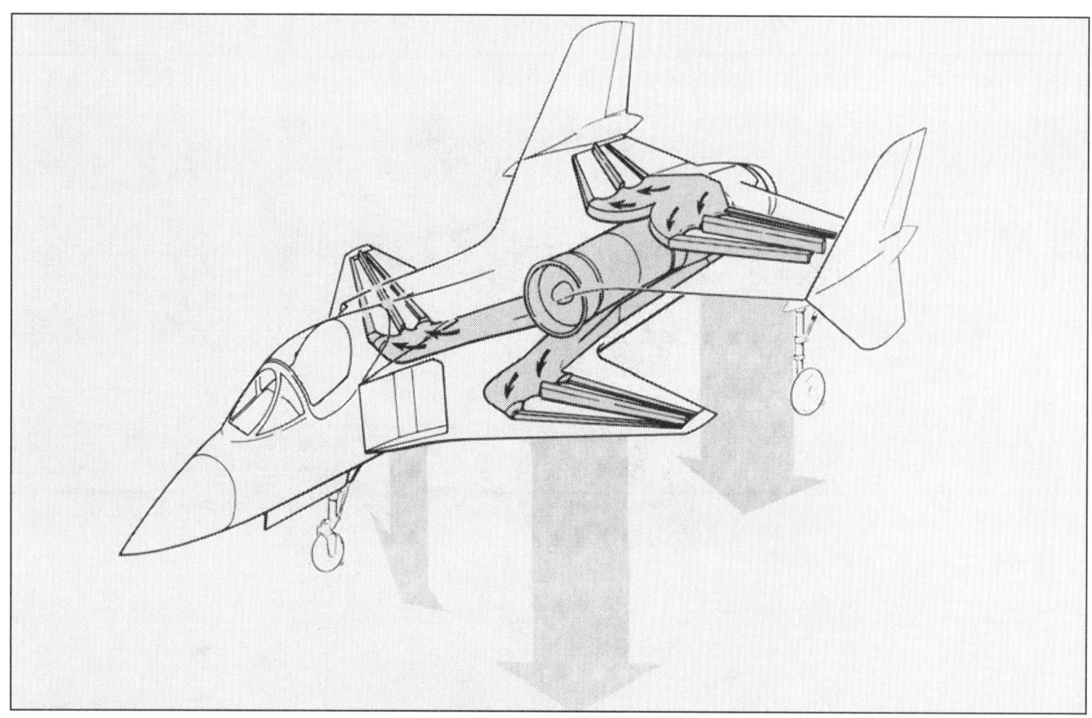

Figure 219 Schematic of the XFV-112 (Courtesy North American, Columbus)

Figure 220 Early Version of the McDonnell-Douglas F-18, Hornet (Courtesy Boeing)

Figure 221 Piper Apache (With Permission from the Royal Aeronautical Society Library)

Figure 222 Lockheed SR71 (With Permission from the Royal Aeronautical Society Library)

Postlude

My sister and I were very lucky to be able to enjoy our parents long after my dad retired in 1970. Mams and Paps, as we called them, built their retirement home in the city of Geel, Belgium. They enjoyed themselves with their garden and with playing a lot of tennis. My dad passed away in 1998, shortly after his 95th birthday. My mother followed him in 1999, shortly before her 91st birthday. They were married for 59 years! We miss them both, very much indeed.

I have been very fortunate to have been involved in so many different airplane projects. Appendix C gives a summary listing.

For young aeronautical engineers who aspire to become airplane designers I would like to offer the following suggestions:

1. Read, read and read some more. This goes not only for professional books and magazines but also for ANY aeronautical publication you can get your hands on. Detailed knowledge of what was tried in past airplane design and development programs is an essential attribute of airplane designers.

2. Learn to fly. It is important to have some appreciation of what pilots have to cope with.

3. Do not yield to the temptation to become a specialist.

4. Conduct yourself as a professional. Always be truthful.

5. Join professional organizations and be active in them. In the airplane business that means AIAA and SAE as a minimum.

6. Always try to do your work right the first time.

Everything comes to an end. I will be retiring from The University of Kansas on December 31, 2003. It has been a great privilege to have been able to influence the professional lives of hundreds of aerospace professionals.

Artist's Rendition of the Safire S-26 (Courtesy Safire Aircraft)

References

1. Francillon, R.J.; McDonnell Douglas Aircraft since 1920; Putnam & Co., Ltd; London, United Kingdom, 1979.
2. Jackson, A.J.; De Havilland Aircraft since 1909; Putnam & Co., Ltd; London, United Kingdom, 1978.
3. Bowers, P.M.; Boeing Aircraft since 1916; Putnam & Co., Ltd; London, United Kingdom, 1966.
4. Hegener, H.; Fokker - The Man and the Aircraft; Harleyford Publications Ltd.; United Kingdom, 1961.
5. Van Ishoven, A.; Messerschmitt, Aircraft Designer; Gentry Books; London, United Kingdom, 1975.
6. Schmitt, G.; Hugo Junkers and his Aircraft; Transpress; Berlin, Germany, 1988.
7. Green, W.; Warplanes of the Third Reich; Doubleday & Co.; N.Y., USA, 1976.
8. Jackson, A.J.; AVRO Aircraft since 1908; Putnam & Co., Ltd; London, United Kingdom, 1965.
9. Mason, F.K.; Hawker Aircraft since 1909; Putnam & Co., Ltd; London, United Kingdom, 1961.
10. Kooy, J.M.J. and Uytenbogaart, J.W.H.; Ballistics of the Future; McGraw-Hill Book Co.; NY, USA, 1946.
11. Wegg, J,; General Dynamics Aircraft and Their Predecessors; Putnam & Co., Ltd; London, United Kingdom, 1990.
12. Avery, N.; North American Aircraft 1934-1998, Volume I; Narkiewicz/Thompson; Santa Ana, CA, USA, 1998.
13. Stoff, J.; The Thunder Factory (History of Republic Aviation Corp.); Motorbooks International; Osceola, WI, 1990.
14. Francillon, R.J.; Lockheed Aircraft since 1913; Putnam & Co., Ltd; London, United Kingdom, 1982.
15. Francillon, R.J.; Grumman Aircraft since 1929; Putnam & Co., Ltd; London, United Kingdom, 1989.
16. Moran, G.P.; The Corsair and other Aeroplanes Vought; Aviation Heritage Books; Terre Haute, IN, 1991.

17. James, D.N.; Gloster Aircraft since 1917; Putnam & Co., Ltd; London, United Kingdom, 1971.
18. Andrews, C.F. and Morgan, E.B.; Supermarine Aircraft since 1914; Putnam & Co., Ltd; London, United Kingdom, 1981.
19. Breihan, J.R., Piet, S. and Mason, R.S.; Martin Aircraft 1909-1960; Narkiewicz/Thompson, Santa Ana, CA, USA, 1995.
20. Rodengen, J.L.; The Legend of Cessna; Write Stuff Enterprises, Inc.; Ft. Lauderdale, FL, USA, 1998.
21. Ransom, S. and Fairclough, R.; English Electric Aircraft and Their Predecessors; Putnam & Co., Ltd; London, United Kingdom, 1987.
22. Heineman, E.H. and Rausa, R.; Ed Heineman, Combat Aircraft Designer; Naval Institute Press; Annapolis; MD, USA, 1980.
23. Silvester, J.; Percival & Hunting Aircraft; R.J. Silvester; Luton, United Kingdom, 1987.
24. Phillips, E. H.; Piper, a Legend Aloft; Flying Books International; Eagan, MN, USA, 1993.
25. Taylor, H.A.; Airspeed Aircraft since 1931; Putnam & Co., Ltd; London, United Kingdom, 1970.
26. Mitchell, K.A.; Fairchild Aircraft 1926-1987; Narkiewicz/Thompson; Santa Ana, CA, USA, 1997.
27. Van Wijngaarden, P.; Van Aviolanda tot Fokker (in Dutch); De Klaroen; Alblasserdam, The Netherlands, 1987.
28. Downie, D. and J.; Rutan Aircraft; Tab Books Inc.; Blue Ridge Summit, PA, USA, 1987.
29. Bruhn, E.F.; Analysis and Design of Flight Vehicle Structures; Tri-State Offset Company; USA, 1973.
30. Creed, R.; PBY The Catalina Flying Boat; Naval Institute Press; Annapolis, MD, USA, 1985.
31. Thompson, W.D.; Cessna Wings for the World (Single Engine Airplanes); Thompson Aero Products; Bella Vista, AR, USA, 1991.
32. Thompson, W.D.; Cessna Wings for the World II (300 Series Twins); Thompson Aero Products; Bella Vista, AR, USA, 1995.

33. Thompson, W.D.; Cessna Wings for the World III (400 Series Twins); Thompson Aero Products; Bella Vista, AR, USA, 2000.
34. McGrogan, D. et al; Legacy of Leadership; TWA Flight Operations Department; 1971.
35. Kolk, R.; Modern Flight Dynamics; Prentice-Hall, Inc.; Englewood Cliffs, NJ, USA, 1961.
36. Hunsaker, J.C.; Dynamic Stability of Airplanes; Smithsonian Miscellaneous Collection, Vol.62, No.5, June 1916.
37. Pelletier, A.J.; Beech Aircraft and Their Predecessors; Putnam & Co., Ltd; London, United Kingdom, 1995.
38. Schweizer, W.; Soaring with the Schweizers; Rivilo Books; Falls Church, VA, USA, 1991.
39. Robinson, D.H. and Keller, C.L.; Up Ship; Naval Institute Press; Annapolis, MD, USA, 1982.
40. Robinson, D.H.; Giants in the Sky, a History of the Rigid Airship; University of Washington Press; Seattle, WA, USA, 1973.
41. Burgess, C.P.; Airship Design; The Ronald Press Co.; NY, USA, 1927.
42. Cook, W.H.; The Road to the 707; TYC Publishing Co.; Bellevue, WA, USA, 1991.
43. Roskam, J.; Airplane Flight Dynamics and Automatic Flight Controls; Parts I and II; DARcorporation; 120 East Ninth Street, Suite 2, Lawrence, Kansas 66044.
44. Students of Professor Van der Neut; Contributions to the Theory of Aircraft Structures; Delft University Press; Delft, The Netherlands, 1972.
45. Ingells, D.J.; Tin Goose, the Fabulous Ford Tri-motor; Aero Publishers, Inc.; Fallbrook, CA, USA, 1968.
46. Roskam, J.; Methods for Estimating Drag Polars of Subsonic Airplanes; University of Kansas Printing Service; Lawrence, KS, USA, 1971.
47. Roskam, J.; Methods for Estimating Stability and Control Derivatives of Subsonic Airplanes; University of Kansas Printing Service; Lawrence, Kansas , USA, 1971.
48. Etkin, B.; Dynamics of Flight; John Wiley & Sons; NY, NY, USA, 1959.
49. Roskam, J.; Flight Dynamics of Rigid and Elastic Airplanes, Volume I; Roskam Aviation and Engineering Corporation*; Lawrence, KS, USA, 1972.

50. Roskam, J.; Flight Dynamics of Rigid and Elastic Airplanes, Volume II; Roskam Aviation and Engineering Corporation*; Lawrence, KS, USA, 1972.
51. Lan, C.T. and Roskam, J.; Airplane Aerodynamics and Performance; Roskam Aviation and Engineering Corporation*; Lawrence, KS, USA, 1980.
52. Andersson, H.G.; SAAB Aircraft since 1937; Putnam & Co., Ltd; London, United Kingdom, 1989.
53. Et al; The Future of Aeronautics; The University of Kansas Printing Service, Lawrence, KS, USA, 1974.
54. Roskam, J.; Airplane Design, Part I: Preliminary Sizing of Airplanes; Roskam Aviation and Engineering Corporation*; Lawrence, KS, USA, 1985.
55. Roskam, J.; Airplane Design, Part II: Preliminary Configuration Design and Integration of the Propulsion System; Roskam Aviation and Engineering Corporation*; Lawrence, KS, USA, 1985.
56. Roskam, J.; Airplane Design, Part III: Layout Design of Cockpit, Fuselage, Wing and Empennage: Cutaways and Inboard Profiles; Roskam Aviation and Engineering Corporation*; Lawrence, KS, USA, 1986.
57. Roskam, J.; Airplane Design, Part IV: Layout Design of Landing Gear and Systems; Roskam Aviation and Engineering Corporation*; Lawrence, KS, USA, 1986.
58. Roskam, J.; Airplane Design, Part V: Component Weight Estimation; Roskam Aviation and Engineering Corporation*; Lawrence, KS, USA, 1985.
59. Roskam, J.; Airplane Design, Part VI: Preliminary Calculation of Aerodynamic, Thrust and Power Characteristics; Roskam Aviation and Engineering Corporation*; Lawrence, KS, USA, 1987.
60. Roskam, J.; Airplane Design, Part VII: Determination of Stability, Control and Performance Characteristics: FAR and Military Requirements; Roskam Aviation and Engineering Corporation*; Lawrence, KS, USA, 1988.
61. Roskam, J.; Airplane Design, Part VIII: Airplane Cost Estimation: Design, Development, Manufacturing and Operating; Roskam Aviation and Engineering Corporation*; Lawrence, KS, USA, 1990.

62. Golley, J.; Whittle, the True Story; Smithsonian Institution Press; Washington, DC, USA, 1987.
63. Dayton-Cincinnati Section of AIAA; Celebration of the Golden Anniversary of Jet Powered Flight, 1939-1989; USA, 1989.
64. Conner, M.; Hans von Ohain, Elegance in Flight; AIAA, Reston, VA, 2001.
65. Kranzhoff, J.A.; Arado, History of an Aircraft Company; Schiffer Publishing Ltd.; Atgen, PA, USA, 1997.
66. Cubitt, D. and Ellis, K.; Vulcan, Last of the V-Bombers; Reed Consumer Books, London, United Kingdom, 1993.
67. Mooney, Al and Baxter, G,; The Al Mooney Story; Shearer Publishing; Fredericksburg, TX, USA, 1985.
68. Pelletier, A.J.; Bell Aircraft since 1935; Putnam & Co., Ltd; London, United Kingdom, 1992.
69. Rashke, R.; Stormy Genius, the Life of Aviation's Maverick, Bill Lear; Houghton Miffin Co.; Boston, MA, USA, 1985.
70. Combs, H.; Kill Devil Hill; Tern Style Press, LTd.; Englewood, CO, USA, 1979.
71. Thompson, W.D.; A Test Pilot's Life; Maverick Publications; Bend, OR, USA, 1997.
72. Diederich, F.W. and Budiansky, B.; Divergence of Swept Wings; NACA TN 1680, August, 1948.
73. Brown, Captain E.; Wings of the Weird and Wonderful, Volumes 1 and 2; Airlife Publishing Ltd.; England, 1985.

---

* These books are now sold through DARcorporation, 120 East Ninth Street, Suite 2, Lawrence, Kansas 66044, USA (http://www.darcorp.com)

References

Appendix A: Published Books, Articles and Papers

1. *A Simplified Method to Identify and Cure Roll Coupling; Journal of the Aerospace Sciences*, Vol. 29, No. 5, May 1962.

2. On Some Linear and Nonlinear Stability and Response Characteristics of Rigid Airplanes and a New Method to Integrate Nonlinear, Ordinary Differential Equations; PhD dissertation, The University of Washington, Seattle, WA, 1965.

3. *A New Method for Numerical Integration of Airplane Equations of Motion; Journal of Aircraft*, Vol. 2, No. 1, Jan.-Feb. 1965.

4. Validity of Linearized Equations of Motion for Elastic Airplanes; paper presented at the Boeing Aerodynamics Technology Forum, Renton, WA, Dec. 19-20, 1966.

5. Preliminary Investigation of Lateral-Directional Dynamic Stability Characteristics of the Cessna Model 421; CRES-FRL Report 67-002, Dec., 1967.

6. Development and Use of Elastic Wind-Tunnel Models in Predicting Longitudinal Stability Derivatives of Elastic Airplanes (co-authored with T. Holgate and G. Shimizu); AIAA No. 68-56, AIAA 6th Aerospace Sciences Meeting, NY, Jan. 22-24, 1968.

7. Equations of Motion for Elastic Airplanes; Proceedings of the Seminar on Elastic Airplane Stability, Control and Response; The University of Kansas, Lawrence, KS, June 1968.

8. Stability Derivatives for Elastic Airplanes: Interpretation and Use; Proceedings of the Seminar on Elastic Airplane Stability, Control and Response; The University of Kansas, Lawrence, KS, June 1968.

9. An Investigation of Methods for Estimating Roll Rate Stability Derivatives of Airplanes (co-authored with A.R. Mulally, C.W. Sapp and J.D. Young); CRES-FRL Report 68-005, July, 1968.

10. A program for Digital Computation of Static and Dynamic Longitudinal Stability Parameters of Propeller Driven Aircraft (co-authored with S.A. Henry); CRES-FRL Report 68-008, Oct., 1968.

11. A Preliminary Design Study of a Light Airplane Configuration with a Pusher Propeller (co-authored with R.C. Colwell and R.D. Agler); CRES-FRL Report 68-009, Oct., 1968.

12. *Elastic Wind Tunnel Models for Predicting Longitudinal Stability Derivatives of Elastic Airplanes* (co-authored by T. Holgate and G. Shimizu); *Journal of Aircraft*, Nov.-Dec. 1968.

13. An Influence Coefficient Method for the Prediction of Longitudinal Stability Derivatives of Rigid and Elastic Airplanes (co-authored with A. Dusto); AIAA No. 69-131, AIAA 7th Aerospace Sciences Meeting, NY, Jan. 20-22, 1969.

14. Comments, Interpretation and Application of a Method for Predicting Aerodynamic Characteristics of Large, Flexible Airplanes; 34th Meeting of the AGARD Flight Mechanics Panel, Marseille, France, April 21-24, 1969.

15. *A Method for Predicting the Longitudinal Stability Derivatives for Rigid and Elastic Airplanes* (co-authored with R. Dusto); *Journal of Aircraft*; Nov. - Dec., 1969.

16. Literature Survey of Lateral Control Spoiler Systems (co-authored by D.L. Kohlman, D. Urban and B. Gorrell); Beech Aircraft Corporation report, Jan., 1970.

17. An Assessment of Performance, Stability and Control Improvements for General Aviation Aircraft (co-authored with D.L. Kohlman); SAE 700240, SAE National Business Aircraft Meeting, March 18-20, Wichita, KS, 1970.

18. *Methods for Estimating Drag Polars of Subsonic Airplanes*; textbook published by RAEC; 1971.

19. *Methods for Estimating Stability and Control Derivatives of Conventional, Subsonic Airplanes*; textbook published by RAEC; 1971.

20. *Flight Dynamics of Rigid and Elastic Airplanes, Part I*; textbook published by RAEC; 1971.

21. *Flight Dynamics of Rigid and Elastic Airplanes, Part II*; textbook published by RAEC; 1971.

22. A Review of the University of Kansas Light Airplane Research Program; SAE 710379, SAE National Business Aircraft Meeting, Wichita, KS, March 24-26, 1971.

23. Preliminary Results of Some Experiments with a Vortex Augmented Wing; (co-authored with M. Gleason); SAE 720321; SAE National Business Aircraft Meeting, Wichita, KS, March 15-17, 1972.

24. Wind Tunnel Data Report on a Hinge Moment and Force Test on a Cessna 210 Half Wing Model; (co-authored with several students); CRINC-FRL Report 72-002; March 1972.

25. Wind Tunnel Data Report on a Force and Moment Test of Separate Surface Ailerons and Rudders on a Cessna 210 Model (co-authored with several students); CRINC-FRL Report 72-003; April 1972.

26. Analysis Report on Wind Tunnel tests of Separate Surface Ailerons and Rudders on Cessna 210 Models (co-authored with several students); CRINC-FRL Report 72-005; May 1972.

27. A Survey of Actuating and Sensing Equipment for General Aviation Airplanes (co-authored with several students); CRINC-FRL Report 72-009; August 1972.

28. Simulating the Airplane Design Environment in the Classroom; Event 1240, American Society for Engineering Education, Annual Conference, Lubbock, TX, June 19-22, 1972.

29. A Computer Program for Calculating α- and q- Stability Derivatives and Induced Drag for Thin Elastic Airplanes at Subsonic and Supersonic Speeds (co-authored with C. T. Lan and S. Mehrotra); NASA CR-112229, Oct., 1972.

30. Method for Computing the Structural Influence Coefficient Matrix of Nonplanar Wing-Body-Tail Configurations (co-authored with H.W. Smith and G. Gibson); NASA CR-112230, Oct., 1972.

31. Method for Computing the Aerodynamic Influence Coefficient Matrix of Nonplanar Wing-Body-Tail Configurations (co-authored with C.T. Lan and S. Mehrotra); NASA CR-112231, Oct., 1972.

32. Procedures Used to Determine the Mass Distribution for Idealized Low Aspect Ratio Two Spar Fighter Wings (co-authored with F.R. Hamler and D. Reynolds); NASA CR-112232, Oct., 1972.

33. Procedures Used to Determine the Structural Representation for Idealized Low Aspect Ratio Two Spar Fighter Wings (co-authored with C.T. Lan, H.W. Smith and G. Gibson); NASA CR-112233, Oct., 1972.

34. *Leading-Edge Force Features of the Aerodynamic Finite Element Method* (co-authored with C.T. Lan); *Journal of Aircraft*, Vol. 9, No.12, Dec., 1972.

35. Steady State Equations of Motion, Equilibrium Shape and Stability Derivatives of Elastic Airplanes Evaluated with Finite Element Methods; pages 305-323 in the book: *Contributions to the Theory of Aircraft Structures*; published in honor of Prof. Dr. Ir. A Van Der Neut by Delft University Press, The Netherlands, 1972.

36. A Parametric Study of Planform and Aeroelastic Effects on Aerodynamic Center, α- and q- Stability Derivatives (co-authored with C.T. Lan); NASA CR-2117; April 1973.

37. Separate Surfaces for Automatic Flight Controls (co-authored with M.R. Barber and P.C. Loschke); SAE 730304, SAE Business Aircraft Meeting, Wichita, KS, April, 1973.

38. An Approach to the Synthesis of Separate Surface Automatic Flight Control Systems (co-authored with Henry, S.A.); AIAA 73-834, AIAA Guidance and Control Conference, Key Biscayne, FL, Aug., 1973.

39. A New Approach to Aircraft Design Education; AIAA 73-787, AIAA 5th Aircraft Design, Flight Test and Operations Meeting, St. Louis, MO, Aug. 6-8, 1973.

40. The Grudging Progress of Lightplane Design (co-authored with D.L. Kohlman); Air Progress, Vol. 34, Jan., 1974.

41. New Airfoils and Higher Wing Loadings: A New Look at General Aviation Airplane Design; paper presented at the Technological University of Delft, The Netherlands, May 20, 1974.

42. Design Philosophy and Hardware Implementation of Separate Surface Automatic Flight Control Systems; paper presented at the Technological University of Delft, The Netherlands, May 21, 1974.

43. A Study of M35 Yaw Damper Performance in a High Inertia Approach Configuration; Gates Learjet Report 26-D288, June, 1974.

44. Spoilers for Roll Control of Light Airplanes (co-authored with D.L. Kohlman and W.H. Wentz); AIAA 74-861, AIAA Mechanics and Control of Flight Conference, Anaheim, CA, July, 1974.

45. Flight Test Results of a Separate Surface Wing-Leveling System; SAE 740369, SAE Business Aircraft Meeting, April 2-5, Wichita, KS, 1974.

46. *Synthesis of a Separate Surface Wing Leveler* (co-authored with S. Henry); *Journal of Aircraft*, Vol. 11, No. 11, Nov., 1974.

47. An Analysis of Lateral Autopilot Modes; Gates Learjet Report 26-D294, Nov., 1974.

48. Opportunities for Progress in General Aviation Technology; AIAA 75-292, AIAA 11th Annual Meeting and Technical Display, Washington, D.C., Feb. 24-26, 1975.

49. Simulation and Simulator Development of a Separate Surface Attitude Command Control System for Light Aircraft; AGARD Flight Mechanics Panel and Guidance and Control Panel Joint Symposium; The Hague, The Netherlands, Oct. 20-24, 1975.

50. Some Comments on Fuselage Drag; NASA/Industry/University General Aviation Drag Reduction Workshop, The University of Kansas, Lawrence, KS, July 14-16, 1975.

51. Some Comments on Trim Drag; NASA/Industry/University General Aviation Drag Reduction Workshop, The University of Kansas, Lawrence, KS, July 14-16, 1975.

52. Drag of the Complete Configuration; NASA/Industry/University General Aviation Drag Reduction Workshop, The University of Kansas, Lawrence, KS, July 14-16, 1975.

53. Proceedings of the NASA/Industry/University General Aviation Drag Reduction Workshop; (edited by J. Roskam); Space Technology Center, The University of Kansas, Lawrence, KS, July 14-16, 1975.

54. Handbook of Aircraft Design Data, Part I, Aircraft Cutaway Drawings; Published by the Department of Aerospace Engineering, The University of Kansas, 1975.

55. Review of the General Aviation Drag Reduction Workshop; SAE 760483, Business Aircraft Meeting, April 6-9, Wichita, KS, 1976.

56. Flight Test Evaluation of a Separate Surface Attitude Command Control System on a Beech 99 Airplane; (co-authored with S.W. Gee, G.E. Jenks and R.L. Stone); AIAA Guidance and Control Conference, San Diego, CA, Aug. 16-18, 1976.

57. *Design for Minimum Fuselage Drag*; (co-authored with G. Fillman); *Journal of Aircraft*, Vol. 13, No. 8, August 1976.

58. Handbook of Aircraft Design Data, Part II, Aircraft Specification Tables; published by the Department of Aerospace Engineering, The University of Kansas, 1976.

59. Handbook of Aircraft Design Data, Part III, Fuselage and Cockpit Arrangements and Interior Dimensions; published by the Department of Aerospace Engineering, The University of Kansas, 1976.

60. *Designing the 1985 VATLIT*; *Journal of Astronautics and Aeronautics*, Oct., 1976.

61. General Aviation Feedback Control Technology Outline; (co-authored with G.E. Jenks); General Aviation Feedback Control Technology Seminar, Wichita, KS, Dec. 1-2, 1976.

62. Applying Advanced Technology to the Corporate Turboprop; *Professional Pilot Magazine*, March, 1977.

63. Utilization of Separate Surface Control Systems on General Aviation Airplanes; SAE 770471, SAE Business Aircraft Meeting, March 29 - April 1, Wichita, KS, 1977.

64. Flight Test Results for a Separate Surface Stability Augmented Beech Model 99 (co-authored with G.E. Jenks and S. Henry); NASA CR-143839, April 1977.

65. Fuselage Shape Simulation for Parametric Design Analyses (co-authored with R.D. Wyatt); AIAA General Aviation Technology Fest, Wichita, KS, Nov. 18-19, 1977.

66. Special Topics in Airplane Stability and Control; 180-page text written for a KU Short Course and printed by The University of Kansas Printing Service; May, 1978.

67. Review of Feedback Technology with Applications; 175-page text written for a KU Short Course and printed by The University of Kansas Printing Service; May, 1978.

68. Linear or Non-linear Analysis Methods: When and How?; AGARD Conference on Dynamic Stability Parameters, Preprint No. 235; Athens, Greece, May 22-24, 1978.

69. Some Noise Transmission Loss Characteristics of Typical General Aviation Structural Materials (co-authored with C.P.G. van Dam and F. Grosveld); AIAA 78-1480, AIAA Aircraft Systems and Technology Conference, Los Angeles, CA, Aug. 21-23, 1978.

70. A Comparison of Hydraulic, Pneumatic, and Electro-Mechanical Actuators for General Aviation Flight Control (co-authored with M. Rice and H. Eysink); SAE 790623, SAE Business Aircraft Meeting and Exposition, Wichita, KS, April 3-6, 1979.

71. Design Description of a Four-Place Business Jet Using Two WR-19 Engines; SAE 790580; SAE Business Aircraft Meeting and Exposition, Wichita, KS, April 3-6, 1979.

72. Summary of Noise Reduction Characteristics of Typical General Aviation Materials (co-authored with F. Grosveld and J. van Aken); SAE 790627, SAE Business Aircraft Meeting and Exposition, Wichita, KS, April 3-6, 1979.

73. *Airplane Flight Dynamics and Automatic Flight Controls, Part I*; textbook published by RAEC, 1979.

74. *Airplane Flight Dynamics and Automatic Flight Controls, Part II*; textbook published by RAEC, 1979.

75. Structural Parameters that Influence the Noise Reduction Characteristics of Typical General Aviation Materials (co-authored with F. Grosveld); AIAA 80-0038; AIAA 18th Aerospace Sciences Meeting, Pasadena, CA, Jan. 14-16, 1980.

76. Correlation of Predicted Longitudinal Aerodynamic Characteristics with Full-Scale Wind Tunnel Data on the ATLIT Airplane (co-authored with C.P.G. van Dam and M. Griswold); AIAA 80-0186, AIAA 18th Aerospace Sciences Meeting, Pasadena, CA, Jan. 14-16, 1980.

77. Forward Swept Wings and Business Airplanes; SAE 800605, SAE Turbine Powered Executive Aircraft Meeting, Phoenix, AZ, April 9-11, 1980.

78. Noise Reduction Characteristics of General Aviation Type Dual Pane Windows (co-authored with R. Navaneethan and F. Grosveld); AIAA 80-1874, AIAA Aircraft Systems Meeting, Anaheim, CA, August 4-6, 1980.

79. Preliminary Design of a Very Advanced Technology, Light Twin for the Mid-80's (co-authored by F. Grosveld, B. van Keppel, J. Eysink and A. van der Hoeven); AIAA 80-1862, AIAA Aircraft Systems Meeting, Aug. 4-6, Anaheim, CA, 1980.

80. The State of the Art of General Aviation Autopilots: Now and in the Future; (co-authored with M.J. See); SAE 810582, SAE Business Aircraft Meeting & Exposition, Wichita, KS, April 7-10, 1981.

81. Development of a Simple, Self-Contained Flight Test Data Acquisition Set (co-authored with R.R.L. Renz, R. Clarke, M.A. Mosser and D. Rummer); SAE 810596, SAE Business Aircraft Meeting & Exposition, Wichita, KS, April 7-10, 1981.

82. Comparison of Selected Lift and Sideslip Characteristics of the Ayres Thrush S2R-800, Winglets-Off and Winglets-On, to Full-Scale Wind-Tunnel Data (co-authored with M. Williams); NASA CR 165710, April, 1981.

83. *Longitudinal Characteristics of the ATLIT Airplane* (co-authored with C.P.G. van Dam and M. Griswold); *Journal of Aircraft*, Vol. 18, No. 6, June, 1981.

84. *Airplane Aerodynamics and Performance*; (co-authored with C.T. Lan); textbook published by RAEC, 1981.

85. Forward Swept Wings and Commuter Airplanes; Proceedings of the International Conference on Forward Swept Wing Aircraft; Bristol, United Kingdom, March 24-26, 1982.

86. Unconventional Commuter Configurations: A Design Investigation (co-authored with R. Srivatsan); SAE 830710, SAE Business Aircraft Meeting & Exposition, Wichita, KS, April 12-15, 1983.

87. AE Educational Design Imperatives; Astronautics and Aeronautics, June, 1983.

88. *Use of Differential Pressure Feedback in an Automatic Flight Control System* (co-authored with D.W. Levy; *Journal of Guidance and Control*, Vol. 7, No. 2, March-April 1984.

89. *Airplane Design, Part I: Preliminary Sizing of Airplanes*; textbook published by RAEC; 1985.

90. *Airplane Design, Part II: Preliminary Configuration Design and Integration of the Propulsion System*; textbook published by RAEC, 1985.

91. *Airplane Design, Part V: Component Weight Estimation*; textbook published by RAEC, 1985.

92. Aircraft Design Education at The University of Kansas; AIAA 86-2636, 1986.

93. Canards, Composites Coming of Age; *Professional Pilot Magazine*; Feb., 1986.

94. *Airplane Design, Part III: Layout Design of Cockpit, Fuselage, Wing and Empennage: Cutaways and Inboard Profiles*; textbook published by RAEC, 1986.

95. *Airplane Design, Part IV: Layout Design of Landing Gear and Systems*; textbook published by RAEC, 1986.

96. *Rapid Sizing Method for Airplanes; Journal of Aircraft*, Vol. 23, No.7; July, 1986.

97. *Airplane Design, Part VI: Preliminary Calculation of Aerodynamic, Thrust and Power Characteristics*; textbook published by RAEC, 1987.

98. The Family Concept; (co-authored with T. Creighton); *Professional Pilot Magazine*, Jan., 1988.

99. *Airplane Design, Part VII: Determination of Stability, Control and Performance Characteristics: FAR and Military Requirements*; textbook published by RAEC, 1988.

100. The Role of Regulations in Aircraft Design Education; AIAA 88-4485, 1988.

101. What Drives Unique Configurations?; SAE 881353, SAE Aerospace Technology Conference and Exposition, Anaheim, CA, Oct. 3-6, 1988.

102. Aft CG and its Effect on Flight Characteristics; *Professional Pilot Magazine*, Dec., 1988.

103. Forward CG Problems; *Professional Pilot Magazine*, Jan., 1989.

104. Problems of High Gross Weight; *Professional Pilot Magazine*, March 1989.

105. Airplane Stability and Control: Past, Present and Future; AIAA Long Island Section, NY, NY, March 16, 1989.

106. Automated Aircraft Configuration Design and Analysis (co-authored with S.Malaek); SAE 891072; SAE General Aviation Aircraft Meeting and Exposition, Wichita, Kansas, April 11-13, 1989.

107. A Family of Low Cost Ground Attack Fighters (co-authored with J. Tuschhoff); AIAA Aircraft Design and Operations Meeting, Seattle, WA, Aug. 2, 1989.

108. Things the Pros Should Know About High Angle of Attack; *Professional Pilot Magazine*, Aug., 1989.

109. *Airplane Design, Part VIII: Airplane Cost Estimation: Design, Development, Manufacturing and Operating*; textbook published by RAEC, 1990.

110. On the Economic Feasibility of Composite (Staged) SST Configurations (co-authored with D. Rogers); NASA Workshop on Innovative Aerodynamics for High Speed Transports; NASA Langley, VA., March 21-23, 1990.

111. Genesis of an Airplane, *Professional Pilot Magazine*, p.70-73, June 1990.

112. The B-2 Bomber: Why? How? and Is it Affordable?; Meeting Proceedings, the Dutch Association for Aeronautical Technology (NVLR), Amsterdam, The Netherlands, July 5, 1990.

113. AAA (Advanced Aircraft Analysis: A User-Friendly Approach to Preliminary Aircraft Design (co-authored with S.M. Malaek and W. Anemaat); 17th ICAS Congress (International Congress of the Aeronautical Sciences), ICAS Paper 2.10.2, Stockholm, Sweden, Sept. 10-14, 1990.

114. What is Needed to Teach Aeronautical Engineering Students How to Design Aircraft?; AIAA 90-3257-CP; AIAA/AHS/ASEE Aircraft Design, Systems and Operations Conference; Dayton, OH, Sept. 17-19, 1990.

115. Preliminary Design of a Supersonic Short Takeoff and Vertical Landing (STOVL) Fighter Aircraft (co-authored with B. Cox); AIAA/AHS/ASEE Aircraft Design, Systems and Operations Conference, Dayton, OH, Sept. 17-19, 1990.

116. Study of the Economic Feasibility of Composite (=Staged) SST Configurations (co-authored with D. Rogers); SAE 901989, SAE Aerospace Technology Conference and Exposition, Long Beach, CA, Oct. 1-4, 1990.

117. Flying Wings; *Professional Pilot Magazine*, p.44-48, Oct., 1990.

118. History of Aircraft Stability and Control; 66th SAE Control and Guidance Technical Committee Meeting, Cape Cod, MA, Oct. 10-12, 1990.

119. Aerodynamic Design Considerations for the Northrop B-2 Bomber; M.I.T. Forum, Massachusetts Institute of Technology, Cambridge, MA, Feb. 20, 1991.

120. Design Developments for Advanced General Aviation Aircraft (co-authored with C. Gomer); SAE 911022, SAE General, Corporate, & Regional Aviation Meeting & Exposition, Wichita, KS, April 9-11, 1991.

121. On the Feasibility of Small, Transcontinental Commuter Aircraft (co-authored with K. Wetzel); SAE 911023; SAE General, Corporate & Regional Aviation Meeting & Exposition, Wichita, KS, April 9-11, 1991.

122. Design Integration Decision Making: What Should be Taught?; SAE Aerotech Atlantic Meeting, Dayton, OH, April 25-26, 1991.

123. *Evolution of Airplane Stability and Control: A Designer's Viewpoint; Journal of Guidance, Control and Dynamics*; Volume 14, Number 3, May-June 1991, pp. 481-491.

124. Commercial Aircraft Design Opportunities in the New South Africa; Keynote address delivered to the Third Aeronautical Engineering Conference, Pretoria, Republic of South Africa, Aug. 14-16, 1991.

125. A Revolutionary Approach to General Aviation Airplane Design (co-authored with C. Gomer); AIAA-91-3126, AIAA Aircraft Design Systems and Operations Meeting, Baltimore, MD, Sept. 23-25, 1991.

126. Configuration Design and Recovery Considerations for a Staged SST (co-authored with N. Mills and T. Lawson); SAE 912232, Aerospace Technology Conference and Exposition, Long Beach, CA, Sept. 23-26, 1991.

127. On the Feasibility of Very Long Range, Small Civil Transports (VLRSCT) (co-authored with K. Wetzel); AIAA-91-3078, AIAA Aircraft Design Systems and Operations Meeting, Baltimore, MD, Sept. 23-25, 1991.

128. Design Developments for Advanced General Aviation Aircraft (co-authored with C. Gomer), SAE 911022, SAE Aerotech Conference, Long Beach, CA, Sept. 24-27, 1991.

129. Aircraft Design: Where Does It Stand?; *Aerospace America*, Sept., 1991.

130. New Design for SST's: The Staged Approach; *Professional Pilot Magazine*, pp.56-60, June 1991.

131. Imagination in New Aircraft Design; *Professional Pilot Magazine*, pp.68-72, Oct., 1991.

132. Wing Loading and Thrust-to-weight Ratio; *Professional Pilot Magazine*, pp.54-55, Nov., 1991.

133. Facing the Crisis in Aircraft Design Education; Aerospace America, pp.24-27, April, 1992.

134. Should Large Business Jets Have Four Under the Wing?; SAE 931256, SAE General, Corporate & Regional Aviation Meeting & Exposition, Wichita, KS, May, 1993.

135. Design Constraints for Oblique Wing Transports (co-authored with S.J. Smith); Workshop on Potential Impacts of Advanced Aerodynamic Technology on Air Transportation System Productivity; NASA Langley, Hampton, VA, June 29-July 1, 1993.

136. Commercial Transport Evolution and the Role of Technology, Keynote Address at the 50th Anniversary of the Department of Aerospace Engineering, The University of Kansas, April 15, 1994.

137. An Easy Way to Analyze Longitudinal and Lateral-Directional Trim Problems with AEO or OEI (co-authored with W. Anemaat); SAE 941143, Aerospace Atlantic Conference and Exposition, Dayton, OH, April 18-22, 1994.

138. Dissimilar-Sized Engines Planned for 3X-Jet (co-authored with R.J. Bacon); *Professional Pilot Magazine*, pp.58-59, Nov., 1994.

139. Ice On Your Tail Can Be Deadly, *Professional Pilot Magazine*, pp.74-76, Dec., 1994.

140. *Airplane Flight Dynamics and Automatic Flight Controls, Parts I*; 576 pages, textbook published by DARcorporation, Lawrence, KS, 1995.

141. *Airplane Flight Dynamics and Automatic Flight Controls, Parts II*; 383 pages, textbook published by DARcorporation, Lawrence, KS, 1995.

142. Making Aircraft Takeoff Friendly, *Professional Pilot Magazine*, pp.70-71, Feb., 1995.

143. The 3X Jet Engine Configuration (co-authored with R. Bacon); SAE Paper 951173, SAE General, Corporate & Regional Aviation Meeting & Exposition, Wichita, KS, May 3-5, 1995.

144. Landing Gear Takes the Load, *Professional Pilot Magazine*, pp.72-74, May 1995.

145. The 3X Jet - An Advanced Engine Configuration for Two Engine Jet Aircraft (co-authored with R. Bacon); AIAA Paper 95-3963, SAE Aerotech and AIAA Aircraft Engineering, Technology and Operations Congress, Los Angeles, CA, Sept. 18-21, 1995.

146. Industry Leaders Look Toward 1026: Visions of the next 30 years; Co-participant, *Professional Pilot Magazine*, p. 42, Jan., 1996.

147. Corporate and Regional Aircraft for the Future: Who Will be in the Cockpit?; *Professional Pilot Magazine*, pp. 84-86, Jan., 1996.

148. Reducing Concept-to-Market Time; *Professional Pilot Magazine*, pp. 66-70, Dec., 1996.

149. No More Props; *Professional Pilot Magazine*, pp. 60-66, Aug., 1997.

150. *Airplane Aerodynamics and Performance* (co-authored with C.T. Lan); 711 pages, textbook published by DARcorporation, Lawrence, KS, 1997.

151. Undergraduate Flight Dynamics Education in a PC Software Environment (co-authored with W. Anemaat); SAE Aerotech and AIAA Aircraft Engineering, World Aviation Congress, Sept., 1997, Los Angeles, CA.

152. Design and Economic Challenges of 10-20 Passenger, Jet-Powered Regional Transports; Conference on "Advanced Design Problems in Aerospace Engineering," Erice, Sicily, Italy, July 11-18, 1999.

153. User-Friendly General Aviation Airplanes: A Revolutionary but Affordable Approach; Conference on "Advanced Design Problems in Aerospace Engineering," Erice, Sicily, Italy, July 11-18, 1999.

154. *Design and Economic Challenges of 10-22 Passenger, Jet-powered Regional Transports; Aircraft Design*, Volume 3, 2000.

155. *Roskam's Airplane War Stories*; DARcorporation, 120 East Ninth Street, Suite 2, Lawrence, KS, USA, 2002.

Appendix B: Graduate Student Theses Chaired

1. Mulally, A.R.; An Investigation of Aerodynamic Design Modifications Which Lead to Performance Gains and the Preliminary Design of a New Light Aircraft; MSAE, 1969.
2. Sapp, C.W.; Experimental Investigation of the Effects of Spoilers on the Aerodynamic Characteristics of Light Aircraft; MSAE, 1969.
3. Cannon, D.; The Aerodynamic Analysis and System Synthesis for a Light Airplane with Spoilers; DEAE, 1970.
4. Colwell, R.C.; Improvement of the Performance, Stability and Control of a Current Light Aircraft; MSAE, 1970 (co-supervised with D.L. Kohlman).
5. Capron, W.R.; An Artificial Force-Feel System for a Fixed-Base Flight Simulator; MSAE, 1970.
6. Agler, R.E.; Experimental Investigation of the Influence of Wing and Spoiler Geometry on Spoiler Effectiveness for Light Aircraft; MSAE, 1970.
7. Gleason, M.; An Initial Three-Dimensional Wind Tunnel Investigation of a Vortex Augmented Wing; MSAE, 1971.
8. Mehrotra, S.C.; A Computer Program for Calculating an Aerodynamic Influence Coefficient Matrix for Thin Wings at Subsonic and Supersonic Speeds; MSAE, 1971 (co-supervised with C.T. Lan).
9. Garrett, R.E.; Experimental Investigation of High Lift Devices for a Light Aircraft; MSAE, 1972.
10. Kaul, S.K.; Wing Planform Parametric Investigation Study and Resulting Improvement in Performance of the Gates Learjet Model-25 Airplane; MSAE, 1972.
11. Henry, H.F.; Flight Test Program for a Separate Surface Stability Augmented Beech Model 99; MEAE, 1972.
12. Buss, M.W.; Flight Test Program-Attitude Command Control System with Separate Control Surfaces on Beechcraft Model 99 Airliner; MEAE, 1973.
13. Prins, J.J.M.; Flight Hardware Design and Analog Model of a SSSA Control System for a Beech Model 99 Aircraft; MSAE, 1973.
14. Bolton, W.R.; User Guide for the Flight Research Laboratory Fixed-Base Simulator; MEAE, 1973.

15. Holmes, B.; Wind Tunnel Investigation of Low Lift to Drag Ratio Wing Modifications for Steep Approaches; MSAE, 1973.
16. Probasco, M.T.; Design and Analysis of a Separate Surface Wing Leveler for a Cessna 172; MSAE, 1974.
17. Hinson, M.L.; An Iron Bird for Static Test and Performance Evaluation of a Separate Surface Attitude Command System; MSAE, 1974.
18. Siegel, W.H.; The Dirigible: A Transportation Study of Lighter-than-Air Aircraft; MSME, 1974.
19. Collins, D.J. and Bolton, W.R.; Separate Surface Stability Augmentation for General Aviation Aircraft; DEAE, 1974.
20. Henry, S.A.; Some Methods for Analyzing Aircraft with Linear Automatic Control Systems; PhDAE, 1974.
21. Schunselaar, H.L.J.; Flight Test Program for a Separate Surface Stability Augmented Beech Model 99 Airliner and An Investigation of its Turbulence Intensity Measuring System; MSAE, 1975.
22. Jenks, G. and Ashburn, M.; Implementation of an Attitude Command System Using Separate Surface Stability Augmentation on a Beech Model 99 Airplane; MEAE, 1975.
23. Holmes, B.J.; Flight Evaluation of an Advanced Technology Light Twin-Engine Airplane (ATLIT); DEAE, 1976.
24. Henderson, T.D.; Design of an Acoustic Panel Test Facility; MEAE, 1977.
25. Peschier, T.D.; General Aviation Interior Noise Study; DEAE, 1977.
26. Durenberger, D.W.; Experimental and Theoretical Sound Transmission Through Aircraft Panels; MEAE, 1978.
27. Rice, M.S.; A Study of Pneumatic and Hydraulic Actuation of a Light Airplane Control Surface; MSAE, 1978.
28. Eysink, J.F.; On the Use of Electro-Mechanical Actuators in Light General Aviation Aircraft; MEAE, 1978.
29. Andrews, D.W.; A Research Program to Study the Interior Noise Characteristics of a Light Twin; MEAE, 1978.
30. Van Keppel, Bob; A Computer Program for the Analysis of the Dynamic Stability Characteristics of Airplanes; MSAE, 1978.

31. Van Dam, C.P.G.; Noise Reduction Through a Cavity-Backed Flexible Plate; MSAE, 1978.
32. Grose, D.L.; The Development of the DAST I Remotely Piloted Research Vehicle for Flight Testing an Active Flutter Suppression Control System, DEAE, 1978.
33. Griswold, M.R.; Comparison of Theoretically Predicted Lateral-Directional Aerodynamic Characteristics with Full-Scale Wind Tunnel Data on the ATLIT Airplane; MSAE, 1980.
34. Konishi, T.; New Design Method for Automatic Flight Control Systems; PhDAE, 1980.
35. Grosveld, F.M.W.A.; Study of Typical Parameters That Affect Sound Transmission Through General Aviation Aircraft Structures; DEAE, 1980.
36. Van Aken, J.M.; The Organization of and Work Completed on the Hydrodynamic Derivatives Project at The University of Kansas Flight Research Laboratory; MSAE, 1980.
37. Van Aken, J.M., Griswold, D.A. and Burnett, J.A.; The Development of an Actuator Test Cell for the Testing of Linear and Rotary Electro-Mechanical Actuators; DEAE for Van Aken and MEAE for Griswold, 1980.
38. Navaneethan, R.; Study of Noise Reduction Characteristics of Multi-Layered Panels and Dual Pane Windows with Helmholz Resonators; MSAE, 1981.
39. Renz, R.R.L.; Development of a Simple, Self-Contained Flight Test Data Acquisition System; MEAE, 1981.
40. Navaneethan, R.; General Aviation Aircraft Interior Noise Problem: Some Suggested Solutions; DEAE, 1982.
41. Van Dam, C.P.G.; Analysis of Nonplanar Wing-Tip Mounted Lifting Surfaces on Low-Speed Airplanes; DEAE, 1982.
42. Clarke, R.; Development of a Simple, Self-Contained Flight Test Data Acquisition System; MEAE, 1982.
43. Graves, E.B.; The Feasibility of a High-Altitude Aircraft Platform System with Consideration of Technological and Societal Constraints; DEAE, 1982.
44. Levy, D.W.; Comparison of Empirical, Finite-Element, and Experimental Methods for Prediction of Aerodynamic Characteristics of a Three Lifting Surface Airplane Configuration; MSAE, 1982.

45. Blacklock Jr., C.L.; Summary of the General Powerplant, Weight and Balance, and the Aerodynamic Characteristics of an Ultralight Aircraft; MSAE, 1984.
46. Turner Hunt, J.; Experimental and Theoretical Comparisons of Two Airplanes Using a Quasi-Vortex-Lattice Method; MSAE, 1985.
47. Stevens, M.E.; An Investigation into the Vertical Axis Control Power Requirements for Landing VTOL Type Aircraft Onboard Non-Aviation Ships in Various Sea States; MSAE, 1985.
48. Rea, P.N.; "XPRFRM" An Interactive Design Program for Estimating The Preliminary Performance Characteristics of Airplanes; MEAE, 1985.
49. McAtee, T.M.; Development of a Flying Qualities Computer Program; MSAE, 1985.
50. Williams, K.L.; Natural Laminar Flow and Regional Aircraft: A Performance Assessment; MSAE, 1985.
51. Malaek, S.M.B.; Development of a Graphics/Interactive Computer Program to Analyze Dynamic Characteristics of an Airplane; MSAE, 1986.
52. Chacko, N.; Preliminary Investigation of an Advanced Short/Medium Range Propfan Powered Commercial Transport; MSAE, 1987.
53. Creighton, T.R.; Results of a Preliminary Design Study for a Family of Commuter Airplanes; MEAE, 1987.
54. Vijgen, P.M.H.W.; Incompressible Boundary-Layer Transition Flight Experiments over a Non-Axisymmetric Fuselage Forebody and Comparisons with Laminar Boundary-Layer Stability Theory; DEAE, 1988.
55. Johnson, V.S.; Life Cycle Cost in the Conceptual Design of Subsonic Commercial Aircraft; PhDAE, 1988.
56. Mills, N.D.; Preliminary Design of an Automatic In-Air Mating and Recovery System for a Staged Supersonic Transport Concept; MSAE, 1989.
57. Hendrich, L.J.; Results of a Preliminary Design Study of Two Transpacific Supersonic Civil Transports; MEAE, 1989.
58. Engelland, S.A.; Evaluation of the Longitudinal Stability and Control Characteristics of the E-7A STOVL Aircraft on Hover; MSAE, 1989
59. Malaek, S.M.B.; Development of a System of Interactive Computer Programs for Airplane Conceptual Design and Advanced Airplane Analysis; PhDAE, 1989.

60. Lampe, A.P.; The Effect of the Horizontal Location of the Main Landing Gear on the Take-Off Rotation Trajectory; MSAE, 1990.
61. Tuschhoff, J.J.; Results of a Preliminary Design Study of a Family of Three Close Air Support Aircraft; MEAE, 1990.
62. Lawson, T.C.; Configurational Design and Comparison of a Staged and Conventional Supersonic Transport; MSAE, 1992.
63. Dirkzwager, A.M.; Determination and Description of Aerodynamic Design Processes for Jet Engine Inlet, Nacelle and Exhaust Configurations, Including Development of Computer Aided Design tools; MSAE, 1992.
64. Gomer, C.O., Jr.; A Feasibility Study on In-Flight Refueling for a Commercial Transport; MSAE, 1992.
65. Greco, P.; Flight Dynamics of an Aeroelastic Forward Swept Wing Glider; MSAE, 1992.
66. Wenninger, E.A.; Results of a Study to Increase the Manufacturability and Utility of Small General Aviation Aircraft; MEAE, 1993.
67. Jones, V.; Comparative Study of a 3X and Conventional Twin Engine Installation on a Typical Medium Sized Business Jet; MSAE, 1995.
68. Smith, S.J.; Elevator Hinge Moment Parameter Identification of a Cessna 182 Using the Maximum Likelihood Estimation Method; MSAE, 1995.
69. Gerren, D.S.; Design, Analysis, and Control of a Large Transport Aircraft Utilizing Selective Engine Thrust as a Backup System for the Primary Flight Controls; PhDAE, 1995.
70. Mustan, R.S.; Development of a Take-off Simulation Algorithm and a Computer Program to Predict Take-off Rotation Behavior; MSAE, 1995.
71. Zyskowski, M.K.; An Alternate Means of Compliance for Composite Structural Fatigue Certification of Small General Aviation Aircraft; MSAE, 1997.
72. Colangelo, M.F.; A Comparative Study of a 3X Jet Regional Airliner to a Conventional Twin-Engine Regional Airliner; MSAE, 1997.
73. Svoboda, C.R., Jr.; Comparative Study of a 6X and Standard Engine Installation on the Boeing 747-400; MSAE, 1998.
74. Von Strombeck, C.; Development of a Very Long Range, Small, Civil Transport; MSAE, 1999.

75. Dunavan, M.A.; Preliminary Aircraft Sizing Using a genetic Algorithm with Varying Levels of Model Detail; MSAE, 2002

Appendix C: Airplanes Flown and Airplanes Worked on

Airplanes flown as pilot or co-pilot:

Piper J-3 (I received my Dutch private pilot license, s.e. land, on this airplane in 1952)

Frits Koolhoven FK-43

DeHavilland Beaver

Percival Prentice

Percival Pembroke

Percival Proctor

Cessna 172 (I received my US private pilot license, s.e. land, on this airplane in 1956)

Cessna 150 and Cessna 152

Cessna 195 on floats

Cessna 182

Boeing B-52

McDonnell F-101

Piper Comanche

Schweizer 2-32

Boeing 727-100

Piper Apache (I received my US multi-engine-land rating on this airplane in 1970)

Beech Sierra

Beech Sundowner

Beech Bonanza

Beech Baron

Beech Model D18S

Beech Staggerwing D17

Ford Trimotor

Learjet M24

Learjet M25

Learjet M36

Grumman S2F Tracker (on and off the carrier Lexington)

Grumman C-2 Greyhound (on and off the carrier Lexington)

Beech Duke

Beech King-Air C-90

Douglas DC-3

Piper Twin Comanche

Rutan Vari-viggen

Rutan Longeze

Bell UH-1

Cessna Cardinal

NASA/KU/Cessna/Roberson Redhawk

NASA/KU/Beech SSSA-M99

Total of 38 types

Airplanes worked on.

Participated in various design and development activities on the following airplanes:

Percival Pembroke

Percival Provost

Aviolanda AT-21

Hawker Hunter

Consolidated PB3Y Catalina

Cessna T-37

Cessna YAT-37

Cessna 405*

Boeing 909*

Boeing 635 Missileer*

Boeing TFX*

Boeing 2707 (SST)*

Boeing 747-100

Learjet M25

Learjet M36

Learjet M55

Canadair Model 600 Challenger

Beech King Air

Cessna Citation I

NASA/KU/Beech SSSA-M99

NASA/KU/Cessna/Robertson Redhawk

SSSA C-172 Skyhawk

NASA/KU/Cessna ATLIT

SIAI-Marchetti S-211

NASA/KU/Delft VATLIT*

Piaggio P-180

Grumman X-29

Buehler Model 103

Piper Model 41

Fairchild 23 Metroliner Advanced*

Nexus*

Air Tractor S22

Visionaire Vantage

Dreamwings Valkyrie*

Dreamwings Hooligan*

Safire S-26**

Total of 36 projects

* airplanes which were not built

** construction to be started in 2003

Appendix D: Curriculum Vitae

Education:

MSAE, Delft University of Technology, Delft, The Netherlands, 1954.

PhD, Aeronautics and Astronautics, The University of Washington, Seattle, WA, 1965.

Professional Experience:

1954-1957 Assistant Chief Designer, Aviolanda Aircraft Company, The Netherlands

1957-1959 Preliminary Design Engineer and Senior Aerodynamics Engineer, Cessna Aircraft Company, Wichita, KS

1959-1967 Senior Group Engineer, The Boeing Company, Wichita, KS and Seattle, WA

1967-1974 Professor of Aerospace Engineering, The University of Kansas, Lawrence, KS

1967-1984 Director, Flight Research Laboratory, Center for Research Inc., Lawrence, KS

1972-1976 Chairman, Department of Aerospace Engineering, The University of Kansas, Lawrence, KS

1972-2001 President, Roskam Aviation and Engineering Corporation, Lawrence, KS

1974-2003 Ackers Distinguished Professor of Aerospace Engineering, The University of Kansas, Lawrence, KS

1976-1985 Member of various Advisory Committees to NASA

1985-1988 Member, Aerospace Engineering Board, National Research Council

1987-1993 Member, USAF X-29 Future Applications Committee

1990-1993 Member, Laboratory Advisory Group, Flight Dynamics Laboratory, WPAFB, Dayton, OH

1991-present President, Design, Analysis and Research Corporation (DAR), Lawrence, KS

Principal Consulting Work:

The Boeing Company, Seattle, WA and Wichita, KS

Gates Learjet Corporation, Wichita, KS

Beech Aircraft Corporation, Wichita, KS

Cessna Aircraft Company, Wichita, KS

Bell Helicopter Company, Fort Worth, TX

Teledyne Brown Engineering, Huntsville, AL

SRI International, Stanford, CA

Piper Aircraft Corporation, Vero Beach, FL

SIAI-Marchetti S.p.A., Sesto Calende, Italy

Rinaldo Piaggio S.p.A., Finale Ligure, Italy

Grumman Corporation, Bethpage, NY

Smith Aircraft Corporation, Bay St.Louis, MS

Airbus Industrie, Blagnac, France

Coleman Research Corporation, FL

Fairchild Aircraft Corporation, San Antonio, TX

Dream Wings, Lawrence, KS

Air Tractor, Olney, TX

Visionaire Aircraft Corp., Chesterfield, MO

Honors:

Tau Beta Pi, Sigma Gamma Tau, Sigma Xi, Omicron Delta Kappa

Gould Award for excellence in undergraduate teaching: 1969 and 1996

SAE Forest McFarland Award: 1983

AIAA General Aviation Award: 1986

University of Kansas Higuchi Award: 1986

AIAA John Leland Atwood Award: 1987

Fellow, AIAA: 1989

Fellow, SAE: 1990

SAE Distinguished Speaker Award: 1990

AIAA Distinguished Lecturer: 1989-1990

University of Kansas Ned Fleming Teaching Award

Outstanding Aerospace Engineering Educator by the aerospace engineering seniors in 1990, 1992, 1996, 1998 and 2000

Governor of Kansas General Aviation Award for 1993

Design Awards for leading a team of 30 students and faculty from KU, WSU and KState to a first place win in the first NASA/FAA General Aviation Aircraft Design Competition of 1995, 1997 and 1998.

Short Courses:

Taught through KU Division of Continuing Education: Dr. Roskam is active in teaching short courses on the subjects of Airplane Design, Airplane Performance, and Airplane Stability and Control through the KU Division of Continuing Education. These courses were taught in the following countries: USA, France, England, Germany, Singapore, Canada and Australia.

Taught through NSF: A two-week short course, sponsored by NSF (National Science Foundation) on Airplane Design for a group of twenty US university professors at KU from Airplane Design at KU, in 1990, July 13-24 (2 weeks), attendees: 19 university professors. In 1991 he did the same course for a group of 20 university professors (July 22 - August 2, 1991).

Sofar Dr.Roskam has taught a total of 144 short courses.

Service:

International Service:

1. Expert Member, Search Committee for a Professorship in Aeronautics at the Royal Institute of Technology (KTH), Stockholm, Sweden.

2. Served as committee member on the PhD committee for Mr. J. Middel of Delft University of Technology, The Netherlands at the request of Professor E. Torenbeek, chairman of that committee. Was invited and accepted to review the dissertation and to attend its public defense in Delft, The Netherlands on April 13, 1992

3. U.S. Editor of the Aircraft Design Journal, a quarterly journal published by Elsevier Publishing, United Kingdom. First issue published in March 1998. This was a three-year appointment. Prof. E. Torenbeek of Delft University of Technology in The Netherlands is the European Editor.

National Service:

1. Member, ETAB (Emerging Technologies Applications Board) for the SAE (Society of Automotive Engineers) 1993-1995.

2. Member, AIAA (American Institute of Aeronautics and Astronautics) Aircraft Design Technical Committee (1982-1994)

3. Member, SAE General Aviation Aircraft Committee for the organization of the 1997 SAE Business Aircraft Meeting, April 29-May 3, 1997 in Wichita, Kansas.

5. Organizer of the Session on Aircraft Design Methodology at the SAE Business Aircraft Meeting, May 17-19, Wichita, Kansas, 1993

6. AIAA Distinguished Lecturer, 1989 - 1991

7. Member, Fellow-Peer-Review committee for AIAA (1990-2000)

8. Member, X-29 Applications Committee, USAF (1991)
9. Member of the USAF/DARPA X-29 Future Applications Committee (1992)

Community Service:

Member, Board of Trustees, Ottawa Public Education Trust (1990 through 1994).

Appendix E Short Courses Taught

1976

Sheraton Hotel, Wichita, KS: General Aviation Feedback Control Technology

1977

KU, Lawrence, KS: Airplane Dynamic Stability, Control and Synthesis of Automatic Flight Control Systems.

KU, Lawrence, KS: Airplane Static Stability and Control and Effects of the Flight Control System.

1978

KU, Lawrence, KS: Airplane Dynamic Stability, Control and Synthesis of Automatic Flight Control Systems.

KU, Lawrence, KS: Airplane Static Stability and Control and Effects of the Flight Control System.

NATC, Patuxent River, MD: Airplane Dynamic Stability and Control and Synthesis of Automatic Flight Control Systems.

1979

KU, Lawrence, KS: Airplane Dynamic Stability, Control and Synthesis of Automatic Flight Control Systems.

KU, Lawrence, KS: Airplane Static Stability and Control and Effects of the Flight Control System.

Boeing, Seattle, WA: Airplane Dynamic Stability, Control and Synthesis of Automatic Flight Control Systems.

NASA, Langley, VA: Airplane Static Stability and Control and Effects of the Flight Control System.

NASA, Langley, VA: Airplane Dynamic Stability, Control and Synthesis of Automatic Flight Control Systems.

1980

KU, Lawrence, KS: Airplane Dynamic Stability, Control and Synthesis of Automatic Flight Control Systems.

KU, Lawrence, KS: Airplane Static Stability and Control and Effects of the Flight Control System.

1981

KU, Lawrence, KS: Airplane Performance Prediction and Sizing to Performance (co-taught).

KU, Lawrence, KS: Airplane Dynamic Stability, Control and Synthesis of Automatic Flight Control Systems.

KU, Lawrence, KS: Airplane Static Stability and Control and Effects of the Flight Control System.

1982

KU, Lawrence, KS: Airplane Performance Prediction and Sizing to Performance

KU, Lawrence, KS: Airplane Dynamic Stability, Control and Synthesis of Automatic Flight Control Systems.

KU, Lawrence, KS: Airplane Static Stability and Control and Effects of the Flight Control System.

1983

KU, Lawrence, KS: Military and Commercial Airplane Performance Prediction and Sizing to Performance (co-taught).

KU, Lawrence, KS: Airplane Dynamic Stability, Control and Synthesis of Automatic Flight Control Systems.

KU, Lawrence, KS: Airplane Static Stability and Control and Effects of the Flight Control System.

1984

KU, Lawrence, KS: Airplane Performance Prediction and Sizing to Performance (co-taught).

KU, Lawrence, KS: Airplane Flight Dynamics, Open and Closed Loop.

KU, Lawrence, KS: Airplane Static Stability and Control and Effects of the Flight Control System.

KU, Lawrence, KS: Airplane Dynamic Stability, Control and Synthesis of Automatic Flight Control Systems.

1985

KU, Lawrence, KS: Airplane Performance and Airplane Design (co-taught).

Basel, Switzerland: Airplane Flight Dynamics, Open and Closed Loop.

KU, Lawrence, KS: Airplane Static Stability and Control and Effects of the Flight Control System.

KU, Lawrence, KS: Airplane Dynamic Stability, Control and Synthesis of Automatic Flight Control Systems.

NADC, Warminster, PA: Airplane Performance Prediction and Sizing to Performance.

NADC, Warminster, PA: Airplane Flight Dynamics, Open and Closed Loop.

Lockheed, Marietta, GA: Airplane Flight Dynamics, Open and Closed Loop.

1986

Williamsburg, VA: Airplane Flight Dynamics, Open and Closed Loop.

Delft University of Technology, Delft, The Netherlands: Advanced Aircraft Design and Performance Prediction (co-taught).

KU, Lawrence, KS: Advanced Aircraft Design and Performance Prediction (co-taught).

KU, Lawrence, KS: Airplane Flight Dynamics, Open and Closed Loop.

Lockheed, Marietta, GA: Airplane Performance Prediction, Performance Sizing and Preliminary Configuration Design.

USAF Test Pilot School, Edwards AFB, CA: Airplane Static Stability and Control and Effects of the Flight Control System.

McDonnell-Douglas, St. Louis, MO: Airplane Static Stability and Control and Effects of the Flight Control System.

NASA-Dryden, Edwards AFB, CA: Airplane Dynamic Stability, Control and Synthesis of Automatic Flight Control Systems.

USAF Flight Dynamics Laboratory, WPAFB, Dayton, OH: Airplane Dynamic Stability, Control and Synthesis of Automatic Flight Control Systems.

1987

KU, Lawrence, KS: Airplane Design.

KU, Lawrence, KS: Airplane Flight Dynamics, Open and Closed Loop.

NASA Dryden, Edwards AFB, CA: Airplane Static Stability and Control and Effects of the Flight Control System.

1988

KU, Lawrence, KS: Airplane Design.

KU, Lawrence, KS: Airplane Flight Dynamics, Open and Closed Loop.

Polytecnico di Milano, Milan, Italy: Advanced Aircraft Design and Performance Prediction (co-taught).

Polytecnico di Milano, Milan, Italy: Airplane Flight Dynamics, Open and Closed Loop.

NASA-Dryden, Edwards AFB, CA: Airplane Dynamic Stability, Control and Synthesis of Automatic Flight Control Systems.

Boeing, Seattle, WA, Airplane Flight Dynamics, Open and Closed Loop.

NADC, Warminster, PA, Airplane Preliminary Design.

1989

USAF, Bergamo Center, Dayton, OH: Airplane Design (co-taught)*

1990

KU, Lawrence, KS: Airplane Design.

KU, Lawrence, KS: Airplane Flight Dynamics, Open and Closed Loop.

Delft University of Technology, Delft, The Netherlands, Advanced Aircraft Design and Performance Prediction (co-taught).

Delft University of Technology, Delft, The Netherlands, Airplane Flight Dynamics, Open and Closed Loop (co-taught).

USAF, Bergamo Center, Dayton, OH: Airplane Design (co-taught)*

1991

KU, Lawrence, KS: Airplane Design.

KU, Lawrence, KS: Airplane Flight Dynamics, Open and Closed Loop.

Airbus, Toulouse, France: Airplane Preliminary Design.

British Aerospace, Hatfield, England: Airplane Preliminary Design.

USAF, Bergamo Center, Dayton, OH: Airplane Design (co-taught)*

KU, Lawrence, KS: Airplane Design for US faculty, financed by NSF (two weeks)*

1992

KU, Lawrence, KS: Airplane Flight Dynamics, Open and Closed Loop.

KU, Lawrence, KS: Airplane Design.

KU, Lawrence, KS: Airplane Flight Dynamics, Open and Closed Loop.

NASA Ames, Moffett Field, CA: Airplane Flight Dynamics, Open and Closed Loop.

Deutsche Airbus, Hamburg, Germany: Commercial Airplane Design.

British Aerospace, Woodford, England: Airplane Flight Dynamics, Open and Closed Loop.

NASA Johnson, Houston, TX: Airplane Flight Dynamics, Open and Closed Loop.

USAF Flight Dynamics Laboratory, WPAFB, Dayton, OH: Airplane Flight Dynamics, Open and Closed Loop.

1993

Williamsburg, VA: Airplane Flight Dynamics, Open and Closed Loop.

KU, Lawrence, KS: Airplane Design.

Polytecnico di Milano, Milan, Italy: Airplane Preliminary Design.

KU, Lawrence, KS: Airplane Flight Dynamics, Open and Closed Loop.

USAF Flight Dynamics Laboratory, WPAFB, Dayton, OH: Airplane Preliminary Design

1994

University of Singapore, Singapore: Airplane Preliminary Design.

Seattle, WA: Airplane Flight Dynamics, Open and Closed Loop.

KU, Lawrence, KS: Airplane Design.

San Diego, CA: Airplane Flight Dynamics, Open and Closed Loop.

British Aerospace (AVRO), Manchester, England: Airplane Preliminary Design.

NAWC, Warminster, PA: Military Airplane Design.

NAWC, Patuxent River, MD: Airplane Flight Dynamics, Open and Closed Loop.

1995

University of Singapore, Singapore: Airplane Flight Dynamics, Open and Closed Loop.

Australian Defense Force Academy, Canberra, Australia: Airplane Preliminary Design.

CTA, Montreal, Quebec: Airplane Flight Dynamics, Open and Closed Loop.

KU, Lawrence, KS: Airplane Design.

1996

Williamsburg, VA: Airplane Flight Dynamics, Open and Closed Loop.

KU, Lawrence, KS: Airplane Performance: Theory, Prediction and Certification.

KU, Lawrence, KS: General Aviation Aircraft Design.

KU, Lawrence, KS: Airplane Design.

Australian Defense Force Academy, Canberra, Australia: Airplane Flight Dynamics, Open and Closed Loop.

Texas Instruments, Dallas, TX: Airplane Flight Dynamics, Open and Closed Loop.

1997

KU, Lawrence, KS: Airplane Performance: Theory, Prediction and Certification.

KU, Lawrence, KS: Airplane Design.

Seattle, WA: Airplane Flight Dynamics, Open and Closed Loop.

Delft University of Technology, Delft, The Netherlands: Performance, Stability, Control, Propulsion Integration and Design of Commercial Transport Aircraft (co-taught, 2 weeks).

KU, Lawrence, KS: Performance Flight Testing, Performance Prediction and Certification of Airplanes (co-taught).

San Diego, CA: Airplane Preliminary Design.

NAWC, Patuxent River, MD: Military Airplanc Design.

NASA Ames, Edwards, CA: Airplane Performance Prediction and Sizing to Performance.

Texas Instruments, Dallas, TX: Airplane Flight Dynamics, Open and Closed Loop.

NASA Johnson, Houston, TX: Airplane Flight Dynamics, Open and Closed Loop.

British Aerospace (AVRO), Manchester, England: Airplane Preliminary Design.

1998

Williamsburg, VA: Airplane Preliminary Design.

Seattle, WA: Airplane Flight Dynamics, Open and Closed Loop.

KU, Lawrence, KS: Airplane Performance: Theory, Prediction and Certification.

Australian Defense Force Academy, Canberra, Australia: Airplane Preliminary Design.

KU, Lawrence, KS: Airplane Flight Dynamics, Open and Closed Loop.

KU, Lawrence, KS: Performance Flight Testing, Performance Prediction and Certification of Airplanes (co-taught).

KU, Lawrence, KS: Airplane Design.

Transport Canada, Canada: Performance Flight Testing, Performance Prediction and Certification of Airplanes (co-taught).

1999

Williamsburg, VA: Airplane Performance: Theory, Prediction and Certification.

Seattle, WA: Airplane Flight Dynamics, Open and Closed Loop.

KU, Lawrence, KS: Airplane Design.

KU, Lawrence, KS: Performance Flight Testing, Performance Prediction and Certification of Airplanes (co-taught).

San Diego, CA: Airplane Flight Dynamics, Open and Closed Loop.

KU, Lawrence, KS: Airplane Design.

2000

Williamsburg, VA: Airplane Flight Dynamics, Open and Closed Loop.

KU, Lawrence, KS: Airplane Design.

Australian Defense Force Academy, Canberra, Australia: Airplane Performance: Theory, Prediction and Certification.

KU, Lawrence, KS: Performance Flight Testing, Performance Prediction and Certification of Airplanes (co-taught).

KU, Lawrence, KS: Airplane Flight Dynamics, Open and Closed Loop.

San Diego, CA: Airplane Preliminary Design.

NASA Glenn, Cleveland, OH: Airplane Preliminary Design.

Rockwell-Collins, Cedar Rapids, IO: Airplane Flight Dynamics, Open and Closed Loop.

2001

Williamsburg, VA: Airplane Preliminary Design.

Embraer, San Jose dos Campos, Brazil: Airplane Performance: Theory, Prediction and Certification.

Embraer, San Jose dos Campos, Brazil: Airplane Preliminary Design.

Cessna Aircraft Co., Wichita, KS: Airplane Flight Dynamics, Open and Closed Loop.

KU, Lawrence, KS: Airplane Flight Dynamics, Open and Closed Loop.

KU, Lawrence, KS: Airplane Design.

KU, Lawrence, KS: Performance Flight Testing, Performance Prediction and Certification of Airplanes (co-taught).

Honeywell, Olathe, KS: Airplane Flight Dynamics, Open and Closed Loop.

San Diego, CA: Airplane Performance: Theory, Prediction and Certification.

2002

NASA Marshall, Huntsville, AL: Airplane Preliminary Design.

KU, Lawrence, KS: Airplane Flight Dynamics, Open and Closed Loop.

KU, Lawrence, KS: Performance Flight Testing, Performance Prediction and Certification of Airplanes (co-taught).

NASA Glenn, Cleveland, OH: Airplane Preliminary Design.

NASA Langley, Hampton, VA: Airplane Preliminary Design.

KU, Lawrence, KS: Airplane Performance: Theory, Prediction and Certification.

KU, Lawrence, KS: Airplane Design.

San Diego, CA: Airplane Flight Dynamics, Open and Closed Loop.

---

* These courses were not sponsored by KUCE.

Appendix E

Appendix F Honors and Awards

1964 Elected member of Sigma Xi Honor Society (University of Washington)

1968 Elected member of Sigma Gamma Tau Honor Society (University of Kansas)

1969 Elected member of Omicron Delta Kappa Honor Society (University of Kansas)

1969 School of Engineering Gould Award for Excellence in Undergraduate Teaching

1974 Elected member of Tau Beta Pi Honor Society (University of Kansas)

1974 Appointed Honorary Tailhooker

1975 Certificate of Recognition for Outstanding Support and Participation in the FAA General Aviation Aircraft Accident Prevention Program

1976 Certificate of Recognition for publication of a 1976 NASA Technical Brief called Aeroelastic Program

1979 SAE Excellence in Oral Presentations Award, Business Aircraft Meeting, Wichita, KS

1983 SAE Forrest R. McFarland Award

1986 University of Kansas Irvin Youngberg Award in Applied Sciences

1986 University of Kansas Higuchi Research Achievement Award

1986 AIAA General Aviation Award

1988 John L Atwood Award for Aerospace Education

1989 Elected Fellow of AIAA

1989 Aerospace Engineering Educator of the Year voted by 1989 KU seniors

1989 SAE Excellence in Oral Presentations Award, Business Aircraft Meeting, Wichita, KS

1990 Elected Fellow of SAE

1990 SAE Distinguished Speaker Award, Detroit, MI

1991 Excellence in Oral Presentations Award, SAE Aerotech, Long Beach, CA

1991 Distinguished Lecturer Award AIAA, Savannah

1992 Excellence in Oral Presentations Award, SAE Aerotech, Long Beach, CA

1992 Aerospace Engineering Educator of the Year voted by 1992 KU seniors

1992 University of Kansas Ned Fleming Outstanding Classroom Teaching Award

1993 Distinguished Service Award AIAA Aircraft Design Technical Committee

Appendix F

1993 Kansas Governor's General Aviation Award

1996 School of Engineering Gould Award for Excellence in Undergraduate Teaching

1996 Aerospace Engineering Educator of the Year voted by 1996 KU seniors

1998 Excellence in Teaching Award, KU Center for Excellence in Teaching

1998 Aerospace Engineering Educator of the Year voted by 1998 KU seniors

1999 Mortarboard Outstanding Educator Award

2000 Aerospace Engineering Educator of the Year voted by 2000 KU seniors